THE CLIMATE OF LONDON

The Climate of London

T. J. CHANDLER, M.Sc., Ph.D.

University College London

HUTCHINSON OF LONDON

HUTCHINSON & CO (*Publishers*) **LTD**
178–202 Great Portland Street, London W1

London Melbourne Sydney
Auckland Bombay Toronto
Johannesburg New York

★

First published 1965

*This book has been set in Times New Roman,
printed in Great Britain on Antique Wove paper
by The Anchor Press, Ltd., and bound by Wm.
Brendon & Son Ltd., both of Tiptree, Essex.*

To the memory of

LUKE HOWARD F.R.S.

(*1772–1864*)

Pioneer of urban climatic studies

Meteorological information can only be depended on when it is the result of the comparison of long continued observations, not the vague surmise founded on a few desultory remarks.

CAPTAIN ALEXANDER MACONOCHIE
First Professor of Geography in Great Britain at University College London.

1818

Contents

Illustrations

Tables

Preface

*Nursed amid her noise, her crowds, her beloved smoke—what
have I been doing all my life if I have not lent out my heart with
usury to such [London] scenes.*

Charles Lamb

THIS BOOK CONSIDERS the nature of London's climate, including the manner and degree to which this varies in sympathy with changes in the city's morphology, and studying in particular the contrasts between the built-up area and the surrounding rural districts.

The variety of records used in this study makes it impossible to use a common period of analysis. Rather has it been the aim to use data for as long and as recent a period as possible or is necessary for studying the climate of the London region. Many of the analyses are based upon records taken before the Meteorological Office changed from the Fahrenheit to the Centigrade scale of temperature in its published records, and as a result of this and the use of degrees Centigrade in weather forecasts and elsewhere, values quoted in this book are normally given in both scales. In general, the units most commonly used in current meteorological and climatological publications have been placed first with their equivalents in other units in brackets.

For a number of reasons this volume is climatically selective. First, much of the literature on the climate of the British Isles is relevant to that of London but is not repeated here; this applies particularly to the dynamic aspects of climate. Also, many London climatological stations have particularly long and detailed records constantly extended by contemporary readings, and although the network in London is open, for each of these stations there is almost no limit to the analyses which could be undertaken. The cellular pattern of the city's climate can, in theory at least, be studied on all scales from the very small to the very large, from a few feet to several miles. Climates differ, in detail, between two sides of a single street or on either side of a garden wall. The problems imposed by this intricacy are obvious, but even the broader spatial picture is frequently incomplete over large areas owing to the paucity of standard recording stations, although regional gaps can often be filled by analogy.

My interest in climatology, and particularly in local climates, was awakened by the teaching I received at King's College, University of London, and commuting between various suburban areas and central London familiarized my senses with the mosaic of London's morphological, structural and atmospheric scene. Later, as a lecturer in geography at Birkbeck College, London, I was able to plan my study of London's climate. This plan was realized following a move to University College London, and the present volume is its fruition.

This is an opportunity to express gratitude to those persons and organizations

B

without whose help the study could not have been undertaken. Amongst these are the many headmasters, teachers and pupils in London schools, lecturers and students in colleges, and independent observers who purchased and maintained climatological stations. Their records were invaluable and their enthusiasm, in spite of considerable personal inconvenience, was a constant inspiration. I am also indebted to the innumerable observers sending their readings to official organizations such as the Meteorological Office and the Department of Scientific and Industrial Research, the heads of which gave their kind permission to consult their records. I am particularly appreciative of the most generous and unfailing help given to me by the staff of the Meteorological Office in all aspects of my work. This venture could never have proceeded without the unceasing support of Professor H. C. Darby who, by his encouragement, provided much more than the material facilities for research. Professor Gordon Manley, the late Professor S. W. Wooldridge and numerous other colleagues in the University of London and elsewhere also contributed a great deal by their interest and friendly advice. I would like to thank my wife Margaret, not only for her clerical assistance but above all for her patience. Recognition is also made of the invaluable cartographic, photographic and secretarial assistance given by the draughtsmen, more particularly Messrs J. Bryant, K. Wass and M. Young, and other members of the Department of Geography, University College London.

I am deeply conscious of my obligation to the Department of Scientific and Industrial Research, the Royal Meteorological Society, the Central Research Fund of London University and University College London, for the financial support which enabled me to give concrete expression to personal enthusiasm.

A project of this nature inevitably touches upon a very wide group of individuals and official bodies, and from these I have received great courtesy, friendliness and willingness to help. To all these people, named and unnamed, I acknowledge a tremendous debt of gratitude.

London, 1964   T. J. C.

1 The physical and cultural setting

That monstrous tuberosity of civilized life, the capital of England.

Thomas Carlyle

AS POPULATIONS INCREASE and social and economic forces persuade more and more people to live in towns, so a rash of bricks and mortar, concrete, stone and macadam fans out to engulf ever-increasing areas. Demographers, economists, town planners and sociologists—all have studied the gathering momentum of urbanization, a circumstance Peter Self aptly described as 'Cities in Flood' (Self, 1957). But amongst this wealth of literature there are relatively few references to the climatic implications of urban sprawl. This is strange, for there are radical and easily perceptible differences between the climates inside and outside towns and the ramifications of these are of considerable architectural (Olgyay, 1963), planning (Hilbersheimer, 1944) and medical (Duhot, 1948) interest. Duhot, indeed, refers to a *'véritable pathologie des grandes villes'* owing, amongst other things, to the inhalation of pollutants and decreased ultra-violet radiation.

Town climates should not, of course, be thought of as uniquely man-made. William Cowper made this mistake when he wrote: 'God made the country and man made the town', whereas the majority of English rural scenes are as artificial as any urban landscape, and in clearing the woodland and draining the marsh, man has unconsciously modified the local physical and dynamic states of the atmosphere above fields and parkland. The contrasts of climate between cities and the countryside into which they constantly encroach are as radical as any of these rural changes, and the surface dissimilarities between town and country have induced equally dramatic atmospheric parallels. Certainly the myriad of contrasting microclimates, in which 80 per cent of the population of Great Britain who are town dwellers spend their lives, are of immediate practical as well as academic interest.

The urban morphology of any town is partly determined by the particular needs for shelter in the prevailing climate. Brooks (1950), amongst others, has considered the climates within buildings and a great deal of recent research has been directed towards a better understanding of the relationship between building materials and architectural styles on the one hand and interior climates on the other. But buildings modify the climates outside as well as inside their walls, and the city dweller not only lives and works in the artificially heated or cooled, humidified or purified air of the inefficiently insulated structures of his home and place of work; he also travels between them in virtually enclosed forms of transport. As an accidental by-product of these attempts to create pockets of controlled climates he has changed the properties of the free atmosphere within and above the city. All the climatic elements are modified, but the evaluation of these contrasts by the comparison of urban and rural records is far from simple. The climate of the city is a function of several variables of which urban development is but one. There are three main determinants: the general climate of the region, the modifying influences of the local morphology, and the 'self-induced' modifications following the congregation of buildings and surfaced roads into the complex of the city. Each house, factory, railway station, wall and pavement creates its own distinctive micro-climatic envelope and these in combination produce a substantial climatic unit—the urban climate.

The general nature of the climate in metropolitan England is covered explicitly or implicitly in many texts (including Bilham, 1938; Brooks, 1954; Howard, 1818, 1820 and 1833; Manley, 1952; London Meteorological Office, 1952) and papers (for example Gregory, 1953; Manley, 1958; Shellard, 1959). Superimposed upon the general theme of the climate in Southeast England which these and many other authors have discussed in terms of the broad climatic setting of the region, there are second order variations owing to both the natural surface and man-made form of London.

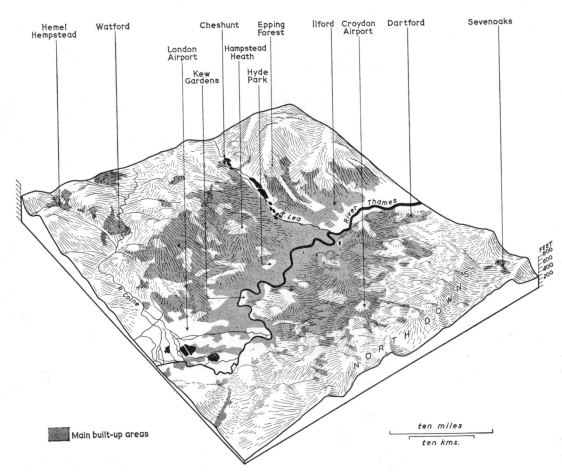

Fig *1* London in its physical setting

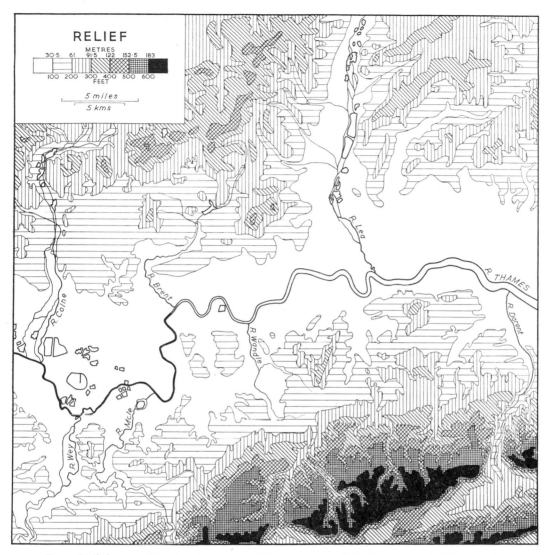

Fig 2 Relief map of the London region. The area covered is the same as in Figs 1 and 3

THE PHYSICAL SETTING

Fig. 1 shows the general physical setting of London. The city has fanned out from nuclei in the City and Westminster to cover almost 750 sq mi (1,942 sq km) of the central London Basin between the chalk outcrops of the Chiltern Hills in the northwest and the North Downs in the south (see also Fig. 2 which covers the same area). The main built-up area, generally known as Greater London, lies between the northern districts of Ruislip, Barnet and Southgate where suburbia climbs on to the higher parts of north Middlesex and south Hertfordshire, and the southern suburbs from Epsom to Dartford which encroach upon the lowers slopes of the Downs. It is, of course, impossible to delimit London precisely and completely. Ribbon development has pushed north from Tottenham and Edmonton as far as Hertford and Ware along the terraces to the west of the Lea, a left-bank tributary of the Thames in northeast London. In the east, houses, shops and factories have sprawled across the low-lying clay plains of south Essex as far as Romford. To the west, where the Green Belt is particularly fractionized, a more

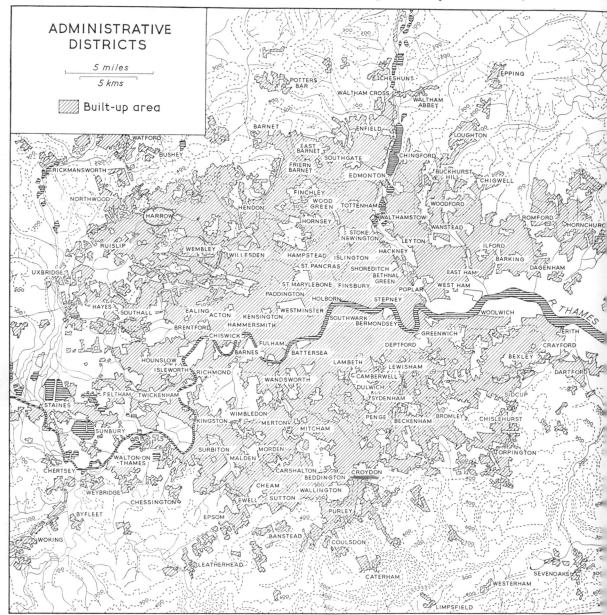

Fig 3 Administrative districts of London

open tracery of buildings reaches westward to Slough, Windsor, Staines and Weybridge (Fig. 3). Other settlements well north of the Chilterns or south of the North Downs are in some respects tributary to the metropolis and help to complicate the definition of London.

Various administrative boundaries in the London region are delimited, amongst others, by the Royal Commission on Local Government in Greater London 1957-60 (1960). For present purposes, coverage is limited to the largely continuous built-up area, generally known as Greater London (and with a population of about 8½ million), shown in Fig. 3. The main features of its surface morphology (Figs. 1 and 2) are:

1 The escarpment of the North Downs rising to 882 ft (268·8 m) north of Oxted and breached by the river Darent north of Sevenoaks.

2 The central axis of the river Thames floodplain, terrace flights and gravel trains, and London Clay lowland from London Airport, 82 ft (25 m), in the west to the low ground and marshes of southwest Essex, 10–100 ft (3–30 m), in the east. Tongue-like extensions of the terraces are found along tributary valleys, especially the lower Lea valley in northeast London, deeply cut between the higher parts of Southgate, Palmers Green and Wood Green to the west and the Epping ridge to the east. There are similar spreads of gravel along the lower Colne valley from Staines to Watford, and the Vale of St Albans in northwest and north London, and southward along the Wandle valley from Wandsworth to Croydon.

3 The upstanding areas of north London including Harrow, Wembley, Willesden, Hendon, Finchley, Totteridge and Southgate, and a ridge from Hampstead through Highgate and Muswell Hill to Alexandra Palace. The closely dissected terrain ranges generally between 125 and 300 ft (38 and 91 m) but rises to over 400 ft (122 m) in such places as Harrow on the Hill, Arkley, Totteridge, Mill Hill and Hampstead.

4 The commons and parks of south London such as those at Richmond, Wimbledon, Clapham, Dulwich and Black Heath rising 100–150 ft (30–45 m) above the surrounding low-lying districts. Few areas apart from the Forest Hill–Sydenham ridge with Crystal Palace Park, 357 ft (108·8 m), rise above 175 ft (53 m) in south London until the lower slopes of the North Downs are reached in the south and southeast near Sutton, Croydon, Bromley, Orpington, Chislehurst and Sidcup.

THE URBAN CHARACTER

The third determinant of London's climate, as already mentioned, is the character of the city itself, involving (for example) the height, density, composition and structure of the buildings, the amount of surface covered by an impervious layer of concrete and macadam, the size, character and distribution of parks and other open spaces, the form and amount of artificial heating, the intensity of road traffic. Here the picture is infinitely complex, as maps of urban land use quickly show. But despite the local intricacy of the conurbation's urban scene, the continuous (until recently) outward cellular

growth from two nuclei in the City of London and Westminster to engulf small settlements, many little more than villages, has given a roughly concentric pattern of basically
similar forms. The details of climate reflect this, for although in the limit of comparison
the atmospheric properties of each street and garden are as unique as their physical
form, the first order unity of building development—frequently reflecting the contemporary building style and planning vogue—give a regional continuity to the basic
climate parallel to that of the urban morphology. There is a marked tendency to an
annular distribution of both city and climatic regions within London.

Fig. 4 shows the broad character of the urban development. At this scale, local
detail is lost to reveal a simple, basic pattern of concentric development. In the centre,

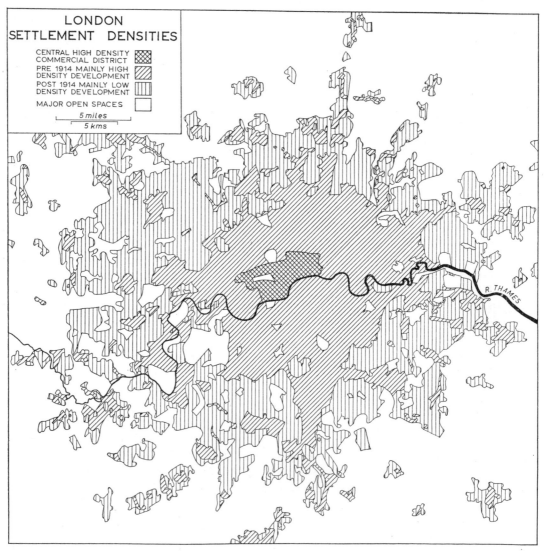

Fig 4 Settlement densities in the primary zones of London's urban morphology

from the West End administrative, shopping and commercial districts to the City, modern buildings of steel, concrete and glass rise above the lower but equally massive and closely spaced Victorian and older buildings. Relief from the pressing chasms of central London is provided by several open spaces, the largest of which are St James's Park, 93 acres (38 hectares), the Green Park, 53 acres (21 hectares), Kensington Gardens, 275 acres (111 hectares) and Hyde Park, 360 acres (146 hectares). Surrounding this is an area developed mainly between 1750 and 1914 and consisting of high density residential, industrial and, in the east, dockside areas with a multiplicity of narrow streets bordered by long rows of tightly packed terrace houses. There are a number of substantial open spaces such as Regent's Park, 402 acres (163 hectares), and Battersea Park, 200 acres (81 hectares), near the junction with the central office district, and a little further out are Hampstead Heath and Kenwood with Parliament Hill Fields, 800 acres (324 hectares), Highgate Woods, 70 acres (28 hectares), Hackney Marshes, 343 acres (139 hectares), Wanstead Flats, 460 acres (186 hectares), Greenwich Park, 197 acres (80 hectares), Dulwich Park, 72 acres (29 hectares), Wimbledon and Putney Common, 1,178 acres (477 hectares), Richmond Park, 2,469 acres (999 hectares), and Kew Gardens, 300 acres (121 hectares). Near these urban lungs there are frequently groups of substantial houses with large gardens, built in the nineteenth and early twentieth centuries. Forming an outer ring of urban development is an area where most of the settlement is post-1914. These areas are characterized by smaller two-storey, semi-detached and detached houses with gardens along fairly wide roads, by close groups or lines of mainly one- or two-storey factories such as those at Park Royal, Colindale and Staples Corner and along Western Avenue and the Great Cambridge Road near Enfield, and by frequent open spaces, playing fields and allotments. The lace-like pattern of residential development near the urban-rural fringe is most extensively developed in southwest London.

SOURCES OF CLIMATOLOGICAL RECORDS

To study the climate of London, analyses have been made of a variety of records. Air temperatures, mostly for short periods, have been taken in and near London since about 1680 (Manley, 1961). But early meteorological enthusiasts were few in number and generally spasmodic in operation until the 1860's. In 1841 Greenwich Observatory began regular observations and in 1868 Kew Observatory, Richmond, started readings from its famous North-Wall Screen. Nine years earlier, George J. Symons had set up a climatological station in the garden of his home at 136 Camden Square, St Pancras, a few hundred yards from 62 Camden Square to which he moved in 1868. Observations here continued until 1958 when there was a further short move to Camden Square Gardens. But Symons's enthusiasm had other meteorological outlets. Reliable rainfall measures in London date from about 1815, but in 1860 appeared the first edition of *British rainfall* with statistics compiled by Symons from the reports of 168 observers of which twenty-four were in London. Today (1964) there are more than 6,000 voluntarily maintained rainfall stations in the organization, of which more than 200 are in Greater London.

There are also (in 1964) eighteen climatological and synoptic stations within or very near London sending their comprehensive daily records to the Air Ministry Meteorological Office. They are:

Station	National Grid reference	Height (O.D.) feet	metres	Period of records
Addington	TQ(51) 352/643	474	144	1891–
Bromley	TQ(51) 399/693	213	65	1927–
Camden Square	TQ(51) 296/845	110	34	1858–1958
		*121	37	1957–
Croydon (Waddon)	TQ(51) 314/639	220	67	1959–
Dartford	TQ(51) 542/736	17	5	1951–
Greenwich (Maritime Museum)	TQ(51) 389/776	24	7	1953–
Hampton	TQ(51) 131/695	39	12	1952–
Hampstead Observatory	TQ(51) 262/863	450	137	1911–
Hoddesdon	TL(52) 371/105	153	47	1960–
Kensington Palace	TQ(51) 259/801	81	25	1918–
Kew Observatory	TQ(51) 171/757	18	5	1868–
London Airport	TQ(51) 077/769	82	25	1948–
Regent's Park	TQ(51) 283/826	129	39	1932–
Southgate	TQ(51) 299/952	221	68	1940–
Swanley	TQ(51) 512/701	177	54	1955–
Wealdstone	TQ(51) 144/897	175	53	1942–
Westminster	TQ(51) 299/799	27	8	1903–
Wisley	TQ(51) 063/583	105	32	1904–

* new site

Kingsway (TQ(51) 307/811) and Bunhill Row (TQ(51) 326/823) take a more limited range of climatic readings. Summaries of all these stations' observations are given in the *Monthly weather report* and daily values are kept at the Meteorological Office. By comparison with most cities, eighteen climatological stations within or immediately beyond the built-up area is a very substantial coverage, but although their records are sufficient to show the main outlines of the city's climate, the network is too open for a detailed spatial study of one of the world's greatest man-modified climates. For this, more readings were needed.

Additional observations came from two sources: supplementary climatological stations taking daily (0900 GMT) or twice daily (0900 and 1500 GMT) readings, and a series of mobile surveys using vehicles equipped with electrical resistance thermometers. These two types of record provide complementary spatial and sectional pictures of temperatures and humidities in London. Initially, between the autumn of 1958 and the spring of 1959, temperature, humidity and rainfall readings, with estimates (in most cases) of wind speed and direction and cloud cover, were obtained from stations in the lower Lea valley district of northeast London, organized in a scheme known as the

Lea Valley Climatological Survey. This involved the co-operation of thirty-nine second-ary schools, training colleges, technical colleges and private observers with the Geography Department of University College London, in an investigation of the local climate (Chandler, 1961a). Stations extended from a northern boundary between Welwyn and Bishop's Stortford (Hertfordshire) southward to the Thames between Stepney and West Ham. The Survey was limited to the northeast quarter of the city for two reasons: to reduce organizational labour when returns were uncertain, and because it was at first falsely assumed that the readings in one sector could be projected to provide a picture for the whole of London. It soon became clear, however, that London would have to be completely covered. Distributions and temporal changes in distribution could not be understood by reference to only one part of the conurbation. For these reasons the Survey was enlarged during 1959 to cover the whole of Greater London and in January 1961 the extended investigation was re-named the London Climatological Survey. Nineteen further climatological stations had already been added and the total grew to sixty by December 1962 (Fig. 5). Within the Survey, monthly analyses of readings were made and distributed to participants, thus in some way compensating for the time and money spent by the schools and individuals in their unselfish devotion to the maintenance of records. All stations were equipped with Meteorological Office pattern, National Physical Laboratory certificated, maximum, minimum, wet- and dry-bulb thermometers, a Stevenson Screen and a rain gauge. A number of schools supplemented this basic equipment with additional purchases and constructions.

Some schools could not afford the total expense of this apparatus, and for this reason one school was persuaded to make and supply standard Stevenson Screens at a very moderate price. Others of the 100 or so schools visited could find no suitable position for the instruments and screen and were unable to take part in the Survey. The problem of site became increasingly difficult towards the heavily built-up areas of inner London. Standard exposure requires a one-to-two ratio between the height of any obstruction and its distance from the instruments. This was maintained at all but six of the new stations established by the Survey but the degree of exposure generally decreased towards the centre. In these six cases obstructions on one side of the screen had an elevation of between 30 and 48 degrees at the station and readings from these were treated with caution when comparisons were made with other stations, particularly on occasions when there was little air movement. They were, on the other hand, useful in providing readings from an urban exposure quite typical of their region.

A mobile survey making observations at closely spaced points along city streets was also begun in the autumn of 1958. This provided data of a type and intensity which helped to construct a more complete and, in some ways, more realistic picture of London's climate. Contrasts could be drawn between conditions in areas of different building type and density and a study could be made of the influence of exposure upon temperature and humidity. With standard climatological stations there remains the uncertainty of the degree to which records, in parks for instance (see Chapter 5), are influenced by the immediate site, and the representativeness of an individual station of conditions in the wider region (Glasspoole, 1959; Manley, 1956).

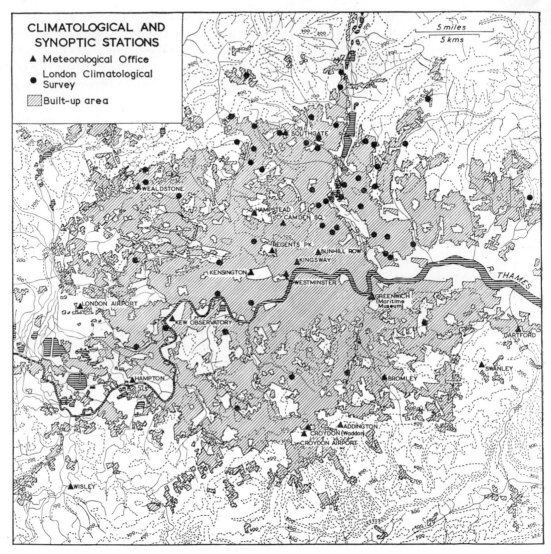

Fig 5 Climatological and synoptic stations in and around London

The instrumentation of the original traverses consisted of electrical resistance thermometers housed in double-louvred radiation shields suspended from the roof-rack of a car so that the element in the lower shield was 4 ft (122 cm) and that in the upper shield was 5 ft (152 cm) above the ground and 6 in. (15 cm) from the side of the car. Temperatures in the first few feet above road surfaces seem, in fact, to be surprisingly uniform (Lawrence, 1958, p. 173) and the precise height of the instrument is less critical than might be supposed. Connections between the platinum elements in the shields and sensitive galvanometers inside the vehicle were made by copper wires whose resistance was less than 0·5 per cent of that of the elements. The copper-sheathed, knife-type element inside the upper shield was covered with a wick dipping into a bottle of distilled water, thus giving wet-bulb readings from which humidities could be calculated. The 90 per cent reaction time of the coiled electrical resistance dry-bulb thermometer element was 18 sec and that of the wet-bulb a few seconds more. This, a measure of the sensitivity, is highly critical. Undersensitive instruments would fail to register quickly enough the important temperature contrasts between built-up and open areas; oversensitivity would result in far too complex a picture, with micro-fluctuations from sources such as car exhausts. In this initial investigation the lag of the instruments was appreciable, but was offset by the 20–25 sec taken to read and note both wet- and dry-bulb elements after the instruments were switched on and the car halted. This was 2 or 3 sec greater than the reaction time of the elements after which dry-bulb readings remained constant for several minutes. Wet-bulb readings were less trustworthy owing to the greater lag and their dependence on the degree of ventilation. For this reason only those values which seemed to be consistent over several closely spaced and topographically similar sites were accepted as typical of their area, and no detailed analyses were made of individual humidity profiles using these instruments.

Any warming of the elements by the car engine would naturally invalidate the readings. This problem has sometimes proved difficult (Godske, quoted by Sundborg, 1952, p. 53), but in the present investigation the position of the radiation shield and elements in relation to the engine and airflow over the car, plus a thick pad of glass fibre over the car bonnet, prevented any warming. It was sought, in general, to keep the car speed to 20 mi/hr (32 km/hr) but in the centre of London it was frequently necessary to drive more slowly. Except on a few noted occasions, speeds were sufficient to secure adequate ventilation of the elements without being too great to induce dynamic warming.

Between October 1958 and November 1960 day and night temperature traverses were made with this equipment along five routes in the lower Lea valley district of northeast London. Four of the routes (with common sections) ran towards two turning points, Liverpool Street and Canning Town, in central London (Fig. 6) and except near stations V, 7, 8, 26 and 27 (Figs. 49 and 52) the general uniformity of relief made it unimportant as a factor of local climate. The fifth traverse made a series of crossings of the Lea valley both in its rural and built-up parts. In all cases readings were taken of wet- and dry-bulb temperatures at the same points along both inward and outward legs of the closed traverses. Thus if regional temperature changes during the period of traverse were linear at each station, and the timing of each leg was roughly the same, then the average of each pair of readings gives the closest possible approximation to the temperature distribution along the line of traverse at the time the midpoint was reached (the end of the first leg and the commencement of the second or return leg). In order to check that variations were linear, three thermographs were sited along the four north-south routes. When their traces were irregular the temperature profile was not calculated. Traverses were also rejected when there were significant regional temperature gradients within the London region. During the second year of the period of traverses with this equipment, readings were made in a similar manner along a route between Marble Arch in central London and London Airport on the western fringes of the city.

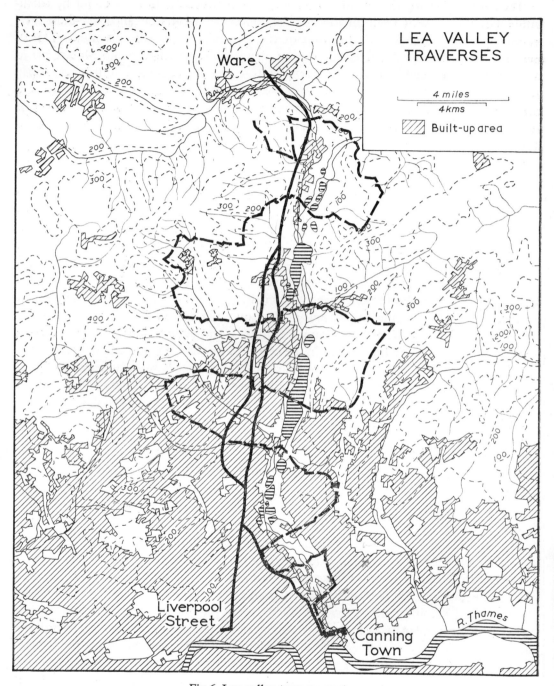

Fig 6 Lea valley traverse routes

The various traverses helped to clarify many uncertainties of temperature conditions within Greater London. For the first time London's heat-island could be studied in section; but the results of both radial traverses and the fixed station survey made it increasingly necessary to sample the whole of London rather than merely a sector. As far as mobile investigation was concerned this necessitated new, automatic, highly sensitive instruments, for the survey routes would be doubled in length and the previous techniques were too slow to cover such distances. Thus, beginning in June 1962, and financed by the Department of Scientific and Industrial Research, traverses were made across the full width of London from northeast to southwest (Fig. 7) in a Land Rover

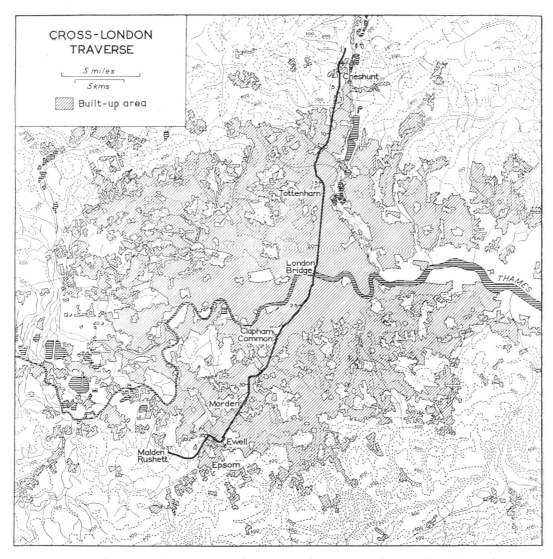

Fig 7 Cross-London traverse route. Stations are numbered

in front of which, at 4 ft (122 cm) above the ground, were shielded electrical resistance thermometer elements connected to a recording a.c. bridge instrument inside the vehicle. The elements were of platinum wire wound on to glass tubes 1·8 in. (45 mm) long and 0·1 in. (2·5 mm) in diameter, and covered by a very thin film of glass. Their sensitivity was well adjusted to the nature and scale of the new investigation which aimed to study not only the heat-island as a whole, but also the influence of different housing densities within London and of parks and other pockets of open land. The lag of the resistance elements was 1·6 sec for a 50 per cent reaction to temperature change, and 4·7 sec for a 90 per cent reaction—equal to half the time interval between successive readings on the recorder.

The two-point Dynamaster recorder worked at 210 volts, 50 cycles per sec, supplied by a vibrator type of transistorized convertor unit from a 12 volt, heavy-duty battery. Many tests were made to ensure uniform power supply characteristics which were found to change only when the battery charge was low. Such circumstances would have affected the chart speed which was normally 24 in. per hr but the battery was, in fact, re-charged after each traverse to prevent this.

One element recorded air temperature, the remaining two formed a hygrometer, and differences in their resistances were converted by the instrument into a record of relative humidity. The wet-bulb element was separated from the dry-bulbs in the thermometer shield. Temperature and humidity were alternately plotted by red and black dots on the chart and each was recorded every 9·2 sec which, at a vehicle speed of 20 mi/hr (32 km/hr), gives readings of both temperature and humidity every 267 ft (81 m). To prevent the flow of engine-heated air over the elements while the vehicle was stationary, at traffic lights for instance, the bonnet of the Land Rover was covered with a pad of glass fibre 4 in. (10 cm) thick. Halts would, of course, affect humidity measures by reducing the ventilation of the wet-bulb, and for this reason a switch operated pen, mounted on a small solenoid, was positioned to give a trace on the right-hand margin of the chart and was used to indicate halts. The effects of reduced ventilation when the vehicle was stationary were later almost eliminated by a small 12 volt extractor fan mounted behind the shield. The trace along the left-hand margin of the chart was also switch operated to give chart positions to fifty locating points along the traverses.

Traverses, mainly during the night, were made along a 36 mi (58 km) route between the Green Belt north of Cheshunt, Hertfordshire, through Tottenham and the City of London, across London Bridge to the Elephant and Castle and then via Clapham, Morden and Ewell to fairly open country at Malden Rushett, west of Epsom, Surrey (Fig. 7). The relief is small except near stations 16a, 17, 18, 26a, 27 and 31–7. (The first three of these stations are the same as those numbered 8, V and IV on the earlier Lea valley traverses). Records were also taken during the return (southwest–northeast) journey along this same route so that a mean temperature profile could be calculated as for the previous Lea valley traverses.

The same equipment was also used in other related investigations. One such series of observations was designed to study temperature and humidity changes near the margins of London. With the Land Rover stationary, and the elements aspirated by the 12 volt fan, temperature changes caused by radiation processes and air movements were taken automatically by the recorder. The incidence and direction of contemporaneous air movements was studied by the drift of soap bubbles. Another programme of experiments was designed to investigate the control of open spaces within the built-up complex of the conurbation upon the pattern of climate. For this purpose, temperature and humidity traverses were made from Paddington to Kensington across Hyde Park (Fig. 8).

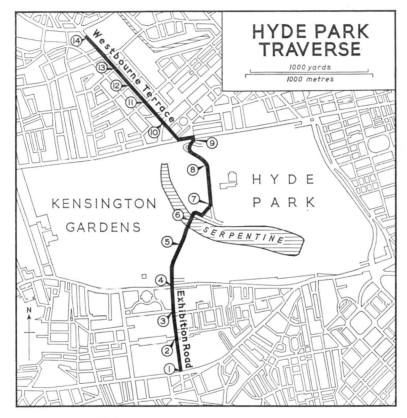

Fig 8 Hyde Park traverse route. Stations are numbered

By these several means, new readings were added to the existing records. More especially, closely spaced observations along London streets supplemented readings from a network of climatological stations, and the thermal and humidity aspects of London's climate could be studied in detail. Not all the elements needed to be so closely sampled, for they vary in the intricacy of their distributions. Cloud cover, for instance, is far more regionally uniform than temperature or humidity. It is not necessary to apply the same density of observations to both variants. Where gradients are slack there are few problems of sampling but where, as in the case of temperatures, appreciable changes are known to occur over distances of a few yards, then the difficulties are obvious. But in these cases it is usual to find a wide spectrum of regional contrast. First order variations

C

can be sampled by a fairly open observation network such as that provided by the fixed station survey and at this scale one can confidently complete the broad spatial picture in districts where records are few, by reasoned analogy. Interpretations, however, must bear in mind the immediate site influences. Second order variations of a more local nature demand closely spaced readings such as those of the mobile surveys, especially using autographic instruments. In these cases the climate is more sensitive to the immediate environment and readings are less easily generalized over a larger region. They do, however, indicate the type of changes to be expected, and though necessarily limited in extent by comparison with the whole of London, provide the best possible solution to the problems set by the size and complexity of the climatic picture at this larger scale of study. The very close measures of the Hyde Park traverses are an example of the third scale of study at which the present survey of London's climate has been conducted.

The fourth dimension of climatic variation has been used in this present study only in so far as it measures the nature and probability of occurrences. Fluctuations of regional climate have been discussed by Drummond (1943), Hawke (1948), Lamb (1963), Lewis (1947) and Manley (1961, 1963a), amongst others, and some of the more recent changes are listed in Marshall's classic study *A century of London weather* (1952). This gives monthly averages and extremes of weather, mainly temperature and rainfall, at Greenwich and Kew Observatories for each year from 1841 to 1949. Others, including Bilham (1938), Luke Howard (1833), Manley (1958) and Shellard (1959b), have considered special aspects of London's climate, but apart from Marshall's work no detailed, comprehensive analysis has previously been made. More especially, little attention has been paid by previous workers to climatic differentiation within the London region. Studies of urban climates, in this country at least, are few in number. Becker's (1925) study of the climate of Glasgow was a statistical analysis of readings at one station, Glasgow University Observatory: records taken at Kew and Greenwich have been treated in a similar way by several authors including Hawke (1941). Tinn (1938, 1939, 1940) published a number of studies of the climate of Nottingham as it differed between its central, suburban and peripheral parts and Gordon Manley (1944) has discussed the records for Manchester. Two of the most comprehensive investigations of town climates in England have been by Balchin and Pye (1947, 1949–50) for Bath, and Parry (1954, 1956a, 1956b, 1957) for Reading. There have also been a number of more limited investigations in other towns such as Edinburgh (Spence, 1936) and Aberdeen (Townshend, 1948) but many of the most notable studies of urban climates have been made in Europe and North America. Much of this work has been listed and summarized by Brooks (1952) and Kratzer (1956).

The arrangement of succeeding chapters is planned to prevent constant forward reference. Climatic elements are, however, remarkably interdependent and it has not been possible entirely to avoid reference to values and relationships derived later. Each chapter begins with a study of conditions at Kew Observatory (Fig. 5) which sets the broad climatic scene; spatial variations are the subject of subsequent sections. A summary chapter (Chapter 12) draws the preceding systematic studies into a framework of regional differentiation.

2 Pressure, weather types, air masses and fronts

Every wind has its weather.
Francis Bacon

THE MAIN PURPOSE of this book is to focus attention upon local patterns in a study of the immediate London district. But one cannot afford to neglect the wider picture for it comprises the basic climatic theme upon which the more intimate local variations are superimposed. The primary features of London's climate are connected with the sequential development and movement of pressure systems, and the air masses and fronts with which they are associated. Here, contrasts occur on scales measured in hundreds, or even thousands of miles. One would not, therefore, expect to find any significant disparity of frequency or type between London and its broader region. For this reason, and because of the extensive literature which already exists on this topic, only the general outlines will be given. The main purpose is to establish the dominant features of the atmospheric circulation as a foundation for the subsequent analyses of elements dependent upon them.

Britain stands in latitudinal and continental positions which, in the pattern of the general circulation, sets it in a sequence of migratory depressions and anticyclones interrupted occasionally by extensions of the more stationary Azores and winter Continental highs. Airstreams moving within and between these atmospheric 'cogs' are varied in character, coming as they do from areas as contrasted as the snowfields of Greenland, the warm waters of the southern North Atlantic and the arid areas of North Africa. Above Britain they contest for atmospheric superiority and their varying fortunes in this 'battle of the air masses' determine the major lineaments of London's climatic scene. The overall impression is one of extreme variety such that spring, summer, autumn and winter lose their normal meaning in what appears to be a disorganized array of weather. But amongst this apparent variety there remains a basic form to British weather throughout the year. The dispersion about the mean may be greater than in many other climates, but the first order variations are no less real and apparent.

THE SEQUENCE OF PRESSURE

Bilham (1938), Brooks (1954), Lamb (1950, 1953) and Manley (1952), amongst others, have discussed what might be called the normal seasonal progression of the British climate and some of the more notable departures from this mean. Many facets of the annual rhythm of weather are related to the periodicities of pressure patterns, although there is by no means an invariable relationship between pressure and weather. The variation of mean monthly pressure, in millibars, based upon readings at exact hours at Kew (1920–60), and the range of individual monthly means are shown in Fig. 9. An expression of the norm is given by the median or central rank value (thick line), whilst the spacing of the upper and lower quartiles (thin lines) measures the scatter of the individual monthly averages. Extreme pressures (1869–1961) are shown by dots.

High median values of monthly mean pressures occur in February, June and September, the lowest values falling in March, August and November. Around the median

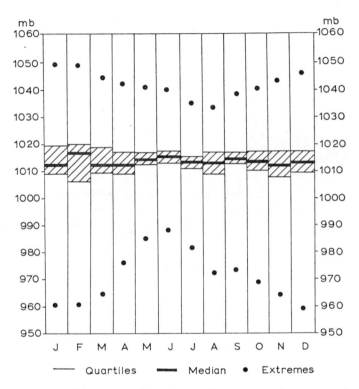

Fig 9 Monthly mean, dispersion and extremes of pressure at Kew, 1920–60; (Source of data: *Monthly weather reports* 1920–60)

is a wide range of values which reflects the changing intensity or frequency from year to year of depressions and anticyclones in any one month. The interquartile range, shaded in Fig. 9, contains 50 per cent of the values and its width is an expression of the scatter of individual records. Differences from the long period mean are obviously smallest in summer. In winter and spring mean monthly pressures change appreciably from year to year, partly owing to variations in the extent of Polar snow and ice, and at these times high-pressure cells are quite frequently replaced by a series of migratory lows. The absolute range of pressure recorded in each month (1869–1961) varies like the average pressure itself, with a gradation from high absolute ranges, above 80 mb, from December to March, to values below 60 mb from May to July. In this context one should note

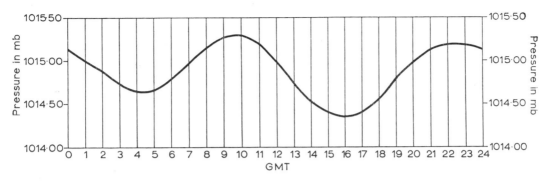

Fig 10 Average diurnal variation of pressure at Kew, 1921–50
(Source of data: *Observatories' year book* 1921–50)

that although November has the lowest average value of monthly mean pressure, the figure was above that in the previous June, the month with the highest average, in 14 of the 41 years between 1920 and 1960.

More detailed analysis of pressure at Kew (and other stations) reveals a small but characteristic diurnal cycle of pressure with maxima around 1000 and 2230 GMT and minima at 0400 and 1600 GMT (Fig. 10). Though no precise explanation exists for this variation, it is clearly related to diurnal changes of temperature and is a form of thermal tide. It has no important weather implications and, in short period analyses, it is masked by a succession of migratory anticyclones and depressions.

Fig. 11 gives some measure of the characteristic day-to-day fluctuations in pressure associated with the incidence or changing intensity of anticyclonic and cyclonic pressure systems. The definition of an 'anticyclonic day', as used by Brooks (1946), is one on which the curvature of the isobars over the British Isles is anticyclonic and pressure is 1,020 mb or more. A 'stormy day' is one on which pressure over or in the vicinity of the British Isles is below 992 mb. Brooks used these parameters to investigate spells of weather over several days and for this purpose ridges of high pressure or anticyclones covering the area for less than 3 days were excluded; similarly, no account was taken of breaks of one or two days in a 'stormy' period. Fig. 11 shows the daily frequency of each type in the 52 years between 1889 and 1940.

The upper graph emphasizes what has already been said of the variation of mean monthly pressure and the scatter about that mean but, in addition, it shows the nature of variations within monthly periods. Some indication of the range of individual mean daily values is given by the interval between the two broken lines in the upper diagram, each separated from the mean curve (heavy continuous line) by twice the standard deviation of the mean. Between these two lines are 95·4 per cent of the recorded values. The band width is therefore proportional to the scatter of mean daily pressure during the period 1881–1940. Winter and early spring, it will be noticed, show not only the greatest divergence of mean daily pressure from year to year but also the most marked changes between short periods or spells within each month. Thus the period from 20–24 January is seen to be characterized by a large number of 'anticyclonic days' giving a

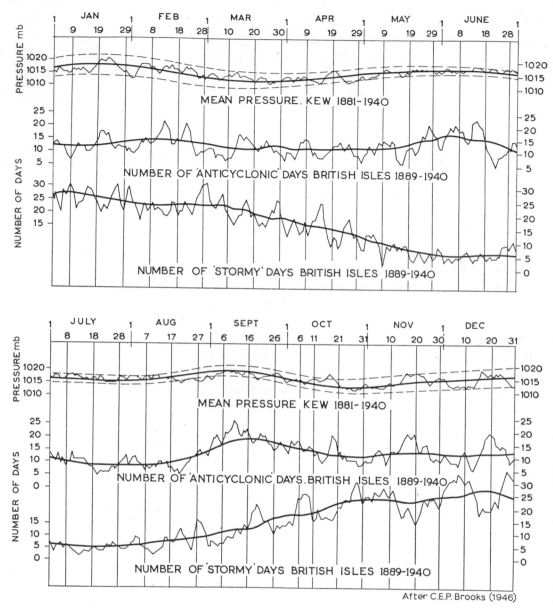

Fig 11 Daily averages of pressure and the frequency of 'Anticyclonic' and
'Stormy' days. Period trend values are shown by thick lines; broken lines are
separated from these by twice the standard deviation of pressure
(Source: Brooks, C.E.P. 1946 Annual recurrences of weather: 'singularities'.
Weather, London, 1, p. 108)

high mean pressure during this period, but conditions are reversed in late January which
is commonly stormy. There is, of course, a close relationship between the graphs of
'anticyclonic days' and 'stormy days' on the one hand and the upper graph of mean
pressure on the other, and it is interesting to note that seasonal variations in the number

of 'stormy days' are appreciably greater than in the occurrence of 'anticyclonic days'. The most marked change in the frequency of 'anticyclonic days' is the substantial increase between late August and early September. 'Stormy days' have a simple mean fluctuation between high values in winter and low in summer, with all the attendant weather implications of this contrast.

WEATHER TYPES

One cannot, of course, make any direct, rigid correlations between pressure values or the number of 'anticyclonic days' and 'stormy days', and weather. The connection is very loose and little more than some broad indication of the intensity of the circulation can be gathered from such brief and incomplete data. Anticyclones can give very different weather according to the season, air mass characteristics and general dynamic structure. They are frequently associated with dry conditions and light winds but thunderstorms are quite common near their margins in summer. Accompanying temperatures are usually high in summer and low or very low in winter. Mist and fog are common in autumn and winter. Emphasis on the evident variety of weather associates does not, of course, deny the very important, even basic, control that pressure systems have upon day-to-day weather, but the connection is indirect and the accompanying weather is a function of more than surface pressure.

Short period departures from the longer period, smoothed, pattern of change are known as singularities if they are outstanding episodes (of about five to ten days) in the seasonal progression, and with a recurrence sufficiently regular to be beyond pure chance. They are, in a sense, notable and frequently repeated departures from the periodic cycle of seasonal weather, or oft-repeated abnormalities in the annual variation of climatic elements, though they remain part of the seasonal pattern. They may even be thought of as micro-seasons. In the graphs of Fig. 11, singularities are clearly shown as departures of mean daily values above or below the smoothed mean value curve. They do not, of course, occure with perfect regularity each year, but probabilities are distinctly better than even.

'Stormy' periods are characterized by the movement of a sequence of depressions, usually frontal, from west to east across the British Isles; southeast England most frequently lying south of the main track of these lows. 'Anticyclonic' periods are commonly associated with a number of well-defined synoptic situations. These include a northeastward extension of the Azores high; the westward spread of a blocking high centred over the Continent in winter, frequently bringing Polar air from the north or northeast or cold continental air off Europe; or the stagnation or more or less autogenous development of anticyclones or extensive ridges of high pressure over northwest Europe which can occur in all seasons.

Lamb (1950, 1953) approached the same basic problem of weather sequences through a very detailed study of the frequency of weather spells of one of the following seven types:

1 *Anticyclonic* Anticyclones centred over, near or extending over the British Isles. Rather settled weather, warm in summer and cold in winter. Autumn fogs.

2 *Southwesterly or Westerly* Sequences of depressions and ridges travelling east across the Atlantic bringing changeable weather.

3 *Northwesterly* Most commonly associated with depressions moving southeast. Unsettled weather. Warm sectors may contain unstable air in late winter and spring. Cooler than the Southwesterly or Westerly type and milder than the Northerly type. Frequent gale-force winds.

4 *Northerly* Depressions forming in southward-moving airstreams on the eastern side of an anticyclone which sometimes extends from Greenland towards the Azores. Cold, disturbed weather with snow and sleet in winter and even spring. Responsible for late and early frosts. Often high winds.

5 *Easterly* High pressure extending from Scandinavia towards Iceland; depressions moving south of their normal course. Cold or very cold in autumn, winter and spring, frequently with showers of snow or sleet. Warm, often thundery weather in summer. Totals of precipitation relatively small.

6 *Southerly* Blocking high over central and northern Europe; Atlantic depressions steered north and northeast around its margins. Rarely persistent for more than a few days, especially in summer. Warm and thundery in spring and summer, mild in autumn. Winter temperatures depend upon the oceanic or continental origins of the air mass.

7 *Cyclonic* Depressions stagnating over, or frequently passing across, the British Isles. Unsettled weather with considerable precipitation. Temperatures rather low except in autumn and early winter. Occasional gales and thunderstorms.

The definitions of Anticyclonic and Cyclonic types differ from Brooks' 'anticyclonic' and 'stormy' weather, as will be seen in a comparison of Figs. 11 and 13.

One might, perhaps, expect each season to be characterized by the dominance, for long periods, of one of the above weather types, or by the persistent association of synoptically related types, such as Westerly and Cyclonic. In the period 1898–1947, analysed by Lamb, there were 158 spells lasting more than 25 days, discounting minor interruptions by ridges of high pressure in a cyclonic sequence, or vice versa, of not more than 3 days. More than 10 per cent of the spells lasted 45 days or more. The winter of 1947, for instance, was characterized by the Easterly type for 52 days. Such spells of weather heavily colour the season in which they occur and analysis shows a marked periodicity of their frequencies (Fig. 12). British weather is, it would seem, most likely to establish itself in a period (25 days or more) of settled, though not necessarily fine, weather in late July and early August and in October. Changeable weather is more typical of April, May, the first half of June and the first half of September.

On the basis of such a collective frequency analysis of all types of weather spells, Lamb (1953) suggested five 'natural seasons' defined by peak periods in the long spell frequency curve (Fig. 12). In each of these there is a strong tendency for the synoptic weather systems to persist. The proposed seasonal division of the year was as follows:

1 *Late Winter and Early Spring* from about 20 January until the end of March. Conditions are more variable than in the other periods except Spring and Early Summer, long weather spells developing in about one year in two but sometimes characteristic of winter and sometimes of early spring. The weather is very variable indeed in those years when no long spell is established.

2 *Spring and Early Summer* between the end of March and approximately 17 June. The start of this period is hard to define for the essence of spring in southeast England is the alternation of short periods of warm, sunny weather with cold, wet days of a Northerly or Northwesterly type. This is the season least given to weather spells of any type but in years when they do occur they are usually Northerly with their

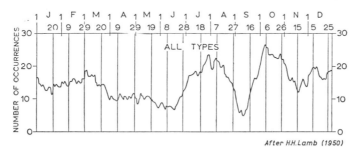

Fig 12 Daily frequency of weather spells of 25 days or more, 1898–1947
(Source: Lamb, H. H. 1950 'Types and spells of weather around the year in the British Isles' *Quart. J. R. Met. Soc.*, London, 76, p. 401)

attendant low temperatures and late frosts or even snow. Day-to-day changes are frequently extreme.

3 *High Summer* from about 18 June until 9 September. Long spells occur in about two years out of three, although only about half of these are Anticyclonic with high temperatures and sunshine amounts. The dominant weather types are Westerly, Northwesterly and Anticyclonic, or combinations of related types such as Cyclonic with either Westerly or Northwesterly. The controlling influence here is the extent and intensity of Atlantic anticyclones, particularly the Azores high.

4 *Autumn* between about 10 September and 19 November. In two years out of three some form of long spell is recorded. The weather in this period is in some years mainly Westerly or Northwesterly giving wet, stormy, unsettled conditions; in other years it is dominantly Anticyclonic with light winds and night fogs.

5 *Early Winter* from about 20 November until 19 January. Long weather spells occur in almost one year in two, Westerly types being most common. Frosts rarely last for more than one week.

Fig. 13 shows the daily frequency of occurrence of the seven types of weather recognized by Lamb (1950, 1953) for the period 1898–1947. The last five days of December and the first ten or twelve of **January** are traditionally ones of wide positive and

FREQUENCY OF WEATHER TYPES 1898~1947

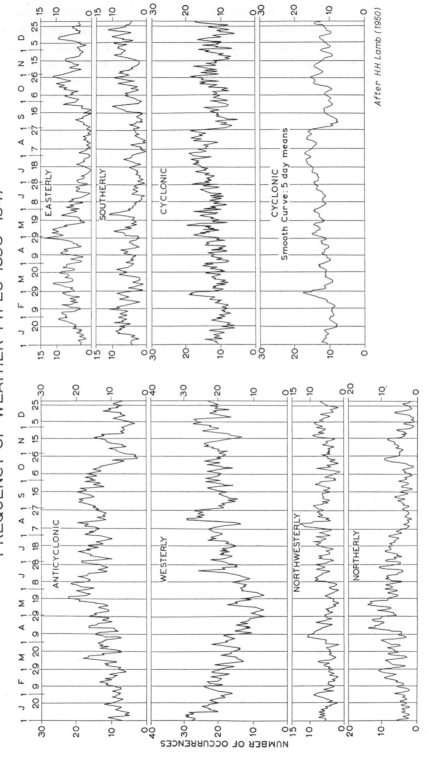

Fig 13 Daily frequency of weather types, 1898–1947 (Source: Lamb, H. H. 1950 'Types and spells of weather around the years in the British Isles' *Quart. J. R. Met. Soc.*, London, 76, p. 401)

negative temperature departures from the smoothed mean. These are associated with families of Atlantic depressions moving into Europe and separated by ridges of high pressure with more settled weather. The days from 6–10 January have, in three years out of five, Westerly weather and this is its period of maximum frequency. By 20 January the dominance of the Westerly type has usually broken down, an increased frequency of Anticyclonic, Easterly and Southerly types marking a westwards expansion and renewal of influence of the Continental winter high. The lowest daily mean temperatures at Kew are generally recorded from 19–29 January in a period of dry, frosty weather with light winds and a marked increase in sunshine during the last five days. High wind speeds accompany a well-defined increase in the incidence of Cyclonic weather between 29 January and 3 **February** in Southeast England (Fig. 13). This spell of unsettled weather usually occurs when a depression or family of depressions moves northeast across the Bay of Biscay or along the English Channel. Snow frequently falls and glazed frosts are a common hazard at this time of the year. In some respects the incidence of this break of Cyclonic weather is critical. When it fails to occur and the Continental high remains dominant until 4 February, the latter usually continues for the remainder of the month giving cold, Easterly weather in London. But February is a month of varied character as continental and maritime air masses alternately overcome what is a marginal balance in southeast England at this time of the year. In cold winters the lowest temperatures are delayed to about 10–12 February. There is a well-defined interruption to the seasonal increase in Kew's mean dry-bulb temperature between 8–12 February associated with a rise in the number of Anticyclonic days (Fig. 13). Late February and early **March** are usually stormy (Figs. 11 and 13), frequently owing to depressions established over the North Sea bringing cold, Northerly, blustery outbreaks to London.

Between 4 March and 16 May long periods are dominated by anticyclones centred over Greenland and the northeast Atlantic, bringing cool, Northerly weather to Southeast England. Interspersed with these are days with Northwesterly and Westerly weather or airstreams which have followed a long, curving path over the Atlantic before turning northeast to reach Great Britain: these give blustery, showery conditions, possibly with snow, but also short periods of sunshine and light winds. There are four well-developed singularities during this period (Figs. 11 and 13). In the fortnight from 4–18 March anticyclones are particularly common at Kew and sunshine totals begin their sharp spring rise about 9 March. Mean daily maximum temperatures at Kew show a similar break about 16 March but night-time temperatures are kept low by clear-sky radiation heat losses. This is a time of accentuated diurnal temperature range. Night frosts are common in this mid-March period, although the average number of days with a mean temperature below 0°C (32°F) at Kew (1871–1950) falls from 3·9 in January and 2·5 in February to 0·9 in March. The last few days of March and the first of **April** see a return to Cyclonic weather but far more regular in occurrence is the cold, stormy period of about 12–19 April with the equal highest frequency of Northerly weather and increased totals of Northwesterly weather. Between 29 April and 16 **May** occurs the second equal highest peak of Northerly weather, the year's highest frequency of Easterly weather and the minimum frequency of Westerly weather. After 16 May there is a decided increase in the frequency of Anticyclonic and, a few days later, Southerly weather, and together these characterize about 70 per cent of the days at this time. The annual peak frequency of Anticyclonic weather (46 per cent of the years 1898–1947) falls on 21 May (Lamb, 1950). The weather is usually sunny, mean daily sunshine totals (1881–1950) at Kew reaching secondary peak values from 22–24 May and 28–31 May (London, Meteorological Office, 1951).

The first four days of **June** are noted for the frequency of Atlantic depressions moving across the British Isles (Fig. 13). There are two further periods, 12–14 June (less pronounced) and 17–21 June, when families of depressions travel eastward in progressively more northerly tracks following the pulsating expansion of the Azores high. It is interesting to note that the three lowest mean daily sunshine totals (1881–1950) at Kew during this month occur on 14, 20 and 24 June. These periods of cyclonic activity are separated by calmer, brighter weather associated with extensions of the Azores high. The frequency of Anticyclonic weather reaches its second highest peak (44 per cent) on 7 June which is noted at Kew for its high mean sunshine hours. During the last of the cyclonic invasions (18–21 June), which form the first waves of the European summer monsoon, Westerly weather achieves one of its outstanding peak frequencies of the year. About 23–24 June there is generally a period of fine Anticyclonic weather with high sunshine totals and low rainfall at Kew, but soon after the beginning of High Summer, usually about 24 June, Northwesterly and Northerly weather returns with some regularity, bringing cloudy skies, high wind speeds, little sunshine and rain. The last two days of June and the first of **July**, on the other hand, are in most years less Westerly and at Kew they are amongst the most consistently sunny of the whole year. The Cyclonic type, with lows centred over the British Isles, has a pronounced peak occurrence in late July and early **August** (generally 21 July–8 August). Depressions are mainly shallow and slow moving and in London there is generally broken cloud with bright periods between heavy rain showers, sometimes with thunder, although occasional deeper, stronger systems are not unknown. The period 20 July—8 August is one of the wettest of the whole year in London although fairly high sunshine hours are maintained in early August. For a few days following this well-marked singularity, there is frequently a short period of Anticyclonic weather from 12–16 August although showery Northwesterly weather reaches its annual peak frequency at this time (13 per cent). From about 17–25 August, there is a well-marked period peak in the Westerly weather frequency curve (Fig. 13); wind speeds increase and rain is associated with fast-moving Atlantic depressions crossing the country. This again is one of the wettest periods of the year in London.

From late August to early October migratory anticyclones and ridges give bright, calm weather with warm, sunny days and cool nights, interspersed between days, such as the last in August and the first two in September, with low cloud and rain. This is known as Old Wives' Summer. Anticyclones reach peak frequencies between 6–16 **September**, 19–22 September and 3–6 October. Rainfall from 13–17 September is very light. In some autumns, anticyclones move in more southerly tracks than usual and the few days around 24 September are in many years a well-developed Cyclonic break, particularly liable to gales and rain. At Kew, 24 September is, on average, one of the rainiest days of the year. The number of anticyclones falls dramatically after 10 **October** and there is a corresponding increase in cyclonic activity with unsettled weather.

From 18 October to about 13 November, Cyclonic weather frequently gives one of the stormiest, wettest periods of the year. Frequencies and intensities are strongest in the week 19–26 October. Interspersed between such days are short periods when high pressure over Europe brings Southerly, Easterly (22 October, 1–2 November) and Northerly (25–26 October) weather. At Kew the seasonal cooling is reversed in the period 28 October–5 **November**. In the literature this is known as St Martin's Summer. Anticyclones increase in frequency to a peak and Westerly and Cyclonic weather to a minimum about 16 November, a notoriously foggy time of the year; mean rainfall at Kew decreases to a well-marked period of much lighter rain from 17–25 November. Early winter begins in the last five days of November and the first ten days of **December** with, in most years, a period of stormy, Westerly weather associated with an intensification of Atlantic westerlies. Soon after mid-December, frequently on 19 December, the Continental winter high begins to dominate the weather, with Anticyclonic, Southerly and Easterly systems. Rainfall amounts are low and clear skies give weak sunshine by day and radiation fogs by night. Immediately after Christmas, from 25–31 December, stormy, cloudy, Westerly conditions usually return with the lowest mean daily sunshine totals of the year, high wind speeds and increased, though far from heavy, rainfall. Thus, but for the short break of Anticyclonic weather in the first four days of January, the year ends as it begins, with unsettled, stormy, dominantly Westerly weather.

AIR MASSES AND FRONTS

For a more limited period than that analysed by either Brooks or Lamb, Belasco (1952) studied the daily frequencies of air masses and the weather associated with fronts at Kew. A summary of his results is given in Table 1.

The most striking feature of the monthly air mass frequency distribution at Kew is the dominance of the basically Polar maritime types (mP′, mP and rP). Generally cool, moist and rather unstable in their lowest layers, and with occasional showers from cumulus clouds, they have a profound influence upon temperatures, radiation amounts, sunshine and humidity values at Kew. Their frequency falls below 35 per cent only in March and reaches 48 per cent in July, accounting for 41 per cent of all daily instances in the years 1938–49. Apart from a markedly lower frequency during March and October, this broad type has no strongly developed monthly periodicity. Polar continental air, on the other hand, is a much rarer airstream, moving over Kew on only four occasions during January and February in 12 years; the length of these spells (9 days in February 1942 and 1947) explains the relatively high mean percentage frequency (Table 1). It is responsible for some of the severest winter weather but it rarely occurs between mid-March and mid-December. Polar air near the centre of depressions has a low frequency of occurrence in all months.

TABLE I

*Monthly and annual percentage frequencies of air masses,
Kew, 1800 GMT, 1938–49*

Air Mass	Jan	Feb	Mar	Apr	May	June
A	7	6	7	7	14	6
mP	24	26	19	28	21	33
rP	10	8	4	5	10	5
cP	7	6	1	0	0	0
D	4	2	3	2	3	3
C	11	10	11	5	13	3
mT	9	10	8	4	4	8
mT'	2	3	4	2	2	1
cT	3	4	5	5	6	3
H	15	19	31	31	19	30
F	8	6	7	11	8	8

Air Mass	July	Aug	Sept	Oct	Nov	Dec	Year
A	5	5	6	4	6	5	6
mP	35	32	27	25	33	31	28
rP	8	7	6	6	5	7	7
cP	0	0	0	0	0	3	2
D	4	4	4	4	5	3	3
C	2	7	3	14	8	7	8
mT	8	6	6	6	10	8	7
mT'	3	1	1	2	2	4	2
cT	4	5	3	9	7	2	5
H	23	24	35	25	17	22	24
F	8	9	9	5	7	8	8

Type		Source Region	Route	Direction
A	Arctic	Arctic ocean north and northeast of Iceland	Oceanic	N or NE
mP	Polar maritime	Northwest and west of Iceland	Oceanic	NW or W
rP	Polar air returning northwards ahead of fronts and depressions	Various, but north of 50°N	Mainly Oceanic	S or SW
cP	Polar continental	North of 50°N and east of 25°E	Land and North Sea	NE, E or SE
D	Polar air near the centre of depressions	Various but north of 50°N	Mainly Oceanic	E and S
C	Continental	South of 50°N and east of 10°E	Land and North Sea	E
mT	Tropical maritime	Southwest of the Azores	Oceanic	SW or S
mT'	Quasi-tropical maritime	43–50°N, 15–25°W	Oceanic	SW, W or NW

cT	Tropical continental	Spain, Mediterranean or northwest Africa; southern Europe in summer	Land and English Channel	S, SE or E
H	Indeterminate anticyclonic air near the centre of anticyclones	—	Various	Various
F	Air in frontal zones	—	Various	Various

Source: Belasco, C.E. 1952 *Characteristics of air masses over the British Isles.* London, Meteorological Office *Geoph. Mem.* No. 87

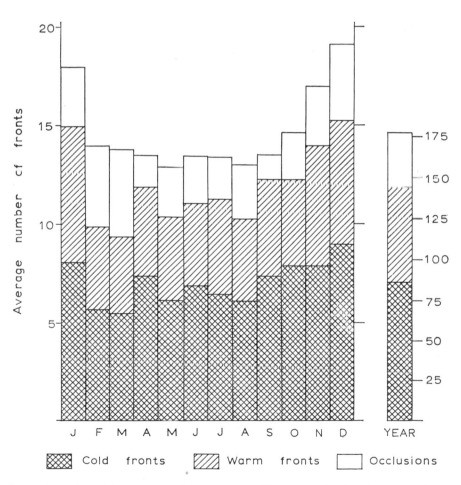

Cold fronts   Warm fronts   Occlusions

Fig 14 Monthly averages of the number of fronts crossing London, 1951–60
(Source of data: *Daily weather reports 1951–60*)

Tropical maritime air, bringing warm, humid conditions and extensive stratiform cloud cover to Kew, accounts for about 9 per cent of occurrences, being most frequent between November and March though with a noticeable increase to a secondary peak in June and July. Tropical continental air, cooler than Tropical maritime in winter and warmer in summer, is drier than the latter in all seasons. It frequently gives very warm, hazy weather but is sometimes thundery. Its frequency is only half that of Tropical maritime air, being most common in spring, early summer and autumn.

Anticyclonic air (with rather intermediate characteristics) accounts for almost one-quarter of the occurrences, being particularly common in March, April, June and September and least frequent in November. Air in frontal zones has a small annual variation from 5 per cent in October to 11 per cent in April. Fig. 14 gives the average monthly frequency of warm, cold and occluded fronts crossing London during the ten years 1951–60. From February to October inclusive, there is remarkably little change in the number of fronts passing across the city, averaging about thirteen per month. In November, December and January, when the Polar Front usually shifts south and air mass contrasts are stronger, fronts are more common, averaging seventeen, nineteen and eighteen per month respectively. Cold fronts account for almost 48 per cent of the annual total, warm fronts average about 33 per cent and occlusions 19 per cent. There is little variation between months in these proportions except for February and March when there is a notable increase in the number of occlusions and a reduction in cold front frequency. The explanation of this may partly lie in an acceleration of the processes of occlusion, probably associated with strong divergence ahead of a well-developed upper trough, but most instances probably result from the tendency, already noted, for depressions to move in more southerly tracks in these months, hence a greater chance that the point of occlusion will pass south of London. September is notable for the small percentage of occlusions amongst all fronts passing over London. This again is probably owing to the nature of the general circulation in this month, when anticyclones over Europe steer depressions around their margins, only the southern, non-occluded parts moving over London. This analysis takes no account, of course, of variations in the intensity, sharpness, speed of movement, breadth and dynamic activity of the fronts; these help to explain the disparity between the statistics for fronts crossing London and the frequency pattern for air in frontal zones. Fronts bring a change in weather but its nature is very variable.

This summary of the periodicity of pressure systems, weather spells and fronts sets the basic form of London's climate and will serve as a foundation for the detailed analysis of individual elements which follows. These have distributions and intensities whose variations both in time and space are partly determined by the broad features of the general circulation. Temperatures in central London, for instance, are modified by the degree of development of London's heat-island, a mass of warm air roughly coincident with the city, and this is closely related to wind velocities and cloud amounts as controlled by weather systems and air mass characteristics. Various elements are intricately interwoven in the final climatic fabric but pressure, wind speed and direction are perhaps basic controls of London's urban climate.

3 Wind

Afloat above ethereal tides,
St Paul's above the city rides.

John Davidson

WINDS, their speed and direction, are not only a primary element of the climate of southeast England, they are also, by reason of their spatial differentiation, an important element and factor (influencing other elements) of London's urban climate. Pollution intensities, visibilities, temperatures and humidities, these amongst others depend upon the character of the wind for both their regional levels and the distinctiveness of the city's climate within the wider environment.

One feature must be recognized from the start: wind is amongst the most fickle of elements, changing appreciably over limited distances and through short periods of time. This is especially true of near-surface winds, and even more of winds in urban areas. Winds near the ground (the standard elevation for anemometers is 33 ft (10 m)) are characteristically turbulent with gusts and lulls and rapid, though temporary, changes in direction. These fluctuations are caused by eddies and are characteristic of nearly all motion in the atmosphere, although the degree of turbulence varies with the accompanying circumstances. Anemograms most commonly illustrate a diurnal cycle of turbulence with oscillations of wind speed and direction building up soon after sunrise to a maximum amplitude around or shortly after noon, then becoming weaker during the afternoon and often dying away almost completely during the night. There is a close relationship between the degree of turbulence and the temperature lapse rate, and thereby the general stability of the atmosphere. Turbulence is strongest by day when surface heating will, especially under clear skies, cause strong thermal gradients through the lowest layers with consequent convection and overturning or eddy motion. By night, the lapse rate is reduced and the atmosphere is normally more stable with much weaker turbulence and a type of air motion closer to laminar flow. Such conditions are, however, modified by the city.

The degree of turbulence and the consequent gustiness of the air near the ground is controlled also by surface 'roughness', hence the city's influence is mechanical as well as thermal, for the typically serrated surface presented by the urban area tends to multiply the eddies. These commonly form between rows of tall buildings, with descending currents on the windward faces and rising currents on the leeward faces, whilst winds are usually channelled along man-made street-gorges orientated in the direction of the prevailing air movement. Thus the most typical attributes of the urban windfield are its regional complexity, its gustiness and temporal nature: these obviously present very serious problems to regional analysis. Instantaneous readings are less representative of the period mean, or of conditions beyond the immediate site, than is true of

D

almost any other element. For this reason, it is customary to consider turbulence as composed of a simple mean motion plus secondary irregular eddies, and to abstract the broad, first order variations from beneath the overlying turbulence 'noise'.

To some extent the standard methods used to measure and calculate wind speed and direction smooth out the more rapid oscillations imposed by turbulence. All wind measuring instruments are characterized by some degree of mechanical inertia, making them less responsive to rapid oscillations of strength and orientation. Many of the familiar cup anemometers have considerable inertia and may fail to respond to rapid gusts which sometimes last for only a fraction of a second, but the standard Dines Pressure Tube Anemograph is more sensitive to the short-lived gusts and lulls which have been seen to typify airflow near the ground, especially in built-up areas. To a varying degree, then, the measuring instruments themselves smooth out the shorter period changes of the turbulence spectrum. Similarly, if we calculate a mean value over a period which is long compared with the frequencies of the eddies of the turbulent flow, then these will be averaged out. The longer the period of the average, the larger are the eddies smoothed out from the period picture. In this context it must be noted that stations with anemographs calculate the mean hourly wind speed and wind direction, and the highest gust speed, in each hour. Stations using cup anemometers calculate the average speed and direction over a short period about each exact hour.

WIND SPEED AT KEW

The outstanding characteristics of the diurnal and annual variations of wind velocity and direction in London can be seen best in an analysis of readings taken on the Dines Anemograph at Kew Observatory in the suburbs of west London. The anemograph is mounted 30 ft (9·4 m) above the dome of the Observatory, with the pressure head at 92 ft (28·04 m) above mean sea level and 75 ft (22·86 m) above the surrounding level ground of the Old Deer Park (17 ft (15·24 m)). The 'effective height' of the instrument is 50 ft (15·24 m): this represents an estimate of the height at which the anemometer would record an equal mean velocity in level country free from obstructions. In spite of nearby obstructions at Kew, the instrument is seen to be over-exposed, with a mean wind speed about 8 per cent higher than would be recorded by an anemometer with its pressure head at the standard level.

It is, of course, far from easy, even in open country, to equate wind speeds taken at these heights with those to be expected closer to the ground. When the temperature lapse rate is large there is a free exchange of momentum by eddies within the turbulent layer and consequently very little change of wind speed with height. In stable air, the vertical transfer of properties is limited and surface drag greatly reduces wind speeds near the ground; in these conditions, winds increase sharply with height. As a very rough general guide, one can expect values at 10 ft (3·05 m) above open country to be about 80 per cent of those at 33 ft (10 m), and at 6 ft (1·83 m), about 75 per cent (Johnson, 1948, pp. 4 and 8). The patterns of change at Kew are nonetheless fairly representative of the London region and values recorded there are only a little above those in air moving above the rooftops of surburban areas.

The mean picture

Fig. 15 shows the characteristic pattern of diurnal change of the mean annual wind strength for each 60 min period ending at an exact hour GMT. Speeds are highest about one and a half hours after noon, averaging at that time about 4·8 m/sec (10·8 mi/hr). In the late afternoon and evening speeds fall to 3 m/sec (6·7 mi/hr) by 0030 GMT, and remain almost constant until 0630 GMT after which they increase in strength to their afternoon maximum. The explanation of this simply progression from

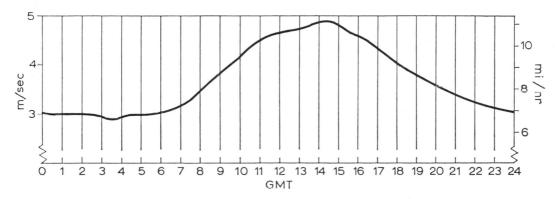

Fig 15 Average diurnal variation of wind speed at Kew, 1932–56
(Source of data: *Observatories' year book* 1932–56)

high daytime to low night-time values of wind strength is the diurnal cycle of temperature and its effect upon the temperature lapse rate and stability of the turbulent layer. When the air is unstable, as during most afternoons, the air in the lowest few hundred feet is mixed, and faster-moving air is carried down, partly compensating for the effect of surface drag. In consequence, mean wind speeds and turbulence are strong. By night the air near the ground commonly becomes more stable with much less mixing, so that fractional drag upon the lowest layers reduces near-surface wind speeds.

Fig. 16 shows that the mean annual pattern at Kew, described above, is in fact the average of a varied monthly form of diurnal variation. The afternoon lag in the time of peak wind speeds, like that of temperature, is greatest in July and least in January. From the afternoon maxima, wind speeds fall rapidly in the two hours before sunset and then more slowly to almost constant values during the early morning hours of darkness. Velocities increase again about two hours after dawn. The diurnal range of mean hourly wind speed varies from month to month (Table 2), being highest in spring, summer and autumn and much lower in winter, that is, in December, January and February.

Between November and December the range is more than halved. These differences

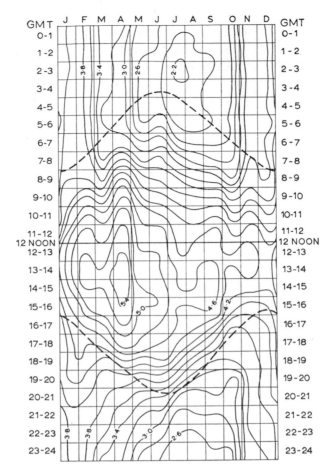

Fig. 16 Average hourly wind speed (in m/sec) at Kew, 1932–56.
Broken lines indicate the times of sunrise and sunset
(Source of data: *Observatories' year book* 1932–56)

are due mainly to changes in night-time rather than daytime speeds. Changes in the diurnal pattern are, of course, a reflection of the diurnal and annual cycle of lapse rates and the effect of these upon turbulence.

The highest mean wind speed, 5·5 m/sec (12·3 mi/hr), occurs between 1300 and 1500 GMT in April; the lowest mean, 2·2 m/sec (4·8 mi/hr), falls between 0200 and 0300 GMT in July (Fig. 16). April does not, on the other hand, record the highest mean monthly wind speed (Table 3). February is clearly the windiest month and August the calmest. Between these two extremes the progression of speeds is far from simple. There is, for instance, a sharp fall in both the average and median velocities between February and March, and in the median values between July and August.

There are also sharp discontinuities, this time increases, between October and November, and between December and January. These changes are of course a reflection of changes in the patterns of pressure and pressure gradients which were considered in

Chapter 1. The picture is, however, a simplification of an interesting day-to-day variation shown in Figs. 17 and 18, but excluding the intercalary date, 29 February. Fig 17 gives the mean daily wind speed for each day of the year (see also Appendix 1) while Fig. 18 shows smoothed (five day moving mean) mean daily wind speeds (thin line) and the general seasonal trend values (thick line). Mean daily wind speeds are

TABLE 2

Diurnal range of average hourly wind speed, Kew, 1932–56

Jan	Feb	Mar	Apr	May	June	July	Aug	Sept	Oct	Nov	Dec	Yr
m/sec												
1·1	1·5	2·0	2·4	2·4	2·5	2·4	2·3	2·3	1·8	2·2	1·0	2·0
mi/hr												
2·5	3·5	4·4	5·3	5·3	5·6	5·3	5·1	5·1	4·1	4·8	2·3	4·4

Source of data: London, Meteorological Office *Observatories' year book* 1932–56

clearly intermediate between usually faster daytime and slower night-time winds but Table 4, though relative to mean monthly values, can be used in conjunction with Figs. 17 and 18 or Appendix 1 to give approximate hourly values.

In **January,** mean daily wind speeds are above the annual average on all days but 20–23 January and fall below the period trend value between 16–26 January (Figs. 17

TABLE 3

Mean monthly wind speed, Kew, 1927–56

Jan	Feb	Mar	Apr	May	June	July	Aug	Sept	Oct	Nov	Dec	Yr
Average												
m/sec												
4·2	4·2	3·9	4·0	3·7	3·6	3·4	3·2	3·3	3·4	3·7	3·8	3·7
mi/hr												
9·4	9·4	8·8	9·0	8·3	8·1	7·7	7·1	7·4	7·7	8·3	8·5	8·3
Median												
m/sec												
3·9	4·0	3·7	3·7	3·5	3·4	3·3	2·9	3·0	3·1	3·5	3·5	
mi/hr												
8·8	9·0	8·3	8·3	7·9	7·7	7·4	6·5	6·7	6·9	7·9	7·9	

Source of data: London, Meteorological Office *Observatories' year book* 1927–56

and 18). This calmer interlude is associated with a fairly recurrent breakdown in the otherwise dominant Westerly and Cyclonic weather (with generally strong pressure gradients in winter) and its replacement by Easterly and Southerly weather associated with an extension of the Continental winter high over Europe. The mean wind speed (non-smoothed) on 22 January is 3·3 m/sec (7·4 mi/hr) and the departure of this from smoothed period trend value (Fig. 18, thick line) for this day is significant at the 1 per cent level. Velocities subsequently increase to a well-defined equal annual maximum, usually on the last day of the month which records a smoothed mean wind speed of

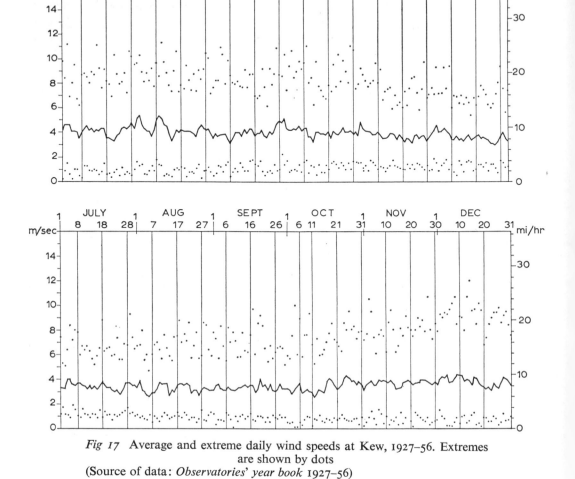

Fig 17 Average and extreme daily wind speeds at Kew, 1927–56. Extremes
are shown by dots
(Source of data: *Observatories' year book* 1927–56)

4·9 m/sec (11·0 mi/hr). The first day of **February** has the highest non-smoothed mean daily wind speed of the year—5·4 m/sec (12·1 mi/hr) (Appendix 1). This value, 1·08 m/sec (2·5 mi/hr) faster than the smoothed, period trend value for this day, is also significant at the 1 per cent level. Eight days later, on 9 February, and following a few days of calmer weather, the annual maximum is almost equalled (the smoothed mean reaches the same value as on 31 January) during a period of dominantly Westerly weather and the departure of this from the period trend value is also significant at the 1 per cent level. But February is very varied in character and the second half is quieter, with speeds little above the annual average, though increasing in the last few days as depressions become more frequent. *March* generally begins with the weather charts dominated by anticyclones over the northeast Atlantic and from 4–18 March, Anti-cyclonic weather is very common at Kew (Fig. 13). Mean diurnal wind speeds are reduced during this period, particularly from 8–11 March, but after 27 March lively Westerly and Cyclonic weather increases in importance and winds are stronger, though because Anticyclonic days are still common, velocities are not as high as in late January. On 30 March the actual (non-smoothed) mean wind speed (1927–56) is 4·9 m/sec (11·0 mi/hr) and the difference between this and the period trend value for this day is significant at the 2 per cent level. At Kew, March winds vary in a contrary manner to the well-known saying; here at least the month comes in like a lamb and goes out like a lion. The picture is reversed in **April,** with an overall fall in wind speeds from 4·6 m/sec (10·4 mi/hr) on 1 April to 3·7 m/sec (8·3 mi/hr) from 12–14 April. The first day of April has the very high (non-smoothed) mean wind speed of 5·1 m/sec (11·5 mi/hr), a singularity significant at the 1 per cent level.

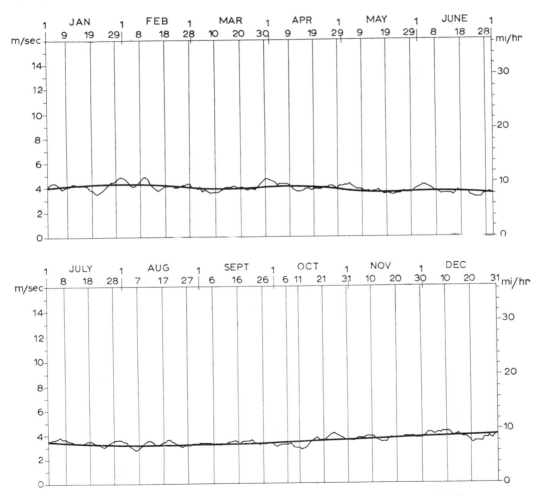

Fig 18 Smoothed mean daily wind speed at Kew, 1927–56. The thin line shows 5-day smoothed mean values, and the thicker line the period trend values through the monthly means
(Source of data: *Observatories' year book* 1927–56)

TABLE 4

Ratio between the averages of wind speed between exact hours GMT and the average monthly speed, Kew, 1927–56

hr	Jan	Feb	Mar	Apr	May	June
0–1	0·90	0·88	0·82	0·78	0·73	0·70
1–2	0·90	0·88	0·82	0·75	0·70	0·70
2–3	0·90	0·88	0·82	0·75	0·70	0·67
3–4	0·93	0·88	0·82	0·75	0·70	0·67
4–5	0·93	0·88	0·80	0·75	0·70	0·67
5–6	0·93	0·88	0·80	0·75	0·70	0·73
6–7	0·93	0·88	0·82	0·80	0·81	0·84
7–8	0·93	0·91	0·85	0·93	0·92	0·94
8–9	0·95	0·93	0·93	1·07	1·05	1·02
9–10	0·97	1·02	1·04	1·17	1·13	1·10
10–11	1·04	1·11	1·17	1·24	1·21	1·19
11–12	1·12	1·18	1·22	1·30	1·27	1·27
12–13	1·17	1·21	1·27	1·32	1·30	1·30
13–14	1·17	1·23	1·30	1·34	1·32	1·30
14–15	1·14	1·21	1·30	1·34	1·35	1·32
15–16	1·09	1·18	1·27	1·32	1·35	1·35
16–17	1·04	1·09	1·22	1·26	1·32	1·30
17–18	1·02	1·02	1·12	1·20	1·27	1·27
18–19	1·00	1·00	1·02	1·07	1·16	1·19
19–20	1·00	0·95	0·98	0·95	1·02	1·05
20–21	0·97	0·93	0·95	0·90	0·94	0·92
21–22	0·93	0·91	0·93	0·85	0·86	0·84
22–23	0·93	0·88	0·90	0·80	0·84	0·78
23–24	0·93	0·88	0·87	0·80	0·76	0·73

hr	July	Aug	Sept	Oct	Nov	Dec
0–1	0·71	0·73	0·76	0·81	0·92	0·92
1–2	0·67	0·73	0·73	0·78	0·92	0·92
2–3	0·65	0·69	0·73	0·78	0·92	0·92
3–4	0·67	0·69	0·76	0·78	0·92	0·92
4–5	0·67	0·69	0·76	0·76	0·92	0·92
5–6	0·71	0·69	0·73	0·81	0·92	0·89
6–7	0·79	0·76	0·76	0·81	0·92	0·92
7–8	0·94	0·88	0·85	0·84	0·95	0·92
8–9	1·06	1·03	1·00	0·94	0·97	0·92
9–10	1·14	1·15	1·15	1·09	1·02	0·95
10–11	1·24	1·24	1·27	1·22	1·14	1·03
11–12	1·26	1·30	1·36	1·31	1·20	1·08
12–13	1·30	1·36	1·36	1·34	1·25	1·16
13–14	1·35	1·39	1·42	1·34	1·25	1·16
14–15	1·35	1·39	1·42	1·34	1·25	1·14
15–16	1·35	1·39	1·39	1·28	1·20	1·08
16–17	1·35	1·36	1·30	1·15	1·08	1·08
17–18	1·30	1·27	1·15	1·06	1·02	1·03
18–19	1·20	1·12	1·03	1·06	1·00	1·03
19–20	1·06	0·97	0·94	0·94	0·97	1·00
20–21	0·88	0·88	0·91	0·94	0·97	1·00
21–22	0·79	0·85	0·91	0·91	0·97	1·00
22–23	0·76	0·79	0·85	0·84	0·97	0·97
23–24	0·71	0·76	0·79	0·81	0·92	0·95

Source of data: London, Meteorological Office *Observatories' year book* 1927–56

After weakening in mid-April there is a partial recovery of wind force in the second half of the month and early **May,** with velocities around 4 m/sec (9 mi/hr). From the middle of May until early October, pressure gradients are particularly slack and mean wind velocities, apart from short breaks, are below the annual average. After 16 May an increase in Anticyclonic and Southerly weather results in mainly calmer weather with wind speeds below the period trend values (Fig. 18) but the calm is often broken by short periods of Westerly and Cyclonic weather and increased wind speeds. One such period falls during the first four days of **June:** the actual mean wind speed of 4·6 m/sec (10·4 mi/hr) on 2 June is a singularity significant at the 1–2 per cent level. There is a second, smaller, increase in wind speeds from 6–21 June, but low values are more characteristic of 24–26 June and are associated with a short but relatively intense period of Anticyclonic weather. The true mean wind speed on 25 June is 3·1 m/sec (6·9 mi/hr) and this is significantly lower than the period trend value for this day (at the 3 per cent level of significance).

A decrease in the frequency of Anticyclonic weather and an increase in Westerly and Northwesterly weather in the first week in **July** is associated with much stronger pressure gradients and higher smoothed mean wind speeds at Kew, reaching 3·8 m/sec (8·5 mi/hr) on 6 July. Non-smoothed mean wind speeds are highest on 4 and 5 July, reaching 4·0 m/sec (9·0 mi/hr), but these departures from the period trend values for these days have significance levels of only about 7 per cent. For the remainder of the month, velocities are variable, but remain below the annual average, more particularly between 21–26 July. Late July and early **August** are, on the other hand, times of stronger winds associated with a pronounced peak in the Cyclonic type of weather (Fig. 13) with lows, though commonly shallow and slow moving, centred over or near the British Isles. The highest smoothed mean wind speed during this period, 3·6 m/sec (8·1 mi/hr), is reached from 29–31 July but the departure from the period trend value on 28 July is significant at only the 6 per cent level.

During the first six days of August, calms increase in frequency and reduce the smoothed mean velocity to its equal annual minimum of 2·8 m/sec (6·2 mi/hr) on 6 August. The actual mean wind speed on this day is 2·6 m/sec (5·8 mi/hr) but its departure from the period trend value for the same day is not statistically significant at even the 10 per cent level. A well-marked interlude of Anticyclonic weather from 12-15 August gives lighter winds than during the ensuing period of mainly Westerly airstreams from 17–25 August. The last week in August sees a dramatic fall in the frequency of Cyclonic weather and a complementary increase in the frequency of Anticyclonic weather. Associated with these changes is a marked decline in mean wind speeds which remain at very low levels during the whole of **September** and early October. September has the second lowest mean monthly wind speed (Table 3) but is more consistently calm than any other month, mean daily velocities departing by only small amounts from 3·3 m/sec (7·4 mi/hr) between late August and early October. This is 'Old Wives' Summer'. There are, of course, breaks in the dominance of migratory anticyclones and ridges during this period and these give short interludes, often no more than one or two days, of stronger winds. One such day is frequently 20 September which has an actual mean wind speed (1927–56) of 4·0 m/sec (9·0 mi/hr), and 24 September with 3·6 m/sec (8·1 mi/hr) (Appendix 1). The former represents a significant deviation from the period trend value (at the 5 per cent level of significance) but not the latter.

Anticyclones affecting the climate of London fall in frequency after 10 **October** (Fig. 13), with a corresponding increase in cyclonic activity, many depressions now with strong pressure gradients and winds. Speeds are well below the seasonal average in early October but from an equal minimum smoothed mean wind speed of 2·8 m/sec (6·2 mi/hr) on 12 and 13 October (a departure from the period trend value significant at the 1 per cent level—in fact the most significant wind speed singularity of the year), smoothed mean values (Fig. 18) increase to a period peak of 4·0 m/sec (9·0 mi/hr) on 25 and 26 October, when departures from the period trend values are significant at the 4 per cent level. This is one of the stormiest periods of the year but it is normally followed by a week, from 28 October to 5 **November,** known as St Martin's Summer, when anticyclones centred over Europe give lighter winds. There is another well-marked peak in the Anticyclonic frequency curve from 15–17 November with an associated fall in smoothed mean wind speeds to 3·4 m/sec (7·7 mi/hr). Thus, apart from lighter winds from 1–4 and 13–17 November, this month has fairly consistent mean wind speeds, little different from the annual average of 3·7 m/sec (8·3 mi/hr).

December can be divided into a windy first half and a calmer second. From 1–19 December, speeds are above both the annual average and period trend values (Fig. 18), reaching peaks in the non-smoothed mean daily values of 4·4 m/sec (9·9 mi/hr) on the 5th and 9th, though these departures have a low statistical significance. Strong winds are brought by recurrent stormy, Westerly weather at this time of the year, but soon after the middle of the month the Continental winter High usually makes its first pulsating expansion to dominate the weather over the British Isles, at least for a few days, during which winds are light. Immediately after Christmas, the anticyclone normally weakens and gives way to deep migratory depressions and mainly Westerly weather with stronger winds, building up to the very much livelier conditions of January.

The average annual cycle, described above, is the long period mean of rather more complicated conditions in any one year and has the limitations of all such generalizations. On any given day, wind velocities may differ significantly from the average. The extreme range, 1927–56, is shown in Fig. 17 and Appendix 1, and Table 5 gives the standard deviation, a measure of the scatter about the average, for each month. Differences between the mean wind speed for each day and the average monthly wind speed are seen to be more marked in winter (October–April) than in summer (May–September). This reflects the more settled and yearly repetitive isobaric patterns of summer in comparison with the more irregular and diversified conditions in winter when actual mean daily wind speeds are likely to differ from the monthly mean by substantial amounts on any one day. The same broad pattern occurs with differences between the actual mean daily wind speed and the period trend value for the same date (Fig. 17). The frequency of various daily means, by months, over a period of 30 years is given in Table 6.

In February, April, May and November the modal, i.e. most frequent mean daily

TABLE 5

Standard deviation of daily mean wind speed, Kew, 1927–56

Jan	Feb	Mar	Apr	May	June	July	Aug	Sept	Oct	Nov	Dec
m/sec											
2·07	2·04	1·91	1·81	1·65	1·55	1·42	1·5J	1·52	1·82	1·95	2·14
mi/hr											
4·6	4·4	4·2	4·0	3·8	3·6	3·3	3·5	3·5	4·0	4·3	4·7

Source of data: London, Meteorological Office *Observatories' year book 1927–56*

TABLE 6

Percentage frequency of average daily wind speed, Kew, 1927–56

m/sec	mi/hr	Jan	Feb	Mar	Apr	May	June
0·0– 0·9	0·0– 2·1	3·2	2·5	2·5	1·0	0·3	0·9
1·0– 1·9	2·3– 4·2	11·6	11·9	11·6	8·4	14·0	11·0
2·0– 2·9	4·4– 6·5	17·9	13·8	21·0	20·2	22·6	25·9
3·0– 3·9	6·7– 8·8	17·6	20·2	19·1	24·7	23·8	24·8
4·0– 4·9	9·0–11·1	15·0	15·6	18·8	19·4	17·8	17·6
5·0– 5·9	11·3–13·1	14·6	15·7	11·2	11·6	10·7	11·0
6·0– 6·9	13·4–15·4	10·4	8·6	8·5	7·9	6·8	6·1
7·0– 7·9	15·7–17·7	5·0	7·0	4·5	4·1	2·6	2·1
8·0– 8·9	18·0–19·8	3·0	3·3	1·9	1·4	1·0	0·2
9·0– 9·9	20·0–22·1	1·1	0·9	0·5	0·7	0·4	0·4
10·0–10·9	22·3–24·4	0·4	0·4	0·4	0·4		
11·0–11·9	24·6–26·7	0·2	0·1		0·2		
12·0–12·9	26·9–28·8						

m/sec	mi/hr	July	Aug	Sept	Oct	Nov	Dec	Yr
0·0– 0·9	0·0– 2·1	0·6	2·2	3·1	5·7	5·8	4·6	2·7
1·0– 1·9	2·3– 4·2	14·2	21·2	15·4	18·3	16·2	17·8	14·3
2·0– 2·9	4·4– 6·5	26·7	25·6	28·2	21·8	17·3	18·2	21·5
3·0– 3·9	6·7– 8·8	24·6	20·4	23·7	18·2	18·4	14·8	20·9
4·0– 4·9	9·0–11·1	18·8	15·5	15·6	17·2	17·7	17·4	17·2
5·0– 5·9	11·3–13·1	10·4	9·8	8·9	9·5	11·3	11·8	11·4
6·0– 6·9	13·4–15·4	3·0	3·8	2·8	4·2	6·8	7·3	6·4
7·0– 7·9	15·7–17·7	1·2	0·9	1·2	3·7	3·3	3·2	3·2
8·0– 8·9	18·0–19·8	0·3	0·6	0·9	1·0	2·1	2·5	1·5
9·0– 9·9	20·0–22·1	0·2		0·2	0·3	0·9	1·9	0·6
10·0–10·9	22·3–24·4				0·1	0·2	0·4	0·2
11·0–11·9	24·6–26·7							0+
12·0–12·9	26·9–28·8						0·1	0+

Source of data: London, Meteorological Office *Observatories' year book 1927–56*

wind speed, is 3·0–3·9 m/sec (6·7–8·8 mi/hr); in all other months it is 2·0–2·9 m/sec (4·4–6·5 mi/hr). Frequencies progressively decrease in grades away from these values but distributions in each month are characteristically skewed towards the lower speeds. Occurrences in the higher ranges are rare but significant and there is an expected prevalence of strong winds in winter. In August there were only 31 days during the 30 years from 1927–1956 when the mean daily wind speed was 7·0 m/sec (15·7 mi/hr) or more; in December there were 76, in January, 90; in February, 99; and in March, 69. On the other hand, very light winds are also more typical of the winter months, or more accurately of the autumn and winter months from September to March. In thirty Octobers between 1927 and 1956, 53 days out of a possible 930, or an average of 1·7 days for the month, had a mean wind speed of less than 1 m/sec (2·3 mi/hr); November had 52 days out of a possible 900 with this value, an average of 1·7 days for the month, and December, 43 out of 930, or 1·4 days per month. In contrast, no month between April and July inclusive recorded a total of more than nine such days during the 30 years; the average was only 0·3 days per month. These features are in part a reflection of the much higher variability of wind speeds in autumn and early winter than in summer already noted. Winters are characterized by days with both very strong and very light mean winds, summers by less variable and extreme conditions. Strong turbulence also contributes to the summer uniformity.

Extreme wind speeds

The mean daily wind speed considered above falls between the normally higher daytime and lower night-time values. The strongest mean hourly winds will usually occur after midday (Table 4 and Fig. 15). Very high wind speeds have, of course, a significance out of all proportion to their frequency and in some senses because of this. Table 7 shows the mean highest hourly wind speed and maximum hourly wind speed at Kew for the period 1913–38.

TABLE 7

Average highest hourly wind speed and maximum hourly wind speed, Kew, 1913–38

	Jan	Feb	Mar	Apr	May	June	July	Aug	Sept	Oct	Nov	Dec
Average												
m/sec	13	12	12	11	10	10	9	9	10	11	12	12
mi/hr	28	26	26	25	23	22	21	20	22	24	26	27
Maximum												
m/sec	16	15	18	13	15	14	13	13	16	13	16	17
mi/hr	35	34	41	30	33	31	28	28	36	28	35	37

Source: London, Meteorological Office 1943 Tables of wind direction and force over the British Isles, 2nd Edition. London, *Meteorological Office Mem.*, No. 370, p. 10

The mean highest hourly wind speed approximates to the sustained velocity which will probably be reached or exceeded in the month in question once in two years; the maximum hourly wind speed represents the sustained velocity which the wind is unlikely to exceed in that month. The annual ranges are really rather small, noticeably smaller than the range of mean monthly wind speeds (Table 3), but this is to be expected of such extremes, for although there is a tendency to stronger winds in winter and early spring than in summer and early autumn, high speeds can and do occur in almost all months.

Moderate gales, or a mean hourly wind speed of 14 m/sec (32 mi/hr) or above, were recorded in all months except April, June, July, August and October in the 26 years analysed. In March there was one reading of fresh gale intensity but it must be remembered that this value, like all those of Table 7, represents the calculated mean over 60 min between exact hours. The short gusts, frequently lasting for only a few seconds, which occur within such periods are also quite obviously of fundamental importance. Table 8 lists these.

TABLE 8

Average highest gust, 1913–38, and maximum recorded gust speed, 1871–1950, Kew

	Jan	Feb	Mar	Apr	May	June	July	Aug	Sept	Oct	Nov	Dec
Average												
m/sec	24	22	21	20	19	18	18	18	19	20	22	23
mi/hr	53	49	48	46	42	41	40	40	42	46	50	51
Maximum												
m/sec	32	30	33	32	25	29	28	27	31	31	33	32
mi/hr	71	66	74	71	57	64	63	61	69	69	73	72

Sources: London, Meteorological Office 1943 Tables of wind direction and force over the British Isles, 2nd Edition, *Meteorological Office Mem.*, No. 370, p. 12; London, Meteorological Office 1951 *Climate of Kew Observatory, 1871–1950*. Appendix, p. 3 (Typescript)

Again, the mean highest gust speed in each month is that which is likely to be reached or exceeded in about one year in two; the maximum gust is unlikely to be exceeded. The peaks of both sets of values fall in winter when suburban London might expect gusts of 22 m/sec (50 mi/hr), equivalent to a strong gale, in almost half the years, causing local damage to trees and perhaps property. Gust speeds of whole gale strength or more have occurred in all months, even August, which is normally the calmest of the year. These high speeds will usually occasion considerable damage; Table 9 gives the number of hours in which certain extreme gust speeds have been exceeded. The threshold values are 17·1 m/sec (38 mi/hr), known as a moderate gale, but for the purposes of statistical summaries not entered as gales; and 24·5 m/sec (55 mi/hr), known as a whole gale.

The broad pattern is similar to that of related analyses with the maximum of the mean curve in January and a minimum in July, also a remarkable increase between December and January. March has a much lower incidence of speeds above these high threshold values because of an increase in the frequency of anticyclones (Figs. 11 and 13). The sudden drop in the mean number of hours with strong winds between April and May is also striking, more especially since it marks the beginning of a long period of almost 8 months when, although high gust speeds occasionally occur (Table 8), they are far less frequent or sustained than from January to April. Summarizing, deep depressions with strong pressure gradients and winds are far from unknown in summer and autumn but they are less frequent then than in winter and early spring. One should, of course, remember that these high winds are exceptional. Even in January, only a

TABLE 9

Average and extreme number of 60 min periods between exact hours GMT containing gusts exceeding the stated speeds, Kew, 1937–51

	Jan	Feb	Mar	Apr	May	June
Average						
>17·1 m/sec (38 mi/hr)	38·5	36·0	22·9	35·7	15·2	13·6
>24·5 m/sec (55 mi/hr)	2·3	1·3	0·7	1·6	0·1	0·7
Maximum						
>17·1 m/sec (38 mi/hr)	89	73	55	103	59	59
>24·5 m/sec (55 mi/hr)	10	6	5	9	1	10

	July	Aug	Sept	Oct	Nov	Dec	Yr
Average							
>17·1 m/sec (38 mi/hr)	8·2	8·5	8·5	16·1	21·7	21·7	20·1
>24·5 m/sec (55 mi/hr)	0·1	0·1	0·1	0·5	0·7	0·7	0·7
Maximum							
>17·1 m/sec (38 mi/hr)	21	43	23	45	63	47	103
>24.5 m/sec (55 mi/hr)	1	1	2	3	8	5	10

Source: London Meteorological Office 1951 *Climate of Kew Observatory, 1871–1950.* Appendix, p. 3 (Typescript)

little over 5 per cent of the hours contain gusts above 17·1 m/sec (38 mi/hr) and less than half of 1 per cent have gusts above 24·5 m/sec (55 mi/hr). But their rarity combined with their severity makes them all the more noteworthy.

Shellard has made a rather different approach to the investigation of strong winds over the United Kingdom (Shellard, 1962, p. 40), with the following results for Kew:

TABLE 10

Average hourly wind speeds likely to be exceeded only once in the stated number of years, Kew, 1931–59

	Years			
	10	*20*	*50*	*100*
m/sec	15	16	17	17
mi/hr	33	35	37	38

Source: Shellard, H. C. 1962 Extreme wind speeds over the United Kingdom for periods ending 1959. *Met. Mag.*, London, 91, p. 40

By reference to Tables 7 and 10, and within the possibly small limits of error imposed by differences in the periods of analysis, we see that the maximum hourly wind speed of 18·3 m/sec (41 mi/hr) recorded at Kew from 1913–38 is likely to occur only once in 100 years, and the 16·6 m/sec (37 mi/hr) recorded in December, only once in 50 years. Similarly, Table 11 gives the maximum gust speeds likely to be exceeded once in the stated number of years.

TABLE 11

Gust speeds likely to be exceeded only once in the stated number of years, Kew, 1931–59

	Years			
	10	*20*	*50*	*100*
m/sec	31	33	35	36
mi/hr	70	73	78	81

Source: Shellard, H. C. 1962 Extreme wind speeds over the United Kingdom for periods ending 1959. *Met. Mag.*, London, 91, p. 41

At the opposite end of the wind force spectrum are times of calm air. Table 12 gives the average number of hours per month with mean wind speeds of 1·5 m/sec (3·5 mi /hr) or less.

TABLE 12

Average number of hours of calm (1·5 m/sec (3·5 mi/hr) or less), Kew, 1937–50

	Jan	Feb	Mar	Apr	May	June	
hrs	97·4	86·6	122·3	107·4	138·6	128·7	

	July	Aug	Sept	Oct	Nov	Dec	Yr
hrs	140·2	172·5	162·5	199·2	153·4	147·4	165·6

Source: London, Meteorological Office 1951 *Climate of Kew Observatory, 1871–1950*. Appendix, p. 3 (Typescript)

It is interesting to compare this table with Table 6 for average daily speeds. The grades are not precisely the same but this does not obscure the general pattern: the varying length of month may have a small influence. January and February have relatively small numbers of both calm days and hours of calm, strong pressure gradients maintaining an active circulation over London by both day and night. Mean wind speeds in March we have already noted to be low and in this month the number of hours of calm increases markedly. April has fewer hours of tranquil air with another reversal in May. What is perhaps most noticeable in a comparison between the annual pattern of days and hours with calm is the differences between these two measures in summer. The tendency is for June and July to have somewhat fewer calm days (as measured by the mean daily wind speed) than January and February (Table 6) but far more hours of calm (Table 12). This is owing to the higher diurnal temperature ranges in summer when gusty, turbulent daytime winds compensate for the often windless nights. The latter are, however, accredited to the total hours with calm. Late summer and autumn, from August to October and, less obviously, November, have the longest periods of winds of 1·5 m/sec (3·5 mi/hr) or less as well as the greatest number of days with mean wind speeds of this order. Lower daytime temperatures, longer nights and generally slack pressure gradients all tend to this end. December sees the beginning of the synoptically disturbed conditions of winter with fewer hours of calm.

The effect of daytime turbulence in summer is also evidenced by the remarkable fact that in 15 years of records at Kew between 1937 and 1951, not a single day in May recorded more than 19 hours of calm and no more than 22 hours were recorded on any one day in March, June, July and August. It is very rare in summer to get a completely still day. The longest periods of continuous calm fall in October and November.

WIND DIRECTION AT KEW

Changes from month to month in the pattern of wind direction for speeds greater than 1·5 m/sec (3·5 mi/hr) are given in Table 13. The direction of winds with speeds below this value tend to be too fickle for analysis and the airflow is frequently too weak to control the vane.

Over the year as a whole the prevailing winds are from the south-southwest and west-southwest. These winds, from 200–250 degrees true, make up 28·3 per cent of all occurrences including calms, or 35·2 per cent of measured wind directions. This is appreciably

TABLE 13

Wind direction for winds of more than 1·5 m/sec (3·5 mi/hr), Kew, 1950–9

Percentage number of 60 min periods ended at exact hours GMT in each of which the mean direction was between the stated limits

	N	NNE	ENE	E	ESE	SSE	S	SSW	WSW	W	WNW	NNW	
							Degrees true						
	350	020	050	080	110	140	170	200	230	260	290·	320	0–1·5
	–010	–040	–070	–100	–130	–160	–190	–220	–250	–280	–310	–340	m/sec
Jan	5·0	6·8	5·7	4·1	2·5	3·0	7·1	14·5	14·1	10·6	4·2	3·8	18·5
Feb	6·3	9·1	7·7	3·9	1·9	2·3	8·5	13·9	14·2	7·5	3·4	4·8	16·4
Mar	4·3	8·6	11·5	10·5	4·4	4·6	8·0	11·0	8·8	4·8	2·8	3·2	17·5
Apr	7·3	12·5	9·0	5·8	2·0	1·3	5·6	11·8	11·3	7·5	3·9	4·9	17·1
May	5·6	12·9	10·0	8·0	2·6	2·0	6·6	13·4	9·7	5·9	3·0	4·2	16·1
June	4·4	8·0	6·3	5·9	1·3	1·4	5·5	16·0	14·4	8·7	5·3	4·8	17·9
July	4·5	7·1	4·9	3·2	1·0	1·3	5·5	15·9	17·9	10·3	5·8	4·8	17·8
Aug	2·6	4·1	3·8	3·6	1·7	2·6	7·2	18·9	17·6	8·2	4·0	4·1	21·6
Sept	2·6	5·7	7·8	5·0	2·3	2·8	6·9	15·4	16·2	8·4	4·1	2·5	20·2
Oct	4·4	5·0	4·5	3·9	3·0	3·4	5·9	15·2	13·6	5·8	4·5	4·4	26·3
Nov	7·7	5·4	4·2	4·4	3·6	4·8	9·0	13·5	11·1	5·4	3·5	5·1	22·3
Dec	3·8	3·3	4·2	3·4	4·1	3·6	10·1	17·4	14·9	6·4	3·4	3·1	22·2
Yr	4·9	7·4	6·6	5·2	2·5	2·8	7·1	14·7	13·6	7·4	4·1	4·1	19·5

Source of data: London, Meteorological Office tabulations, Form 3433 (MS)

greater than in any neighbouring direction grade. Equally interesting is the very low frequency of winds from the east-southeast and south-southeast (110–160 degrees true). These and other characteristics are, of course, related to changes in pressure patterns over southeast England and conform with previous discussions of weather types. Winds from a general southwesterly direction are important in all months but especially, it will be noted, in August. There is a tendency for a stronger southerly element in November, December, March and May, and a westerly element in July and January. Northeasterly winds are also frequent, with a gradual build-up of occurrence from January to May, followed by a secondary maximum in September. Northeasterly (020–070 degrees true) winds become more important than southwesterly (200–250 degrees true) winds in March and are nearly so in April and May. March also sees a clear peak frequency of easterly (080–100 degrees true) winds. We have, of course, previously noted similar patterns of air movement in the discussion of pressure sequences and weather types.

Table 14 relates wind direction and speed over the year.

TABLE 14

Percentage frequency distribution of average hourly wind directions and speeds, Kew, 1950–9

		Percentage number of hours from:					
		N	NNE	ENE	E	ESE	SSE
				degrees true			
m/sec	mi/hr	350 -010	020 -040	050 -070	080 -100	110 -130	140 -160
<0·3	<0·8						
0·3– 1·5	0·8– 3·5						
1·6– 3·3	3·7– 7·4	1·9	2·1	1·7	1·8	1·3	1·1
3·4– 5·4	7·7–12·1	1·8	2·8	2·6	2·0	0·9	1·0
5·5– 7·9	12·3–17·7	1·0	2·2	1·9	1·2	0·3	0·6
8·0–10·7	18·0–24·0	0·2	0·3	0·3	0·2	0+	0·1
10·8–13·8	24·2–29·9	0+	0+	0·1	0+		0+

		S	SSW	WSW	W	WNW	NNW	
				degrees true				
		170 -190	200 -220	230 -250	260 -280	290 -310	320 -340	Total
<0·3	<0·8							2·7
0·3– 1·5	0·8– 3·5							16·8
1·6– 3·3	3·7– 7·4	2·6	4·2	5·0	3·0	1·8	1·8	28·3
3·4– 5·4	7·7–12·1	2·5	4·9	4·9	2·9	1·5	1·6	29·4
5·5– 7·9	12·3–17·7	1·7	4·2	3·0	1·3	0·7	0·6	18·7
8·0–10·7	18·0–24·0	0·3	1·3	0·6	0·2	0·1	0·1	3·7
10·8–13·8	24·2–29·9	0+	0·1	0·1	0+	0+	0+	0·3

Source: London, Meteorological Office tabulations, Form 3433 (MS)

E

The highest speeds accompany winds from the south-southwest (200–220 degrees true), although southerly and west-southwesterly winds (170–190 and 230–250 degrees true) are quite frequently stronger than 5·5 m/sec (12·3 mi/hr) as are winds from the north, northeast and east. Of the recorded wind directions between 200 and 250 degrees, 33 per cent are of 5·5 m/sec (12·3 mi/hr) or more; 34 per cent of those between 020 and 070 degrees are of this speed. Some of the lightest winds, below 3·4 m/sec (7·7 mi/hr), also accompany winds from the southwest. Winds from the east-southeast (110–130 degrees true) are usually light. This, like the main characteristics of Table 14 and the discussion of winds generally to this point, paints the broad picture for much of Greater London and in large measure for southeast England as a whole. Even so, there are variations within London owing to the surface morphology and urban development.

MODIFICATIONS OF THE WINDFIELD BY THE SURFACE MORPHOLOGY

In making comparisons between winds in the various parts of Greater London, as in any other town, one is faced with several problems of analysis. Paramount amongst these is the complexity of the areal pattern and its temporal nature. Anyone walking through London on a windy day will soon realize the contrasts between streets facing in different directions and even between two sides of the same street, some of these small-scale circulations being derived from temperature differences between courtyard, street and park surfaces (Whiten, 1956; Gold, 1956). Eddies behind buildings may extend downwind 10–20 times their height (Evans, 1957, p. 3) and near street level in an area surrounded by tall buildings, speeds will usually be very much less than with normal exposure. In one investigation in London, the wind speed at 4 ft (1·2 m) in the middle of a road between tall blocks of flats averaged 0·8 m/sec (1·8 mi/hr) while that at Kew was 2·3 m/sec (5 mi/hr), and 1·8 m/sec (4·1 mi/hr) when that at Kew was 9 m/sec (20 mi/hr) (Bedford et al., 1943, p. 8). But synoptic and climatological stations avoid, as far as possible, these dominant site influences and some correction for local interference is usually made using the measure of effective height. Also, by averaging over a period of an hour or more, the instantaneous differences can be smoothed out in a broader view which is simpler to analyse. But it should always be remembered that the measures taken at official recording stations are equivalent to conditions above roof-level.

Another problem in the study of urban winds is how to isolate relief influences from those owing to the city *per se*. They act together to modify the regional picture, but by careful selection and analysis it is possible to trace at least the broader facets of the separate controls.

On days when there is hardly any air movement between the closely ranked buildings of city streets, many Londoners seek the refreshing breezes which blow across Hampstead Heath and Horsenden Hill, Harrow Hill, Highgate, Alexandra Palace Park, Crystal Palace Park and Shooters Hill, all those parts of the conurbation in fact which raise their heads above the general low-lying areas whose air is enmeshed in a maze of macadam, bricks and mortar. The rate of increase of mean wind speed with height in the lowest layers is usually logarithmic (Frost, 1947, pp. 14–17; Hellman, 1917, p. 174; Sutton, 1937, pp. 105–7) but locally it is very complex, varying with the lapse rate of temperature, the geometry of the surface and the direction and speed of the wind, and no simple correction can be generally applied. But when the velocity gradient is steep, as will frequently occur during inversions and/or when winds are strong (Pooler, 1963, p. 449), the wind speed at 500 ft (152·5 m) may be twice that at rooftop level. The diurnal variation of wind speed also changes its characteristics with height and at 300–1,000 ft (about 100–300 m) above open, level country, speeds are faster by night than day. Conditions in the higher parts of London are probably intermediate between those near the ground at low altitudes and conditions at greater heights above open country.

Aspect and the form of the ground are also important controls. The leeward slopes of hills are usually more sheltered, although in certain circumstances there may be convergence in these areas with strong, gusty winds. The low mean wind speed (for all winds) of 3·6 m/sec (8·1 mi/hr) at Croydon in south London is appreciably less than at London Airport in a similar position of the urban fringe in west London (Fig. 5 and Table 19). Its (corrected) mean annual speed is in fact lower than at any other station in the area and this in spite of its quite high elevation—208 ft (63·4 m) O.D. The real cause is the exceptionally large number of calms and light airs (wind strengths of 1·5 m/sec–3·5 mi/hr or less), most probably owing to shelter by the North Downs, on the north-facing backslope of which the station lay. Urban development may also contribute to this effect, as we shall see later.

Channelling between higher ground, such as along the Lea valley between the heights of north London and the Epping ridge (Figs. 1 and 2), may frequently concentrate and accelerate the airflow, particularly when the air is stable. Speeds in central London (represented by the Kingsway record), for instance, seem to be unusually high, with winds blowing parallel to the higher (by 100–400 ft (46–122 m)) ground running from west-southwest to east-northeast between Hampstead and Highgate in north London (Figs. 1 and 2, Table 15).

Croydon recorded its highest mean wind speed from a more westerly direction than Kew, London Airport or rural districts outside the city. This may be the consequence of topographic steering and concentration by the North Downs immediately south of the station. The curiously small mean speed associated with winds from the north-northeast (020–040 degrees true) at Kingsway is more difficult to understand, but, if topographically influenced at all, may be associated with some divergence at the widening, funnel-shaped southern exit of the lower Lea valley, otherwise orientated at this angle on Kingsway (Fig. 5).

Wind directions are also affected by London's underlying surface form, disturbing the pattern of flow, forming eddies, channelling and initiating lee waves. It is difficult to generalize about the nature of this interference, but it may explain the otherwise puzzling differences in wind direction frequencies at Kingsway and Kew (Table 16).

The Kingsway anemometer was (until 1959) mounted above the Air Ministry roof,

TABLE 15

Average wind speeds from given directions

Mean wind speed from:

m/sec	N	NNE	ENE	E	ESE	SSE
	350 –010	020 –040	050 –070	080 –100	110 –130	140 –160
			degrees true			
Kingsway 71 ft (21·6 m)	4·1	3·8	4·2	4·1	3·7	3·6
Kew 17 ft (5·2 m)	4·3	4·7	4·6	4·5	3·7	4·3
Croydon 208 ft (63·4 m)	4·4	4·3	4·6	4·3	3·9	4·2
London Airport 82 ft (25·0 m)	4·1	4·6	4·7	4·6	4·3	4·7
SE England*	4·6	5·3	4·8	4·8	4·8	5·0

m/sec	S	SSW	WSW	W	WNW	NNW	all
	170 –190	200 –220	230 –250	260 –280	290 –310	320 –340	
			degrees true				
Kingsway	4·2	4·8	5·0	4·7	4·2	4·0	4·5
Kew	4·5	5·0	4·5	4·2	4·0	4·0	4·6
Croydon	4·7	5·3	5·5	5·1	4·4	4·4	4·9
London Airport	5·2	6·0	4·9	5·4	4·7	4·4	5·1
SE England*	5·7	6·0	5·5	5·2	4·8	4·7	5·2

Mean wind speed from:

mi/hr	N	NNE	ENE	E	ESE	SSE
	350 –010	020 –040	050 –070	080 –100	110 –130	140 –160
			degrees true			
Kingsway	9·2	8·5	9·4	9·2	8·3	8·1
Kew	9·7	10·6	10·4	10·2	8·3	9·7
Croydon	10·0	9·7	10·4	9·7	8·8	9·4
London Airport	9·2	10·4	10·6	10·4	9·7	10·6
SE England*	10·4	11·9	10·8	10·8	10·8	11·3

mi/hr	S	SSW	WSW	W	WNW	NNW	all
	170 –190	200 –220	230 –250	260 –280	290 –310	320 –340	
			degrees true				
Kingsway	9·4	10·8	11·3	10·6	9·4	9·0	10·2
Kew	10·2	11·3	10·2	9·4	9·0	9·0	10·4
Croydon	10·6	11·9	12·2	11·5	10·0	10·0	11·1
London Airport	11·7	13·4	11·1	12·1	10·6	10·0	11·5
SE England*	12·7	13·4	12·2	11·7	10·8	10·6	11·7

* mean of Abingdon, 210 ft (64·0 m); Shoeburyness, 11 ft (3·4 m); South Farnborough, 249 ft (75·9 m)

The values for Kingsway (1948–54), Kew (1950–9) and Croydon (1950–8) are compiled from mean hourly anemograph readings; those for London Airport (1949–58) are based upon short period means at 6 hr intervals. Corrections, where necessary, have been made for effective height and defective records

Source of data: London, Meteorological Office tabulations, Form 3433 (MS)

TABLE 16

Frequency of given wind directions for winds of more than 1·5 m/sec (3·5 mi/hr) at Kingsway and Kew

	N	NNE	ENE	E	ESE	SSE	
Percentage number of hours from:							
				degrees true			
	350	020	050	080	110	140	
	–010	–040	–070	–100	–130	–160	
Kingsway (1948–54)	3·7	5·1	6·7	5·7	2·6	1·8	
Kew (1950–9)	4·9	7·4	6·6	5·2	2·5	2·8	
Difference							
Kingsway–Kew	–1·2	–2·3	0·1	0·5	0·1	–1·0	

	S	SSW	WSW	W	WNW	NNW	
			degrees true				
	170	200	230	260	290	320	Total:Year
	–190	–220	–250	–280	–310	–340	
Kingsway	3·6	10·1	18·3	13·9	6·8	4·1	82·4: 1948–54
Kew	7·1	14·7	13·6	7·4	4·1	4·1	80·4: 1950–9
Difference							
Kingsway–Kew	–3·5	–4·6	4·7	6·5	2·7	0·0	

Kingsway values corrected for a 1·5 per cent defective record

Source of data: London, Meteorological Office tabulations, Form 3433 (MS)

north of the Thames in central London (Fig. 5), 160 ft (48·8 m) above ground level and 231 ft (70·4 m) O.D. The effective height of the instrument is 40 ft (12·2 m). The contrasts in Table 16 may be due to the disparity in the years covered by the analyses or to the slightly higher frequency of winds of 1·5 m/sec (3·5 mi/hr) or more at Kingsway, but such marked shifts of wind direction are unlikely to result solely from such inconsistences. The immediate influence of nearby streets and office blocks on the Kingsway record, if it occurs at all, would be some near-surface channelling along a north-north-west to south-southeast alignment. Comparison between the Kingsway and Kew records shows, however, a marked increase in the frequency of winds at Kingsway from the west-southwest and west and, less obviously, from the east (Table 16). This alignment mirrors the general run of the local topography, the Thames valley between the southern edge of the north London heights from Hampstead to Alexandra Palace (Wood Green) north of Kingsway and the upstanding commons and Downs to the south.

Kew, by comparison, stands where the Thames's general orientation is southwest-northeast, an alignment continued by its right-bank tributaries, the lower Mole and Wey (Figs. 1 and 2). At Kew, northerly and northeasterly (350–040 degrees true) and southerly and south-southwesterly (170–220 degrees true) winds are particularly frequent, probably reflecting some influence on the near-surface airflow by the valleys of the Colne (a north-bank tributary) and Wey (a south-bank tributary) of the Thames

(Figs. 1 and 2). The physical setting seems to bear upon wind direction frequencies at both Kingsway and Kew, but were this the sole explanation one would expect positive disparities between the two sets of readings in any given wind direction to be balanced by negative relationships in neighbouring ranges. This is not the case, as will be seen from Table 16. The higher frequency of easterly (050–130 degrees true) winds at Kingsway is over-compensated by winds on either side of this direction. Increased westerly (230–310 degrees true) winds are under-compensated by winds from neighbouring quarters. There would seem to be other influences upon the records; perhaps, as already suggested, of the non-coincidence of years covered by the separate analyses.

The anemometer which was, until September 1959, sited on Croydon Airfield, also shows somewhat different wind direction frequencies from those at either Kingsway or Kew (Table 17).

TABLE 17

Frequency of given wind directions for winds of more than 1·5 m/sec (3·5 mi/hr), Croydon, 1950–8

Percentage number of hours from:

N	NNE	ENE	E	ESE	SSE	S	SSW	WSW	W	WNW	NNW
					degrees true						
350	020	050	080	110	140	170	200	230	260	290	320
–010	–040	–070	–100	–130	–160	–190	–220	–250	–280	–310	–340
2·7	4·2	5·0	3·3	1·5	3·2	8·3	12·7	11·6	9·0	4·4	2·9

(percentage< 1·5 m/sec: 31·1)

figures corrected for effective height

Source of data: London, Meteorological Office tabulations, Form 3433 (MS)

The main difference is the notably higher frequency of south-southwesterly winds by comparison with the Kingsway and Kew records. The explanation seems to be at least partly topographical, for the Croydon station lay near the focus of a remarkable set of deep dry-valleys cut with these same alignments into the back slope of the North Downs (Figs. 1, 2 and 5). The channelling effect of these valleys probably goes a long way towards explaining this particular characteristic of the Croydon record.

Near-surface winds in other parts of London must be similarly affected by the local topography. There is little doubt that the north-northeast to south-southwest orientation of most of the lower Lea valley in northeast London must give a higher frequency of possibly stronger winds with this alignment. This will be true of areas such as Cheshunt, Waltham Cross, Waltham Abbey, Enfield, Chingford, Edmonton, Tottenham and Walthamstow. To the south, the Lea valley opens out near its confluence with the Thames, and in the Hackney, Bethnal Green and Leyton districts westerly and easterly elements will become more important. In north and northeast London, where the relief is more intricate, winds are likely to be more variable but locally they will be modified by the dominant topographic grain. Thus the valley drained by the Dollis Brook and

Brent, running between North Finchley southwest to Golders Green, will influence local wind directions and speeds, as will the Colne valley further to the northwest. With certain lapse rates and wind shears, strong eddies are likely to form when winds blow across these and similar valleys, and in their lower parts the wind direction may then be the reverse of that of the free air above the eddy.

MODIFICATIONS OF THE WINDFIELD BY LONDON

The complicated, dynamically rough surface presented by London, and the mass of warm air, or heat-island, which normally covers the city also bear on wind strength and direction. The increased roughness parameter causes increased frictional drag upon air moving between and immediately above the buildings, reducing mean wind speeds near

TABLE 18

Average wind speed at London Airport and its excess over that at Kingsway, 1961–2

| | 0100 GMT | | | | 1300 GMT | | | |
| | m/sec | | mi/hr | | m/sec | | mi/hr | |
	Mean Speed	Excess Speed	Mean Speed	Excess Speed	Mean Speed	Excess Speed	Mean Speed	Excess Speed
Dec–Feb	2·5	−0·4	5·6	−0·9	3·1	0·4	6·9	0·9
Mar–May	2·2	−0·1	5·0	−0·2	3·1	1·2	6·9	2·8
June–Aug	2·0	−0·6	4·4	−1·3	2·7	0·7	6·0	1·7
Sept–Nov	2·1	−0·2	4·6	−0·5	2·6	0·6	5·8	1·5
Year	2·2	−0·3	4·9	−0·7	2·9	0·7	6·4	1·7

Source of data: London, Meteorological Office tabulations, Forms 3431 and 3257(B) (MS)

the ground. There is also increased turbulence owing to both the mechanical and thermal attributes of the built-up area. The degree of drag and of turbulence depends upon the wind speed and wind shear, the horizontal thermal field, the temperature lapse rate and the form of the surface, in this case a function of the size, shape and spacing of the buildings.

It has already been seen that wind speeds are generally stronger by day than by night and stronger in winter than in summer; heat-islands are, as we shall see in Chapter 5, most intense during summer and early autumn nights, and inversions are common in both winter and summer. These climatological changes have a marked bearing upon the differences in wind speed between central and fringe areas of London. The form of these changes is shown in an analysis for the two years, 1961–2, of wind speeds at Kingsway in the centre, and London Airport on the western margins of London (Fig. 5). Table 18 lists the mean excess of wind speed at London Airport over that at Kingsway at 0100 and 1300 GMT in each of four seasons.

Over the year as a whole, night-time winds increase their speed as they move into central areas, and the stronger daytime winds decrease in speed, but the percentage night-time increase is about half the daytime decrease. The explanation of this at first sight strange daily reversal of the urban influence lies mainly in the diurnal cycle of wind speeds and stability. By night, winds (outside London) are usually light and the air stable. In consequence, there will be a steep vertical wind gradient with more slowly moving air near the ground. Above the city, increased mechanical turbulence will bring down faster-moving air and the mean near-surface wind speed will be increased. By day, wind speeds are stronger and the air less stable, and there will be much more vertical exchange of momentum so that wind speeds outside London will be more uniform in the lowest layers. In this case the reduction of near-surface winds by frictional drag with the buildings of central and other parts of London is more important than any small influx of faster-moving air from above. Air movements resulting from contrasted temperatures within and about the conurbation also play their part and help to explain some features of the seasonal fluxes in this basic pattern.

Fig. 19 shows the excess of wind speed at London Airport over that at Kingsway as a function of the wind speed at London Airport for each day of the two years 1961–2. Some interesting differences emerge. At times of light winds, speeds are increased in central areas (and presumably, though by smaller amounts, in suburban areas) but with strong winds there is a decrease. The actual rate of increase and also the critical wind speed which divides these two responses, changes with the time of day and with the seasons. The figure and relationships quoted in Fig. 19 should not be taken too precisely for the period of analysis is necessarily rather short, but the relative order of values is likely to be correct.

When winds are light, turbulence (outside London) will usually be weak and wind speed will increase quite sharply with height (Johnson, 1948, p. 13). Thus by both day and night, the extra turbulence induced by the city will bring down faster-moving air which will enhance near-surface velocities. By night, however, lapse rates will be reduced (or even reversed in inversions) and the vertical wind profile will be steepened. Thus we have higher and more frequent increases of speed in air moving into central London at 0100 than at 1300 GMT (Fig. 19).

The critical value below which winds will strengthen rather than weaken in central London is highest on winter nights and days, and on summer nights. During winter, the lower atmosphere tends to be relatively stable owing to both advection and radiation cooling. Summer night air is also quite commonly stable owing to radiation cooling in the light winds common at this time of the year. For the reasons mentioned, these conditions will result in increased wind speeds in London, even with quite strong winds outside—about 5·0–5·5 m/sec (11·3–12·3 mi/hr) in all three cases. In spring (March–May), by day, we have the greatest reductions in speed at the centre for given wind strengths at the margin of London; spring nights have the smallest reductions in speed. Part of the explanation might be the strong winds and considerable instability by day and the less frequent night-time inversions at this time of the year.

Having in mind these features of the changing diurnal pattern of urban interference with the regional windfield, we can better understand the longer period picture shown in Table 19. The overall feature is one of speeds within the built-up area reduced by an

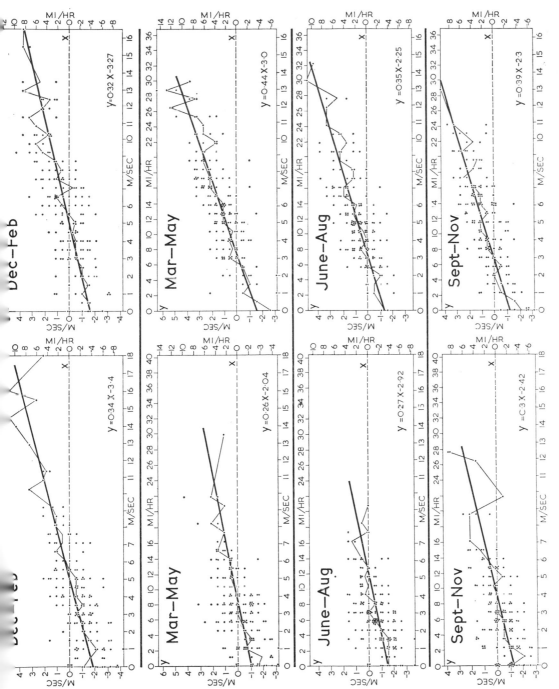

Fig 19 Excess of wind speed at London Airport over that at Kingsway (y), as a function of the wind speed at London Airport (x), 1961–2. Thin lines join the median values of this difference and the thicker, straight lines have been drawn by the method of least squares. The equations are for wind speeds measured in knots (Source of data: London, Meteorological Office—Hourly values of wind speed, Form 3431)

TABLE 19

Average wind speeds at London stations

	Winter (a)	Winter (b)	Spring (a)	Spring (b)	Summer (a)	Summer (b)	Autumn (a)	Autumn (b)	Year (a)	Year (b)
MEAN										
All winds										
Kingsway	4·3	9·7	3·8	8·5	3·5	7·9	3·6	8·1	3·8	8·5
Kew	4·0	9·0	4·1	9·2	3·6	8·1	3·6	8·1	3·8	8·5
Croydon	4·1	9·2	3·6	8·1	3·3	7·4	3·3	7·4	3·6	8·1
London Airport	4·4	10·0	4·4	10·0	4·0	9·0	4·0	9·0	4·2	9·4
Southeast England*	4·6	10·4	4·1	9·2	3·5	7·9	3·9	8·8	4·0	9·0
Winds of more than 1·5 m/sec (3·5 mi/hr)										
Kingsway	4·8	10·8	4·5	10·2	4·2	9·4	4·4	10·0	4·5	10·2
Kew	4·8	10·8	4·7	10·6	4·3	9·7	4·4	10·0	4·6	10·4
Croydon	5·3	11·9	4·9	11·1	4·6	10·4	4·9	11·1	4·9	11·1
London Airport	5·4	12·1	5·2	11·7	4·9	11·1	5·0	11·3	5·1	11·5
Southeast England*	5·7	12·7	5·1	11·5	4·8	10·8	5·3	11·9	5·2	11·7
Winds of more than 7·9 m/sec (17·7 mi/hr)										
Kingsway	9·8	21·9	9·5	21·2	9·4	20·9	9·6	21·4	9·6	21·4
Kew	9·7	21·7	9·6	21·4	9·6	21·4	9·7	21·7	9·6	21·4
Croydon	10·2	22·8	10·0	22·4	9·8	21·9	10·0	22·4	10·0	22·4
London Airport	10·2	22·8	10·1	22·6	9·7	21·7	10·0	22·4	10·0	22·4
Southeast England*	10·3	23·0	10·2	22·8	10·1	22·6	10·5	23·5	10·3	23·0

	Winter	Spring	Summer	Autumn	Year
PERCENTAGE FREQUENCY					
Winds of 1·5 m/sec (3·5 mi/hr) or less					
Kingsway	12·3	17·7	19·8	20·1	17·6
Kew	19·0	16·9	19·1	22·9	19·5
Croydon	26·8	29·3	32·9	35·4	31·1
London Airport	19·3	17·8	19·4	22·6	19·8
Southeast England*	22·0	24·4	32·0	29·0	26·8

Winter: December, January, February; spring: March, April, May; summer: June, July, August; autumn: September, October, November

(a): m/sec; (b): mi/hr

* mean of Abingdon, Shoeburyness and South Farnborough

The values for Kingsway (1948–54), Kew (1950–59) and Croydon (1950–8) are compiled from mean hourly anemograph readings; those for London Airport (1949–58) are based upon short period means at 6 hr intervals. Corrections, where necessary, have been made for effective height and defective records

Source of data: London, Meteorological Office tabulations, Form 3433 (MS)

amount which increases with distance from the city margins, but again there are appreciable differences between seasons and in the several speed ranges.

Over the year as a whole, winds in the centre of London (represented by Kingsway) and in the suburbs (represented by Kew) are weaker than those ouside the city, although the overall reduction in speed is quite small, about 5 per cent. The mean values for all winds at Croydon and London Airport are somewhat anomalous: Croydon's mean is unusually low and that at London Airport is high, higher in fact than the calculated average wind speed for Southeast England outside London. Both Croydon and London Airport stand in the urban-rural fringe areas in south and west London respectively (Fig. 5).

The abnormally low values of mean wind speeds at Croydon (in spite of its elevation, 208 ft (63·4 m)), are probably due to shelter by the North Downs as evidenced in the remarkably high percentage frequency of calms and light airs in all seasons. In winter, when winds are strong, there are fewer calms at Croydon and the mean wind velocity (for all winds) is more in tune with that at London Airport, being slightly higher than at Kew nearer the centre of London. Very high mean wind speeds (for all winds) at London Airport occur in all seasons, and in all but winter the mean value is even greater than the average for the three stations in Southeast England outside London. Part of the explanation is probably some channelling of the near-surface flow by the local relief, more particularly the valleys of the middle Thames to the west, and its north- and south-bank tributaries the rivers Colne and Wey (Figs. 1 and 2). In winter, the faster winds will be less clearly streamed by the ground (Pooler, 1963) and this probably explains the less anomalous picture at London Airport in comparison with other stations in this season. Some of the increase may also be explained by the effects of increased turbulence, both thermal and mechanical, near the margins of the city.

In spite of the speeding up of night-time winds and light winds generally, Kingsway in central London has a mean wind speed consistently below that of the surrounding country, and a little below that at Kew (very small differences in Table 19 are hidden by 'rounding-off' to the nearest decimal place) except in winter when the mean velocity (for all winds) is well above that at Kew. This is probably related to differences in the intensity and scale of turbulence in the strong winds of winter at Kew and Kingsway. At both, owing to the day and night conditions we have just considered and the very long nights over which lighter winds prevail in winter, many winds will be increased in speed as they run towards central London. Turbulence is likely to be stronger and deeper at the centre than in the suburbs (whatever the direction of the wind), owing to contrasts in the nature of the buildings. In central areas the serried concrete, stone and glass cliffs of buildings are likely to cause turbulence deep enough to bring down faster-moving air from levels higher than the top of the turbulent layer in the suburbs with their lower skyline. Kew Observatory stands in a fairly large open space and this may also materially affect the intensity and scale of local turbulence.

It will be noted (Table 19) that the urban influence upon mean speeds (for all winds) disappears in summer, mainly owing to a substantial increase in the percentage frequency of light winds (1·5 m/sec–3·5 mi/hr, or less) in rural areas outside London, so reducing the overall mean velocity and at the same time enhancing those in the city. One out-standing characteristic of wind speeds in London compared with conditions outside is, in fact, the small number of calms and light airs. Apart from the Croydon record, this is a feature displayed in all seasons. Its explanation lies in the turbulence induced by the physical and thermal attributes of buildings, frequently overturning and mixing the lowest layers of the atmosphere with the faster moving air above, while the air above parks and farmland is almost at rest.

As we have seen, this process does not operate with stronger winds and here the pic-ture is simpler, mean speeds decreasing fairly systematically towards the centre of Lon-don and with Croydon recording wind speeds comparable with those at London Air-port (Table 19). For winds of more than 1·5 m/sec (3·5 mi/hr), the mean annual differ-ence between speeds outside and at the centre of London is a little over 13 per cent, being about 16 per cent in autumn and winter and about 12 per cent in spring and summer. Wind speeds of more than 7·9 m/sec (17·7 mi/hr) suffer a smaller reduction in central areas, averaging 7 per cent throughout the year and varying between 5 per cent in winter, through 7 per cent in spring and summer to 9 per cent in autumn. The reduc-tion in suburban areas is smaller.

Tables 20 and 21 show the likely frequency of extreme wind speeds at four stations in London. Hampton stands at 38 ft (11·6 m) O.D., only a little lower than London Airport at 82 ft (25·0 m) O.D. and 5·6 mi (9·0 km) to the northwest (Fig. 5). Both are in a similar urban setting. In general, maximum hourly wind speeds are lower in London than outside but they are least, not in the centre, but in the suburbs. In the centre, as evidenced by the Kingsway record, expected hourly speeds are relatively high (Table 20) and expected gust speeds (Table 21) are very much higher at Kingsway than in the suburbs (Kew), the urban-rural fringe (Hampton and Croydon), or even outside London (South Farnborough). These features are very puzzling in the light of previous evidence

TABLE 20

Average hourly wind speeds likely to be exceeded only once in the stated number of years

	years			
m/sec	10	20	50	100
Kingsway	17	18	19	21
Kew	15	16	17	17
Hampton	15	16	17	18
Croydon	18	19	21	22
South Farnborough	21	22	25	27
mi/hr				
Kingsway	37	40	43	46
Kew	33	35	37	38
Hampton	33	35	38	40
Croydon	41	43	46	49
South Farnborough	46	50	56	60

The Hampton and Croydon records have been corrected for effective height
Source: Shellard, H. C. 1962 Extreme wind speeds over the United Kingdom for periods ending 1959. *Met. Mag.*, London, 91, p. 40

TABLE 21

Gust speeds likely to be exceeded only once in the stated
number of years

	years			
m/sec	*10*	*20*	*50*	*100*
Kingsway	35	38	43	45
Kew	31	33	35	36
Hampton	31	33	36	38
Croydon	33	35	38	39
South Farnborough	34	35	38	39
mi/hr	10	20	50	100
Kingsway	79	86	95	102
Kew	70	73	78	81
Hampton	69	74	80	84
Croydon	74	78	84	88
South Farnborough	75	79	84	87

The Hampton and Croydon records have been corrected for effective height

Source: Shellard, H. C. 1962 Extreme wind speeds over the United Kingdom for periods ending 1959
Met. Mag., London, 91, p. 41

(Fig. 19). They may be connected with differences in the periods of records at the several stations and the difficulties of fine distinctions at these extremities of the wind spectrum (Shellard, 1962, p. 39).

Tables 22, 23 and 24 give the percentage frequency of winds in the standard velocity grades at Kingsway, Kew and London Airport respectively. The differences between each of these and the mean conditions outside London (the average of those at Abingdon, Shoeburyness and South Farnborough) are listed in Tables 25, 26 and 27. Annual wind strength frequencies at Kingsway and Kew, it will be noted, are below those in Southeast England in the lower and higher speed ranges and above the latter for speeds of 1·6–5·4 m/sec (3·7–12·1 mi/hr).

At London Airport the pattern is slightly different. Here the range of speeds in which frequencies are above those in Southeast England are 0·0–0·2 m/sec (0·0–0·7 mi/hr) and 3·4–7·9 m/sec (7·7–17·7 mi/hr). The general explanation bears upon matters previously considered, low speeds being strengthened in the city and strong winds weakened, with a consequent reduction in the extreme speed frequencies and an increase in the intermediate ranges. Differences in the ranges in which frequencies are higher than in Southeast England between both Kingsway and Kew on the one hand and London Airport on the other are explained first by the smaller reduction, through friction, in the speed of the higher velocities near the city margin (London Airport) compared with the centre (Kingsway and Kew), and secondly by turbulence so weak and shallow in light winds as to be ineffective in increasing near-surface speeds at the city margin; rather they are reduced by friction. Only with slightly stronger winds than are necessary in the more heavily built-up areas can this process operate, hence the shift of velocity range.

We might reasonably ask whether there are any differences in the urban effect upon wind speeds with winds from different directions; and more particularly whether, for

TABLE 22

Percentage frequency distribution of average hourly wind speeds, Kingsway, 1948–54

m/sec	mi/hr	Jan	Feb	Mar	Apr	May	June
<0·3	<0·8	1·0	1·1	2·0	1·5	1·7	1·3
0·3– 1·5	0·8– 3·5	8·3	10·8	14·6	15·6	17·8	16·4
1·6– 3·3	3·7– 7·4	19·3	23·5	27·0	23·5	27·6	29·2
3·4– 5·4	7·7–12·1	38·5	34·1	33·6	33·9	37·8	38·0
5·5– 7·9	12·3–17·7	27·1	25·0	19·8	21·9	14·6	14·1
8·0–10·7	18·0–24·0	5·4	5·1	2·7	3·1	0·5	0·9
10·8–13·8	24·2–29·9	0·4	0·3	0·2	0·5		0+
13·9–17·1	31·1–38·0		0·1				

		July	Aug	Sept	Oct	Nov	Dec	Yr
<0·3	<0·8	1·5	2·8	2·1	2·7	3·6	3·4	2·1
0·3– 1·5	0·8– 3·5	15·4	22·0	17·7	20·5	13·8	12·4	15·5
1·6– 3·3	3·7– 7·4	29·3	25·7	25·4	29·9	25·1	24·0	25·7
3·4– 5·4	7·7–12·1	39·1	33·1	35·9	34·1	32·6	36·3	35·7
5·5– 7·9	12·3–17·7	14·1	15·9	17·5	12·5	23·2	20·6	18·8
8·0–10·7	18·0–24·0	0·6	0·4	1·2	0·3	1·6	3·2	2·0
10·8–13·8	24·2–29·9			0·1	0+	0·1	0·1	0·2
13·9–17·1	31·1–38·0					0+		0+

Corrections have been made, where necessary, for defective records
Source of data: London, Meteorological Office tabulations, Form 3433 (MS)

TABLE 23

Percentage frequency distribution of average hourly wind speeds, Kew, 1950–9

m/sec	mi/hr	Jan	Feb	Mar	Apr	May	June
<0·3	<0·8	1·8	1·7	2·3	2·1	2·4	3·4
0·3– 1·5	0·8– 3·5	16·7	14·7	15·2	15·0	13·7	14·5
1·6– 3·3	3·7– 7·4	26·8	27·9	25·1	25·6	26·6	29·5
3·4– 5·4	7·7–12·1	27·2	29·0	29·5	31·1	32·2	32·6
5·5– 7·9	12·3–17·7	21·3	20·4	21·9	22·4	20·9	18·1
8·0–10·7	18·0–24·0	5·3	5·7	5·3	3·8	4·0	1·8
10·8–13·8	24·2–29·9	0·8	0·5	0·7	0+	0·2	0+
13·9–17·1	31·1–38·0	0+					

		July	Aug	Sept	Oct	Nov	Dec	Yr
<0·3	<0·8	3·4	4·0	1·9	3·6	2·5	2·9	2·7
0·3– 1·5	0·8– 3·5	14·4	17·6	18·3	22·7	19·8	19·3	16·8
1·6– 3·3	3·7– 7·4	30·4	29·8	29·7	30·7	30·1	27·5	28·3
3·4– 5·4	7·7–12·1	33·1	30·5	30·3	26·7	26·1	25·3	29·4
5·5– 7·9	12·3–17·7	16·1	16·0	17·3	13·6	17·3	18·0	18·7
8·0–10·7	18·0–24·0	2·4	1·9	2·2	2·4	3·7	6·3	3·7
10·8–13·8	24·2–29·9	0·2	0·2	0·2	0·2	0·5	0·6	0·3
13·9–17·1	31·1–38·0					0+		

Source of data: London, Meteorological Office tabulations, Form 3433 (MS)

instance, the excess of wind speeds at London Airport (in west London) over those at Kingsway (in the centre) applies only or mainly to westerly winds and is reversed with easterly winds, or whether there is any material difference in the character of westerly and easterly winds (the latter having crossed the city) at London Airport. Any results must remain somewhat inconclusive owing to the concentration of flow from certain quarters by the local topography, the bearing of which upon the Kingsway and London Airport records has been considered earlier in this chapter. Some insight into the problem is, however, provided in Table 15. Westerly winds (from 260–280 degrees true) at London Airport are faster than those at Kingsway by an annual mean of 0·7 m/sec (1·6 mi/hr), and easterly winds (080–100 degrees true) are 0·5 m/sec (1·2 mi/hr) faster. The difference is small and this, plus the fact that speeds are strongest at London Airport for either direction, indicates how closely the winds are adjusted to the local parameters, increasing in speed as they move away from the city centre. The comparison of speeds at London Airport with the calculated values for Southeast England (Table 27) is even more strongly coloured by the local relief, for westerly winds at London Airport are 0·2 m/sec (0·5 mi/hr) faster than the average for Southeast England. But easterly winds having crossed London will obviously be more turbulent than those from fairly rural country to the west, and this will at least partly explain their reduced speeds although the difference is small. It is clear that as the frictional drag of London decreases, so the wind velocity increases from central areas to the urban-rural fringe.

TABLE 24

Percentage frequency distribution of wind speeds at 0300, 0900, 1500 and 2100 GMT, London Airport, 1949–58

m/sec	mi/hr	Jan	Feb	Mar	Apr	May	June
<0·3	<0·8	8·9	8·8	9·2	8·1	8·2	7·6
0·3– 1·5	0·8– 3·5	7·7	8·2	8·9	10·5	8·1	10·4
1·6– 3·3	3·7– 7·4	16·7	18·3	17·5	16·7	19·3	22·4
3·4– 5·4	7·7–12·1	30·9	30·2	31·1	31·1	34·7	34·8
5·5– 7·9	12·3–17·7	27·2	23·8	24·4	25·5	22·5	20·6
8·0–10·7	18·0–24·0	6·8	7·5	6·7	6·2	6·1	3·7
10·8–13·8	24·2–29·9	1·4	2·6	1·9	1·9	0·8	0·5
13·9–17·1	31·1–38·0	0·4	0·5	0·3		0·3	
17·2–20·7	38·4–46·1		0·1				

m/sec	mi/hr	July	Aug	Sept	Oct	Nov	Dec	Yr
<0·3	<0·8	7·0	11·4	9·3	15·3	12·2	14·5	10·1
0·3– 1·5	0·8– 3·5	10·1	11·3	9·1	12·2	9·7	9·2	9·5
1·6– 3·3	3·7– 7·4	21·1	19·9	20·5	20·5	20·5	18·2	19·4
3·4– 5·4	7·7–12·1	34·7	29·2	30·7	27·6	30·1	26·9	31·0
5·5– 7·9	12·3–17·7	21·7	21·6	22·7	19·0	19·8	21·0	22·7
8·0–10·7	18·0–24·0	4·4	5·8	6·2	4·7	5·8	7·1	5·8
10·8–13·8	24·2–29·9	0·7	0·8	1·3	0·7	1·4	3·0	1·3
13·9–17·1	31·1–38·0	0·3		0·2		0·2		0·2
17·2–20·7	38·4–46·1					0·2	0·1	0+
20·8–24·4	46·5–54·5					0·1		0+

Source of data: London, Meteorological Office tabulations, Form 3433 (MS)

TABLE 25

Differences in the percentage frequency of average hourly wind speeds, by months, at Kingsway and in Southeast England (Kingsway–Southeast England*)

m/sec	mi/hr	Jan	Feb	Mar	Apr	May	June
<0·3	<0·8	−5·4	−5·0	−4·9	−5·1	−5·0	−6·8
0·3– 1·5	0·8– 3·5	−6·0	−4·9	−1·8	−2·4	−0·7	−6·8
1·6– 3·3	3·7– 7·4	1·8	14·5	8·0	3·7	6·1	7·4
3·4– 5·4	7·7–12·1	14·0	8·7	8·3	7·6	10·2	12·4
5·5– 7·9	12·3–17·7	2·4	2·6	−3·1	−0·5	−5·5	−3·3
8·0–10·7	18·0–24·0	−3·2	−2·5	−4·0	−2·5	−3·9	−2·3
10·8–13·8	24·2–29·9	−2·8	−3·0	−2·0	−0·8	−1·0	−0·6
13·9–17·1	31·1–38·0	−0·7	−0·3	0·5	−0·1	−0·2	−0·1
17·2–20·7	38·4–46·1	−0·1	−0·1	0·2			

m/sec	mi/hr	July	Aug	Sept	Oct	Nov	Dec	Yr
<0·3	<0·8	−6·3	−6·6	−6·0	−7·4	−4·4	−4·1	−5·6
0·3– 1·5	0·8– 3·5	−8·3	−1·9	−2·9	−0·9	−5·1	−3·6	−3·6
1·6– 3·3	3·7– 7·4	7·7	4·9	6·1	11·4	7·1	7·2	6·2
3·4– 5·4	7·7–12·1	14·0	9·2	11·5	11·3	8·1	13·6	11·8
5·5– 7·9	12·3–17·7	−3·0	−1·8	−3·2	−6·9	2·0	−2·6	−2·0
8·0–10·7	18·0–24·0	−3·1	−2·9	−4·2	−4·7	−4·4	−5·7	−3·8
10·8–13·8	24·2–29·9	−0·9	−0·8	−1·2	−1·4	−2·4	−3·7	−1·6
13·9–17·1	31·1–38·0	−0·1	−0·2	−0·2	−0·3	−0·6	−0·7	−0·3
17·2–20·7	38·4–46·1				−0·1	−0·2	−0·2	−0·1

* mean of Abingdon (1950–9), Shoeburyness (1950, 1952, 1954–9) and South Farnborough (1950–9)

Kingsway: (1948–54)

Computed from mean hourly wind speeds

Corrections have been made, where necessary, for effective height and defective records

Source of data: London, Meteorological Office tabulations, Form 3433 (MS)

TABLE 26

Differences in the percentage frequency of average hourly wind speeds, by months, at Kew and in Southeast England (Kew–Southeast England*)

m/sec	mi/hr	Jan	Feb	Mar	Apr	May	June
<0·3	<0·8	−4·6	−4·4	−4·6	−4·5	−4·3	−4·7
0·3– 1·5	0·8– 3·5	2·4	−1·0	−1·2	−3·0	−4·8	−8·7
1·6– 3·3	3·7– 7·4	9·3	8·9	6·1	5·9	5·1	7·7
3·4– 5·4	7·7–12·1	2·7	3·6	4·2	4·9	4·6	7·0
5·5– 7·9	12·3–17·7	−3·4	−2·0	−1·0	0·1	0·8	0·7
8·0–10·7	18·0–24·0	−3·3	−1·9	−1·4	−1·8	−0·4	−1·4
10·8–13·8	24·2–29·9	−2·4	−2·8	−1·5	−1·3	−0·8	−0·6
13·9–17·1	31·1–38·0	−0·7	−0·4	−0·5	−0·1	−0·2	−0·1

m/sec	mi/hr	July	Aug	Sept	Oct	Nov	Dec	Yr
<0·3	<0·8	−4·4	−5·4	−6·2	−6·5	−5·5	−4·6	−5·0
0·3– 1·5	0·8– 3·5	−9·3	−6·3	−2·3	1·3	0·9	3·3	−2·3
1·6– 3·3	3·7– 7·4	8·8	9·0	10·4	12·2	12·1	10·7	8·8
3·4– 5·4	7·7–12·1	8·0	6·6	5·9	2·9	1·6	2·6	4·5
5·5– 7·9	12·3–17·7	−1·0	−1·7	−3·4	−5·8	−3·9	−5·2	−2·1
8·0–10·7	18·0–24·0	−1·3	−1·4	−3·2	−2·6	−2·3	−2·6	−2·1
10·8–13·8	24·2–29·9	−0·7	−0·6	−1·1	−1·2	−2·0	−3·2	−1·5
13·9–17·1	31·1–38·0	−0·1	−0·2	−0·2	−0·3	−0·6	−0·8	−0·3
17·2–20·7	38·4–46·1				−0·1	−0·2	−0·2	−0·1

* mean of Abingdon (1950–9), Shoeburyness (1950, 1952, 1954–9) and South Farnborough (1950–9)

Kew: (1950–9)

Computed from mean hourly wind speeds

Corrections have been made, where necessary, for effective height and defective records

Source of data: London, Meteorological Office tabulations, Form 3433 (MS)

TABLE 27

Differences in the percentage frequency of average hourly wind speeds, by months, at London Airport and in Southeast England (London Airport–Southeast England*)

m/sec	mi/hr	Jan	Feb	Mar	Apr	May	June
<0·3	<0·8	2·5	2·7	2·3	1·5	1·5	−0·5
0·3– 1·5	0·8– 3·5	−6·5	−7·5	−7·5	−7·5	−10·4	−12·8
1·6– 3·3	3·7– 7·4	−0·8	−0·7	−1·5	−3·0	−2·2	0·6
3·4– 5·4	7·7–12·1	6·4	4·8	5·9	4·9	7·1	9·2
5·5– 7·9	12·3–17·7	2·5	1·4	1·6	3·2	2·4	3·2
8·0–10·7	18·0–24·0	−1·8	−0·1	0·0	0·6	1·7	0·5
10·8–13·8	24·2–29·9	−1·8	−0·7	−0·3	0·6	−0·2	−0·1
13·9–17·1	31·1–38·0	−0·3	0·1	−0·2	−0·1	0·1	−0·1
17·2–20·7	38·4–46·1	−0·1	0·0	−0·2			

		July	Aug	Sept	Oct	Nov	Dec	Yr
<0·3	<0·8	–0·8	2·0	1·2	5·2	4·2	7·0	2·4
0·3– 1·5	0·8– 3·5	−13·6	−12·6	−11·5	−9·2	−9·2	−6·8	−9·6
1·6– 3·3	3·7– 7·4	−0·5	−0·9	1·2	2·0	2·5	1·4	−0·1
3·4– 5·4	7·7–12·1	9·6	5·3	6·3	3·8	5·6	4·2	6·1
5·5– 7·9	12·3–17·7	4·5	3·9	2·0	−0·4	−1·4	−2·2	1·9
8·0–10·7	18·0–24·0	−3·2	2·5	0·8	−0·3	−0·2	−1·8	0·0
10·8–13·8	24·2–29·9	−0·2	0·0	0·0	−0·7	−1·1	−0·8	−0·5
13·9–17·1	31·1–38·0	0·2	−0·2	0·0	−0·3	−0·4	−0·8	−0·1
17·2–20·7	38·4–46·1				−0·1	0·0	−0·1	−0·1
20·8–24·4	46·5–54·5					0·1		

* mean of Abingdon (1950–9), Shoeburyness (1950, 1952, 1954–9) and South Farnborough (1950–9), and compiled from mean hourly wind speeds

London Airport (1949–58) values are based upon short period means at 6 hr intervals

Corrections have been made, where necessary, for effective height and defective records

Source of data: London, Meteorological Office tabulations, Form 3433 (MS)

F

4 Atmospheric pollution

A mighty mass of brick and smoke, and shipping,
Dirty and dusky, but as wide as eye
Could reach, with here and there a sail just skipping
In sight, then lost amidst the forestry
Of masts; a wilderness of steeples peeping
On tiptoe through their sea-coal canopy;
A huge dun cupola, like a foolscap crown
On a fool's head—and there is London Town!

George Gordon Byron

IN MOVING ACROSS LONDON, the air changes not only its physical properties but also its chemical composition. As building development covered more and more of what was previously open country, so an atmospheric shroud of solid and gaseous pollutants was released from a growing forest of chimneys and engine exhausts to mask the buildings in a sea of swirling smoke, noxious gases, ash and dust. From a vantage point on the North Downs, south of the city, one cannot help but be impressed by the contrast in visibilities north over Greater London and south across the Weald. The difference is, in large measure, due to the dome of pollutants which commonly envelops the city.

Although atmospheric pollution has long been recognized as a serious health hazard (see Chapter 12), no really effective measures were taken to alleviate the problem until quite recently. In the thirteenth century a law was passed forbidding the burning of coal but it quickly lapsed because of an acute shortage of wood. Four hundred years later, John Evelyn (1661, p. 19), author of *Fumifugium* (Flight from Fumes) and one of the earliest apostles of clean air, had this to say about the pall of smoke above seventeenth-century London:

> Whilst these [chimneys] are belching forth their sooty jaws, the City of London resembles the face rather of Mount Etna, the Court of Vulcan, Stromboli, or the suburbs of hell, than an assembly of rational creatures, and the Imperial seat of our Incomparable Monarch.

and again:

> The weary traveller, at many miles distance, sooner smells than sees the city to which he repairs. This is that pernicious smoke which foils all her Glory, super-inducing a sooty crust or fur upon all that it lights.

Pollution is, of course, a comprehensive term covering mineral dusts from soils, quarries and roads, and pollen from plants as well as carbon and other solid and gaseous products of combustion. It is thought that the burning of coal and oil is responsible for less than half the pollution in country areas, but in most towns the bulk of the pollutants

are from coal and oil. The Department of Scientific and Industrial Research has estimated that domestic sources are responsible for just over half the Country's smoke, but
in the County of London the figure is between 80 and 90 per cent. In contrast, only
30 per cent of the sulphur dioxide in London's air comes from house fires, 41 per cent
being from electricity power stations and 29 per cent from factories (Dept. of Sci. and
Industr. Res., 1960, p. 9).

POLLUTION AT KEW

Different instruments are used to measure the gaseous pollutants (mainly sulphur
dioxide), suspended particulates (smoke) and deposited matter (tar, ash and other
undissolved combustible matter, and dissolved matter, more especially the chlorides,
sulphates and calcium washed out by rain). Until about 1960 smoke measurements were
made by comparing the darkness of stain formed by drawing air through a filter, with
a series of standard, calibrated stains. The method is open to several sources of error—
for example those which stem from the colour and size distribution of the smoke particles and the diameter of the stain, as well as human errors in shade matching; improved photo-electric methods have now been introduced. But whilst comparisons
of values, more particularly of results from different districts, must be made with
caution, the general pattern of differences can be discussed with some confidence.
This is especially true of smoke and sulphur dioxide distributions; deposit gauge
readings are much less representative of their wider environment, for the heavier,
insoluble particles at least are generally deposited close to their source (Meetham,
1956, p. 182).

It must be remembered that a large proportion of the solid deposits—apart from the
heaviest particles which settle quickly and spontaneously—are washed down by rain,
or are dispersed by the turbulent winds of associated fronts, so that during dry settled
weather, more of the fine particles tend to remain suspended in the air. On the other
hand, the sulphur dioxide caught by lead peroxide instruments and the smoke and
sulphur dioxide extracted in volumetric analyses represent only what remains after a
proportion has settled naturally or been brought down by turbulent winds and rain. But
the rate of settling of deposits also depends on the direction and character of air movements in relation to the main sources of pollution.

The mean picture

From January 1932 to July 1953 an Owens pollution recorder gave a consistent series of
hourly smoke values (between exact hours GMT) at Kew Observatory. Fig. 20 shows
the characteristic pattern of diurnal change in the mean annual concentrations of smoke
(in milligrams per hundred cubic metres) for each 60 min period ended at exact hours
GMT. To convert the values into the number of smoke particles per 100 m^3, multiplica-
tion by a factor of the order of 10,000 million is necessary. Peak intensities occur at

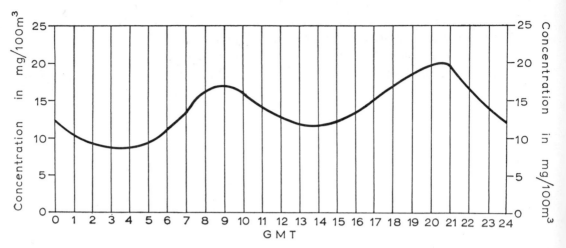

Fig 20 Average diurnal variation of smoke concentration at Kew, 1932–52
(Source of data: *Observatories' year book* 1932–52)

0900 and 2030 GMT, separated by minima at 0330 and 1330 GMT. This typical cycle is due partly to climate and partly to fluctuations in the output of pollutants from domestic and industrial sources.

Pollution is dispersed from its source both vertically and laterally and the efficiency of these processes is controlled, amongst other things, by the speed of the wind linked with the scale and intensity of turbulence; the form of the temperature lapse rate is obviously important here. It has been shown (Fig. 15) that winds are generally strongest one and a half hours after noon, and at this time turbulence is also most active. The afternoon fall in pollution concentration is related to these changes in the windfield. Higher values during the morning and late evening result from the stoking of many thousands of house fires and industrial boilers at times of frequent low inversions, light winds and weak turbulence. Fuel combustion is least efficient and creates most pollution when the burning temperature is low, that is when fires are first lit, or less obviously, when replenished, and this helps to accentuate the very steep rise in average concentrations between 0600 and 0800 GMT, although gentle early morning turbulence may sometimes bring down smoke trapped beneath a low inverson. Many domestic fires are allowed to burn themselves out during the late evening with a consequent falling off in the output of smoke from a forest of low chimneys above suburban London. During the night, winds become lighter and turbulence weakens as the air becomes more stable, but the fall in pollution output dominates the pattern of change in spite of atmospheric conditions conducive to high concentrations.

As might be expected, this overall pattern is a generalization of a varied monthly form of diurnal change shown in Fig. 21. In summer there is a very much lower output of pollutants and a more active thermal turbulence for a longer period each day than during winter. The diurnal cycle of concentrations in June, July and August is simpler than in other months, owing to the virtual removal of domestic output. There is just one peak about 2 to 3 hours after sunrise when some industrial sources are started and turbulence and winds are light, followed by a long period of evenly low concentrations from before noon to early evening. This is a time when the output of pollutants is small and its dispersal efficient, being carried upwards and diffused by convection in a deep haze layer. There is no marked evening peak of concentrations during summer, values

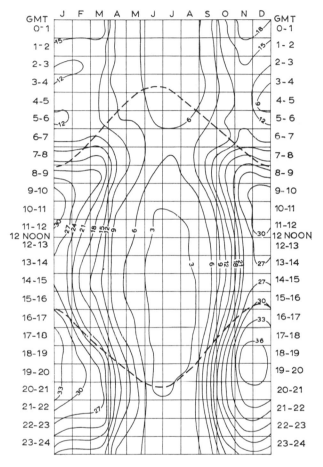

Fig 21 Average hourly smoke concentration (in milligrammes/
100 cubic metres) at Kew, 1932–41. Broken lines indicate the
times of sunrise and sunset
(Source of data: *Observatories' year book* 1932–41)

remaining almost constant from sunset to sunrise. In the remaining months, but especially November and December, the diurnal cycle we have already outlined, with double peaks, is strongly developed. The heaviest mean concentrations fall between 1800 and 2000 GMT in November and December with averages of 37 mg/100 m³, more than eighteen times the summer minimum of 2 mg/100 m³.

Table 28 gives the range of average hourly pollution concentrations in each month. It shows, as does Fig. 21, a simple progression from large fluctuations between winter

TABLE 28

Diurnal range of average hourly smoke concentrations, Kew, 1932–41

Jan	Feb	Mar	Apr	May	June	July	Aug	Sept	Oct	Nov	Dec	Yr
					mg/100 m³							
22	21	17	9	5	5	4	5	7	16	24	26	11

Source of data: London, Meteorological Office *Observatories' year book* 1932–41

days and nights to very much smaller hour-to-hour changes during summer: these are, of course, the times of London's most polluted and cleanest air respectively. The minimum concentrations in winter, in the hours before dawn, are almost twice the maximum early-morning concentrations of summer, and evening peak concentrations in winter are more than five times these maximum summer values. Minimum mean hourly values on winter days are a little less than five times those of mid-summer.

The broad character of the yearly cycle is given in Table 29.

TABLE 29

Mean smoke concentration by months, Kew, 1932–52

	Jan	Feb	Mar	Apr	May	June	July	Aug	Sept	Oct	Nov	Dec	Yr
						mg/100 m³							
Average	23	20	19	10	8	4	3	4	8	17	25	26	14
Median	25	16	21	12	8	3	2	4	8	17	23	24	14

Source of data: London, Meteorological Office *Observatories' year book* 1932–52

December has the highest mean pollution concentration and January the highest median (central rank) value, and although differences are small, it is clear from both measures that November and December tend to record more atmospheric pollution than January and February, even though the consumption of fuel is greatest during the latter pair of months. The reason for this difference is the higher wind speeds and mechanical turbulence of January and February, with more efficient dispersal of pollutants. Concentrations are almost halved between March and April, the time when house fires cease to be necessary in most years and convection is deep and active: they are more than doubled between September and October when conditions are reversed. The summer levels must very nearly represent the general industrial contribution to near-surface concentrations at Kew and probably remains fairly constant throughout the year although the figures must be used with caution owing to differences from month to month in the efficiency of atmospheric dispersal. Also, Kew Observatory is some distance from a major concentration of solid-fuel powered industry, the nearest being 4–5 mi (6–8 km) away at Park Royal: conditions close to this and other concentrated industrial areas in London are rather different.

Many factories shut down at weekends and their power plants are damped down or closed, with a marked influence upon pollution values in their vicinity. Table 30 shows that there is an appreciable reduction in smoke concentrations at Kew during weekends, more especially in winter.

TABLE 30

Average smoke concentration by days of the week, Kew, 1957–62

	Mon	Tues	Wed	Thurs	Fri	Sat	Sun	Mean
				mg/100 m³				
Winter (Oct–Mar)	14·8	16·1	16·0	16·0	14·2	13·3	12·7	14·7
Summer (Apr–Sept)	6·2	6·2	6·3	6·3	6·5	6·0	5·5	6·1

Source of data: London, Meteorological Office tabulations, Form 3745 (MS)

Since over a long period there is no definite difference between weekday and weekend weather (the only suggested differences in cities being a debatable reduction in precipitation, an increase in visibilities and an increase in sunshine hours at weekends consequent upon changes in pollution densities), the lower concentration of pollution at weekends and the smaller reduction on Fridays and Mondays must follow a diminution of emission after the closing or damping down of many industrial power plants between Friday evening and Monday morning.

Mean winter smoke concentrations at Kew for the period 1957–62 (Table 30) were much lower than for 1932–52 (Table 29), although summer intensities remained almost the same. This long-term reduction in smoke has been a feature of most areas of Great Britain during the past few decades (Meetham, 1956, p. 203; Dept. of Sci. and Industr. Res., 1955, p. 21, and 1960, p. 8) though the changes are far from uniform or consistent in either time or space. Improvements have followed the use of more efficient fuel burners, and a change from coal to oil and electricity by industrial and (to a lesser degree) domestic consumers, accelerated more recently by smoke control regulations. But changes in atmospheric conditions from year to year, more particularly in wind speed and turbulence, will alter pollution concentrations near the ground apart from any fluctuations in the rates of emission. Certainly any significant reduction can only be conclusively established by analysis over many years. Fig. 22 shows the smoothed (five-year moving mean) values of smoke concentration at Kew for the period 1932–61, and from this very little comfort can be drawn. Summer values fell fairly consistently until the late 1940's when they again rose to intensities equalling or (in 1951) exceeding those 20 years earlier. Since that time, concentrations have fallen again. Winter values have fluctuated in a more complicated fashion, though they have been lower in recent years owing to a decline in domestic and industrial emissions. The spread of smoke control areas can take some of the credit here (Dept. of Sci. and Industr. Res., 1960, p. 9). Since 1952, and more particularly since the Clean Air Act of 1956, the total emission of smoke in the County of London has fallen from 141,000 tons in 1952 to 89,000 tons in 1960, a decrease of some 37 per cent (Dept. of Sci. and Industr. Res., 1963, p. 5).

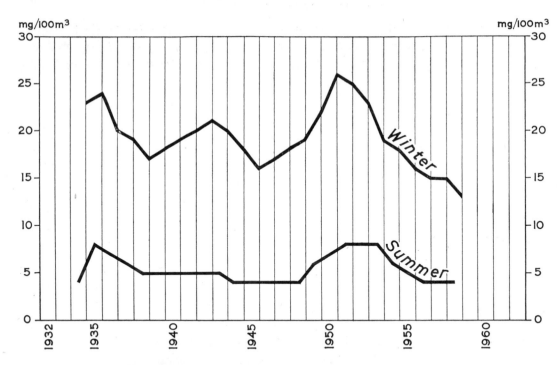

Fig 22 Smoothed mean winter (October–March) and summer (April–September) smoke concentrations at Kew, 1932–61: 5-year moving mean
(Source of data: *Observatories' year book* 1932–61)

This mainly reflects a big fall in domestic coal consumption. But during the winters of 1951–2 and 1952–3, average concentrations of smoke at Kew were only a little less than during the notable winter of 1933–4. The winter mean for 1960–1 (9 mg/100 m³), on the other hand, was the lowest at Kew since records began.

Extreme concentrations of smoke at Kew

Although the emission of smoke and other atmospheric pollutants seems to be declining, under certain conditions (mainly of airflow and temperature lapse) concentrations can and do build up to dangerous levels. This happened in December 1952 and Table 31 lists the hourly values at Kew during this period.

Recalling that the average concentration of smoke at Kew (1932–52) in December is 26 mg/100 m³ (and only 18 mg/100 m³ for 1957–61), the seriousness of these choking concentrations will be realized, although people who have experienced one of these smogs need no persuasion. Trying to breathe an atmosphere in which the pollutants, unable to escape through a strong temperature inversion, have built up to concentrations vaguely reminiscent of those in the chimneys from which they have been released, is never forgotten. In central London, more particularly the low-lying areas of high density building development, amounts were even higher, the average daily smoke concentration for the 6 and 7 December 1952 ranging here between 200 and 400 mg/100 m³, but

Kew's values are fairly typical of most of the suburbs. The generally accepted smog level for medical purposes in London is defined, in part, by a smoke concentration of 200 mg/100 m³ (Medical Officer of Health, L.C.C., 1956, Appendix B; and 1958, pp. 99 and 367): there were thus 14 hours with critical smog levels in December 1952.

TABLE 31

Hourly and daily averages of smoke concentration, Kew, December 1952

	December 1952							December 1952					
	4th	5th	6th	7th	8th	9th		4th	5th	6th	7th	8th	9th
			mg/100 m³							mg/100 m³			
GMT							GMT						
00–01	15	95	255	110	145	145	12–13	15	145	145	45	95	30
01–02	15	65	255	110	145	145	13–14	15	145	145	45	65	45
02–03	15	95	255	110	110	110	14–15	45	145	145	45	65	30
03–04	15	65	255	95	110	45	15–16	45	145	145	45	65	30
04–05	15	65	230	95	110	45	16–17	65	230	170	65	95	30
05–06	15	65	230	65	110	45	17–18	65	230	170	65	95	30
06–07	15	65	195	65	110	45	18–19	95	255	145	95	95	30
07–08	15	45	195	65	110	30	19–20	95	255	145	110	110	30
08–09	30	65	170	65	145	45	20–21	95	255	145	145	145	15
09–10	15	65	145	65	145	65	21–22	95	255	145	170	145	15
10–11	15	110	110	65	145	45	22–23	95	255	145	145	145	15
11–12	15	145	145	65	195	45	23–24	95	255	110	145	145	15
							00–24	42	138	175	87	118	47

Source of data: London, Meteorological Office tabulations, Form 3745 (MS)

Miasmal conditions produced by smoke are far from rare. Within the past decade smog hazard levels (as defined above) were exceeded for several hours at Kew in January 1956 and December 1962, and in central areas also in December 1957. The greatest health hazards exist when concentrations of smoke are above 200 mg/100 m³, sulphur dioxide amounts are in excess of 40 parts per 100,000,000 parts of air, and the prevailing weather is raw. Table 32 lists the highest hourly value of smoke concentration reached in each year at Kew between 1929 and 1961.

TABLE 32

Highest hourly smoke concentration, Kew, 1929–61

mg/100 m³

1929	1930	1931	1932	1933	1934	1935	1936	1937	1938	1939
480	320	260	350	320	420	610	350	320	180	130
1940	1941	1942	1943	1944	1945	1946	1947	1948	1949	1950
180	170	230	150	230	170	200	190	280	210	230
1951	1952	1953	1954	1955	1956	1957	1958	1959	1960	1961
230	250	170	110	170	230	190	150	190	170	200

Because of a change of instruments, the comparable 1962 value cannot be given but was probably about 220 mg/100 m³

Source of data: London, Meteorological Office *Observatories' year book* 1929–61

Dangerous concentrations of smoke (above 200 mg/100 m³) were reached in 20 of the 34 years between 1929 and 1962. The early 1930's were particularly prone to smogs of a severity not equalled until 1962. On 23 December 1935, for instance, concentrations of smoke built up during the morning and early afternoon and reached the astonishing level of over 600 mg/100 m³ by 1800 GMT, a situation hard to imagine, especially when one realizes how much greater the densities must have been in central London. The conditions, though extensive in the London area, were fortunately short-lived, having fallen to 70 mg/100 m³ at Kew by midnight.

Variation of smoke concentration at Kew with wind direction and velocity, relative humidity and cloud amount

Wright (1932) has shown how the intensity of smoke concentration at Kew, measured at 1500 GMT, varies with several elements of the weather. Although the analysis covered only three years (1928–30), the results are likely to be fairly representative. Table 33 and Fig. 23(b) show the relationship between smoke concentration and wind direction. The very high concentrations of smoke with winds from the east-northeast, east and

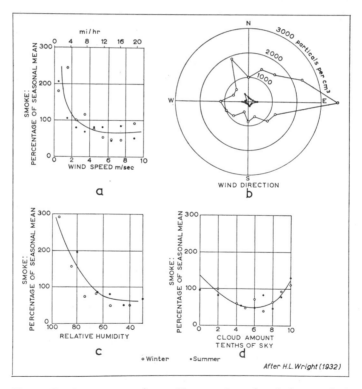

Fig 23 Smoke concentration at Kew, 1928–30, in relation to wind
speed, wind direction, humidity and cloud amount
(Source: Wright, H. L. 1932 'Observations of smoke particles and
condensation nuclei at Kew Observatory' London, Meterological
Office, *Geoph. Mem.*, 6, No. 57)

TABLE 33

Median smoke concentration with different wind directions as a percentage of the seasonal mean, Kew, 1928–30

	N	NNE	NE	ENE	E	ESE	SE	SSE
				per cent				
Oct–Mar	77	110	121	187	289	97	88	53
Apr–Sept	118	90	79	123	220	100	93	176
	S	SSW	SW	WSW	W	WNW	NW	NNW
				per cent				
Oct–Mar	63	36	65	78	88	50	52	145
Apr–Sept	52	47	39	66	126	45	42	189

Source of data: Wright, H. L. 1932 Observations of smoke particles and condensation nuclei at Kew Observatory. London, Meteorological Office, *Geoph. Mem.*, 6, No. 57, p. 7

north-northwest is striking. The excess from the south-southeast in summer is probably spurious for there were only four observations from this direction and three of these fell in April when concentrations are still well above the general summer level (Wright, 1932, p. 8). Some of the pollutants were from quite local sources but the exceptionally high values (about two and a half times the average) with easterly winds were also the result of accumulation in air moving across London. This was borne out by the higher percentage increase in winter with winds from the northeast to east. South-southwesterly, southwesterly and west-northwesterly winds, on the other hand, gave concentrations 50 per cent or more below the average. A shorter traverse of London's chimneys is no doubt partly responsible, but the frequently high wind speeds (Table 15) from the south-southwest, and instability in westerly and northwesterly airstreams (Belasco, 1952, pp. 15–16) presumably contribute to the reduction. Similarly, easterly winds are associated, particularly in winter, with stable air (Belasco, 1952, p. 18) which helps to keep pollution near the ground. Changes of wind direction are likely to cause smaller fluctuations in pollution levels in central areas than in suburban districts because the urban traverse is about the same length whatever the orientation.

Table 34 and Fig. 23(a) illustrate the dependence of smoke concentration upon wind velocity. Light winds with weak turbulence and frequently stable air quite clearly give the heaviest concentrations of smoke both in winter and summer. But the reduction, more regular in winter than in summer, is not perfectly progressive in either season, the irregularities being explained by the small sample which fails to assure a fair representation of wind direction within each velocity grade. The general form of the relationship (Fig. 26(a)) is a very rapid fall in concentrations with increased wind strength up to about 3 m/sec (6·7 mi/hr), followed by a more gradual fall to 5 m/sec (11·3 mi/hr), beyond which smoke concentrations remain almost independent of wind speed. But the dependence upon wind velocity of smoke concentrations near the ground is, in fact, less than might be supposed. More important is the efficiency of upward dispersal, although in most cases an increase of wind is accompanied by an increase in turbulence.

The relationship between smoke concentration and relative humidity at Kew is illustrated in Fig. 26(c). Intensities change hardly at all with humidities below 60 per cent, but above this they increase with humidity at a fairly uniform rate. There is little doubt that the relationship in this case is mainly indirect, for both humidities and pollution concentrations are highest in stable air.

The median concentration of smoke particles associated with specific cloud amounts is shown in Fig. 26(d). Changes are slight but it is quite clear that the lowest concentrations of smoke occur with intermediate cloud cover and this will typify days when convection is strong. The very high median value of smoke on cloudless days in winter may be due to associated conditions, for more than half the occasions from which the

TABLE 34

Median smoke concentration with different wind speeds as a percentage of the seasonal mean, Kew, 1928–30

	per cent				
m/sec	0·0–0·9	1·0–1·9	2·0–2·9	3·0–3·9	4·0– 4·9
mi/hr	0·0–2·1	2·3–4·2	4·4–6·5	6·7–8·8	9·0–11·1
Oct–Mar	180	244	100	115	73
Apr–Sept	205	104	78	67	78

	per cent			
m/sec	5·0– 5·9	6·0– 6·9	7·0– 7·9	8·0–10·0
mi/hr	11·3–13·1	13·4–15·4	15·7–17·7	18·0–19·8
Oct–Mar	52	45	44	92
Apr–Sept	78	44	83	49

Source: Wright, H. L. 1932 Observations of smoke particles and condensation nuclei at Kew Observatory. London, Meteorological Office, *Geoph. Mem.*, 6, No. 57, p. 9

median is derived had either easterly winds or calms, situations known to result in high smoke densities. Excluding these days, the median value lies very close to the summer value on the graph. The increased pollution with high cloud amounts is readily understandable, for overcast skies will commonly be associated with an inversion of temperature which will reduce turbulence and act as a barrier to the higher dispersal of smoke particles.

There are, of course, other irregularities in pollution concentrations resulting from changes in air temperature and the consequent output of domestic smoke. Severe cold weather may increase the density of smoke more than five-fold, but just as critical is the temperature lapse with height, inversions acting as atmospheric lids, trapping pollution near street level and sometimes causing a spectacular build-up of densities. Rain plays an important role in cleansing the air by washing down smoke, sulphur dioxide and other soluble pollutants, although near fronts there is also a beneficial increase in turbulence.

Little has been said about the gaseous and solid pollutants, other than smoke, at Kew. This is because no records have been kept at the Observatory of the amount of sulphur dioxide in the air and although a deposit gauge has been maintained since 1927, its record, like all others, is dominated by the very local rather than regional urban morphology and could not be used to indicate anything more than the immediate site conditions. In general, concentrations of gaseous and solid pollutants vary in sympathy with those for smoke. Spatially, sulphur dioxide (except perhaps in foggy conditions), dust, grit and other deposited matter are less widely diffused than smoke. The average life of a smoke particle before deposition is perhaps one or two days, that of a molecule of sulphur dioxide is probably less than 12 hr (Meetham, 1950, p. 369). The density of sulphur dioxide at ground level in London in winter varies from place to place as will be shown, but in general it is about two-thirds that of smoke, the ratio being higher in summer than in winter (when the percentage industrial contribution is reduced) and very much higher near factory chimneys.

In the country as a whole, the emission of sulphur dioxide has increased in recent years, but in London there has been a small decrease since 1955 (Dept. of Sci. and Industr. Res., 1960, p. 9; Carroll et al., 1960). The Clean Air Act of 1956 did not legislate for sulphur dioxide for, as stated by the Minister of Housing and Local Government in the House of Commons on 28 July 1959, the designation of sulphur dioxide-free zones is rendered impracticable by 'the present state of scientific and technical knowledge'. The situation over sulphur dioxide remains unsatisfactory in London where concentrations are nearly 20 per cent higher than the urban average for the country and there is no significant downward trend in concentrations (Craxford, 1961, p. 138). A fall in the domestic emission of sulphur dioxide from coal seems to be more than offset by a sharp increase in the low-level output from industrial oil-burning plants.

POLLUTION WITHIN GREATER LONDON

We have mentioned that deposit gauges are really typical only of their immediate environment, making it difficult to construct meaningful maps based on their records. This is less true of figures for smoke concentration. There are over 100 stations taking smoke readings in Greater London but their distribution is far from even, being more numerous in the centre than in the outer suburbs. Thus although maps of reasonable accuracy can be drawn for Greater London, in those which follow broken lines are used to indicate some uncertainty in their precise location, while dotted lines reflect even greater subjective judgement. As most of the records are comparatively recent and because of the piecemeal instigation of smoke-control areas, it would be difficult to average over more than one year, but in any case the picture for this short period must be fairly typical.

Fig. 24 shows the average concentration in mg/100 m³ of smoke in London during the summer of 1957, the last for which statistics are at present published (Dept. of Sci. and Industr. Res., 1960, pp. 45–90). Values, everywhere rather small, decrease away from the centre, but noteworthy are the small totals in the City of London (C) and in an area from Hampstead (H) to Westminster, and the heavier pollution in Stepney and

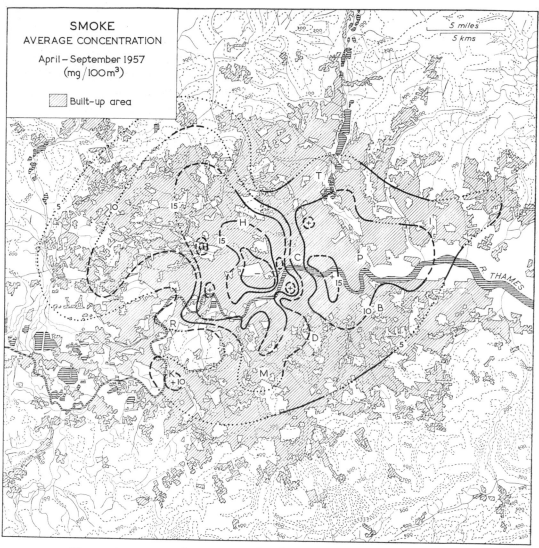

Fig 24 Average smoke concentration in London, summer 1957. Capital letters refer to districts mentioned in the text: B Blackheath, C City, D Dulwich, H Hampstead, I Ilford, K Kingston, M Mitcham, P Poplar, R Richmond, T Tottenham

(Source of data: Department of Scientific and Industrial Research 1960 *The investigation of atmospheric pollution*, No. 31. London H.M.S.O.

Southwark. Low values in the City of London are a result partly of the small resident population and the salutary effects of smoke-control regulations upon both domestic and industrial emissions. But, remembering the low domestic output in summer, the main explanation would seem to be the small number of smoke-producing industries in the area. Several large parks and the local importance of commercial offices and shops explain the cleaner air south of Hampstead. The parks are of great consequence for trees act as filters to air passing through them as John Evelyn (1661) recognized in his recommendations for reducing the intensity of smoke in seventeenth-century London, and parks are themselves smokeless zones. Deposits on laurel leaves near the periphery of Hyde Park, covering 360 acres (146 hectares), are about ten times as heavy as at the centre (Dept. of Sci. and Industr. Res., 1945, pp. 151–3) and, on average, the density of smoke at the centre of Hyde Park is about two-thirds that outside, ranging from one-quarter when turbulence and upward diffusion are active to five-sixths when both are sluggish. There is also some improvement downwind of the Park. Concentrations in the Park are reduced most when there is little smoky pollution in London generally, but when London is dirty, Hyde Park is almost as dirty as the surrounding streets (Dept. of Sci. and Industr. Res. 1945, pp. 71–5). Sulphur dioxide is also less in the Park than outside. With winds of more than 1·5 m/sec (3·5 mi/hr), as recorded on the Air Ministry roof 2 mi (3 km) east-northeast of Hyde Park, concentrations decrease steadily with distance from the upwind edge, whereas in winds of less than 1·5 m/sec (3·5 mi/hr) the initial decrease is usually followed by an increase (Wainwright and Wilson, 1962, p. 338). The latter may be explained by descending air into the Park, but from a higher level than that envisaged by Gold (1956), as part of a circulation linked with rising air above the surrounding built-up areas. This idea will be considered in Chapter 5. Investigations have shown that the rate of decrease, though closely correlated with the lapse rate, has little or no relationship with wind speed.

High smoke values during the summer of 1957 (Fig. 24) in an area on either side of the Thames from Stepney to Southwark were caused by a remarkably intense concentration of older-type factories and terrace houses in a low-lying area inimical to the efficient dispersal of pollutants.

Conditions during the winter of 1957–8 are shown in Fig. 25. Everywhere values are higher than during the previous summer but the decrease from central to suburban and rural districts is by no means uniform. In the Hackney, Bethnal Green, Poplar (P), Stepney and Bermondsey districts of the lower Lea valley, average smoke concentrations were more than three times those of the outer suburbs, more particularly those south, west and northwest of the centre and including Kew. In these northeast districts, a product of mainly eighteenth- and nineteenth-century urban expansion, thousands of domestic and industrial chimneys pour their pollutants into the atmosphere of a low-lying area. Fulham and Battersea to the southwest gave a secondary peak in smoke concentrations for similar reasons. The relative purity of air in the City of London can be attributed both to its small resident population and smoke-control regulations. Pindard and Wilkins (1958, p. 7) estimated a reduction of 40 per cent in the average smoke concentrations over half the city's smokeless zone and at a time when it was surrounded by built-up uncontrolled areas, unlike today (Fig. 26), but others have expressed more guarded views and the figure must now be regarded as suspect for it was based upon readings from different sizes of stain which are not directly comparable. A recent investigation by the Department of Scientific and Industrial Research in a small smoke-control area in Hackney (northeast London) yielded very interesting results. The area subject to smoke-control was about one mile long by half a mile wide, the longer axis being normal to the direction of the prevailing winds. It was surrounded by eighteenth- and nineteenth-century, closely spaced terrace housing with some industry. The average

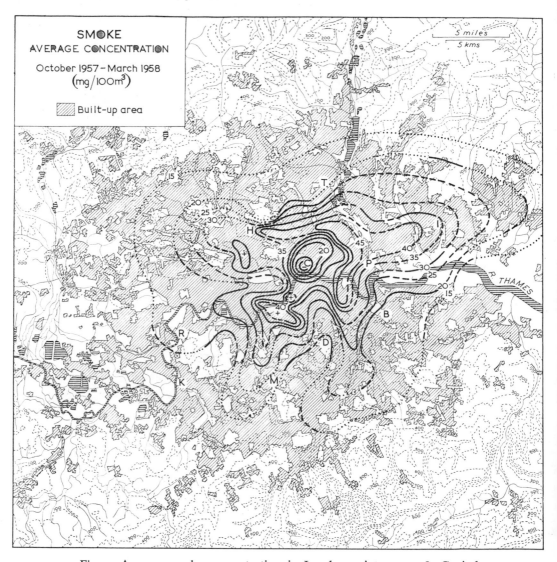

Fig 25 Average smoke concentration in London, winter 1957–8. Capital
letters refer to districts mentioned in the text and listed with Fig. 24
(Source of data: Department of Scientific and Industrial Research 1960 *The
investigation of atmospheric pollution*, No. 31. London H.M.S.O.)

reduction in smoke within this small area was only about 16 per cent at 400 yards
(366 m) from the windward edge, but perhaps more significant was the fact that reduction was by about the same absolute amount regardless of the weather, being greatest
in the evening.

It is obvious that smoke-control regulations are most effective when the regulated
areas are large and compact, but more research over a period of years is needed. Mean-
while there is an encouraging if somewhat fragmentary spread of smoke-control areas
in London (Fig. 26).

The asymmetric distribution in Fig. 25 with a northeast displacement of zones seems

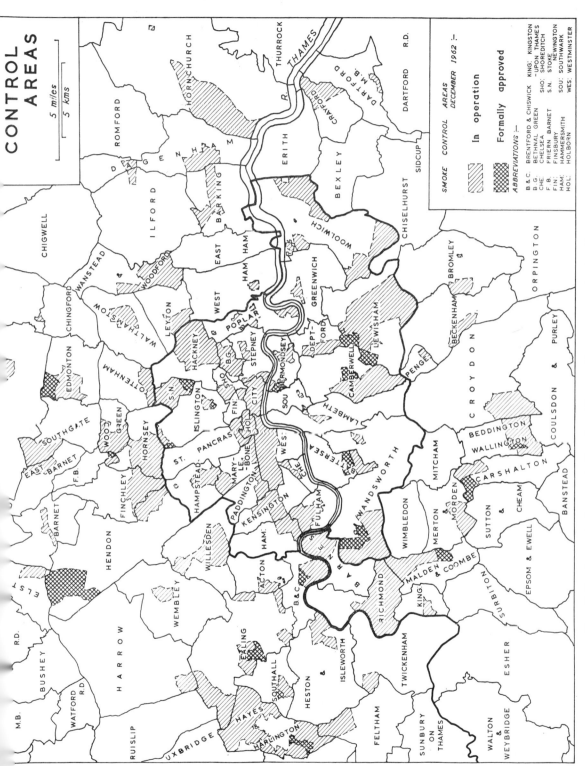

Fig 26 Smoke control areas in London (Source: Department of Scientific and Industrial Research, Warren Spring Laboratory, MS map)

at first sight to result from the prevailing southwesterly winds but it is likely that the explanation is as much topographic as climatic for comparisons between the emission of pollutants and near-surface concentrations of smoke and sulphur dioxide indicate that upward escape is more important than sideways drift as a means of dispersal, and there is no great progressive accumulation of smoke in surface air as it blows across a town (Dept. of Sci. and Industr. Res., 1945, pp. 60 and 125). In these circumstances, the areas of highest smoke and sulphur dioxide concentrations will remain broadly the same no matter what the wind direction may be, although a proportion of the pollutants will be carried downwind. The concentration isopleths are then shifted towards the lee side of the city without any drastic changes in their general form and without any significant move of the points of maximum concentration. In a city of symmetrical urban development and with the main pollution sources at the centre, the distribution would become asymmetric but with its peak in central areas and cleaner air on the windward rather than the lee side of the built-up area. It would seem that the intensity of smoke and sulphur dioxide concentrations is dominated by conditions near the point of measurement (Williams, 1960) and on turbulent days in particular a very large proportion of the suspended pollution is of extremely local origin, for pollution from more distant sources rapidly diffuses upwards. Densities sometimes differ appreciably between two neighbouring streets with contrary orientations and conditions of airflow.

Some indication of the extent of lateral shift in the general pattern of smoke is given by Fig. 27 which is a map of the mean smoke concentration for 10 days with light winds during the winter of 1958–9, on each of which winds remained in an easterly quarter (70–110 degrees true). The mean wind speed for all 10 days was 4·6 m/sec (10·4 mi/hr) at both 0000 and 1200 GMT.

During easterly winds, and when turbulent diffusion is not excessive, it would seem that the main areas of heavy pollution by smoke remain broadly the same, but there is a decided increase of concentration in western districts and a fall below average in eastern areas. The pattern of smoke density, though still reflecting the asymmetry of London's urban morphology with the main source regions in northeast rather than central London, is far more concentric to the built-up area than is the mean annual picture (Fig. 29). Cleaner air seems to move down the Lea valley and also into lower Thames-side, while more polluted air is carried westward along the valley of the Thames. The related features of airflow have already been noted in Chapter 2. Fig. 28 shows a similar distortion of the pattern of sulphur dioxide in the atmosphere by easterly winds during the same 10 days, but with an even more pronounced westward shift, as might be expected with a pollutant which is less easily carried upwards to be dispersed high above street level.

The bearing of wind direction upon smoke concentrations at Kew has already been considered and from this and other evidence we can infer that although shifts in wind direction are unlikely to make any great changes in the peak areas, in the suburbs the highest concentrations will accompany winds with the longest traverse of the city, more particularly those which move across the heavily polluted northeast districts. But much depends upon the prevailing atmospheric conditions, as anyone familiar with the

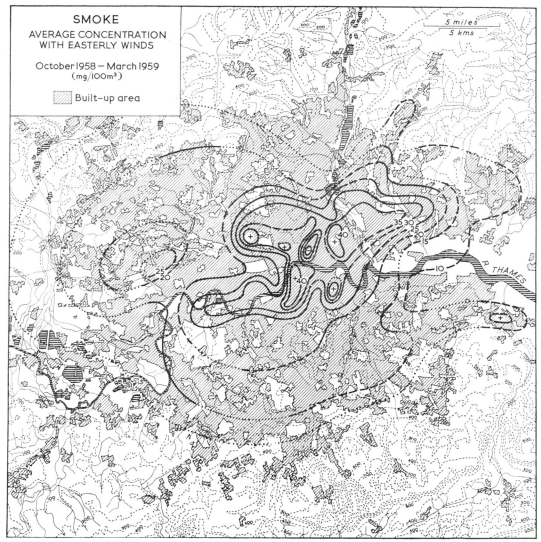

Fig 27 Average smoke concentration in London with easterly winds, October
1958–March 1959
(Source of data: Department of Scientific and Industrial Research, Warren
Spring Laboratory, MS records)

changing view from Hampstead Heath well knows. That there is some transport of smoke
(and sulphur dioxide) into and beyond the lee areas of the city is beyond doubt, but the
small amounts involved are perhaps surprising. Nevertheless, Figs. 24 and 25 suggest that
the prevailing southwesterly winds probably accentuate the northeastward extension of
concentration isopleths in northeast London and the pollution of rural areas beyond
the city margin. Until the recently instigated National Survey of Air Pollution, there
were few measurements in rural areas, including those around London. It is, however, a
matter of common observation that there is considerably more smoke near the ground
in country areas of the Green Belt when the wind is blowing from London than when
it is coming from other directions. The effect seems to be most marked with fresh winds

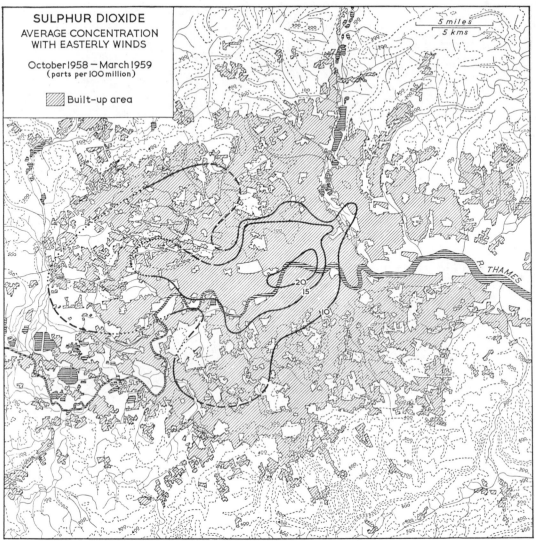

SULPHUR DIOXIDE
AVERAGE CONCENTRATION
WITH EASTERLY WINDS

October 1958 – March 1959
(parts per 100 million)

Built-up area

Fig 28 Average sulphur dioxide concentration in London with easterly winds,
October 1958–March 1959
(Source of data: Department of Scientific and Industrial Research, Warren
Spring Laboratory, MS records)

of more than 4·4 m/sec (10 mi/hr). The pollution is sometimes carried much further, even as far as Leicester, 100 mi (161 km) away (Dept. of Sci. and Industr. Res., 1945,p. 125).

Orographic influences are also evident in the distribution of smoke (Fig. 25). A tongue of cleaner air from Mitcham Common (M) inward to Crystal Palace Park and Dulwich (D) covers an upstanding area with substantial open spaces, raised above the pollution hood of the surrounding low-lying areas; Richmond Park (R) and Wimbledon Common are similarly positioned, as is the open, windswept area of Hampstead in north London. At the foot of these elevated areas there are intense pollution gradients with rapid changes in the dirtiness of the air.

Fig. 29 shows the mean distribution of smoke for a whole year. It is a composite

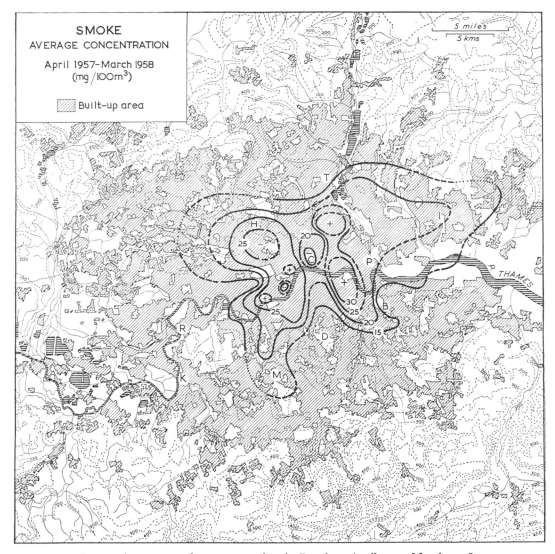

Fig 29 Average smoke concentration in London, April 1957–March 1958.
Capital letters refer to districts mentioned in the text and listed with Fig. 24
(Source of data: Department of Scientific and Industrial Research 1960 *The
investigation of atmospheric pollution*, No. 31. London H.M.S.O.)

map bringing out the main features of the previous seasonal maps, that is, reduced
concentrations in St Marylebone, Hammersmith, Kensington and Westminster, and in
the City of London; heavily polluted air in the lower Lea valley residential and industrial
area between Stoke Newington and Stepney, and in a tongue between Bermondsey
and Lewisham south of the river; a tendency to higher concentrations in the northeast
suburbs than elsewhere; and relatively clean air in the higher, more open areas of
south, west and north London.

The pattern of average sulphur dioxide concentrations for the same twelve months
(Fig. 30) is less complicated, with values in outer London less than half those of central

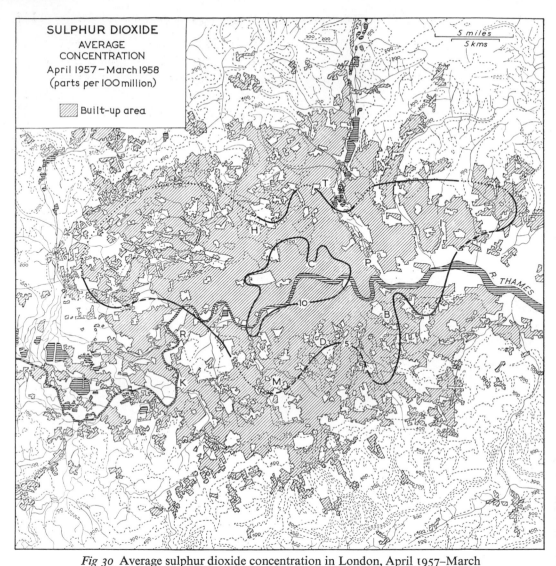

Fig 30 Average sulphur dioxide concentration in London, April 1957–March 1958. Capital letters refer to districts mentioned in the text and listed with Fig. 24
(Source of data: Department of Scientific and Industrial Research 1960 *The investigation of atmospheric pollution*, No. 31. London H.M.S.O.)

areas from Fulham to Stepney and from St Pancras to Southwark. In winter the ratio is of the order of 1:3, similar to that of smoke. There was not at this time, nor is there now, any restriction on the emission of sulphur dioxide in the City of London or any other control area, and changes in the types of fuel used in these areas have had less effect upon the production of this noxious gas than upon smoke: in some areas there has been an increase in the output of sulphur dioxide.

As already explained, the distribution of soluble and insoluble deposits of atmospheric pollutants is far less susceptible to areal analysis than are suspended impurities. Their general distribution is similar to that of smoke or sulphur dioxide: in Poplar, deposit rates are locally as high as 450 ton/mi²/yr (174 ton/km²/yr) and over most of Greater London deposition is at the annual rate of 200 ton/mi² (77 ton/km²) or about 2 oz/yd². Near Epping, 6 mi (9·7 km) beyond the northeastern fringe of the main built-up area, values are less than 100 ton/mi²/yr (39 ton/km²/yr) (Dept. of Sci. and Industr. Res., 1960, pp. 49 and 58) and in open country well beyond London it falls to less than 10 ton/mi²/yr (4 ton/km²/yr). London as a whole is coated with about 110,000 tons of tar, ash and other pollutants each year.

The depth of smoke over London

The view of a city's pollution haze from an aircraft is most interesting. The smoke canopy sometimes rises to greater and greater heights downwind but is frequently domed above the city itself. Its edges, particularly on the windward side, are usually clearly defined with a rapid build up of intensity and depth over a very short distance across the rural-urban fringe, more especially when winds are light. There is also a mainly high-level drift of pollution downwind of the city which has sometimes been reported to extend for hundreds of miles and, during the day, to heights of several thousand feet. The pollution trail will frequently concentrate and flow laterally beneath a temperature inversion leaving a rather purer layer sandwiched between it and the contaminated streets below.

Up to the present there have been few measurements of the vertical distribution of pollutants and only a small number of these have been above cities. Only one published investigation of this nature exists for London. Braun and Wilson (1961) used captive balloons to determine sulphur dioxide concentrations at heights up to 500 ft (152 m) above a built-up area of Kensington near the southern boundary of Hyde Park, and at Kew Observatory. These experiments showed that when the wind velocity gradient is large, a situation commonly associated with stability and more characteristic of night than day, then concentrations decreased with height. Reductions by a quarter to two-thirds of that at 100 ft (30 m) were greatest on clear nights when the air was usually stable and with steep velocity gradients, whilst clear days gave a far more uniform concentration consistent with instability and turbulent mixing. At times of fog there was little difference between conditions at 100 and 500 ft (30 and 152 m). On the other hand, there is good reason for believing that much of the pollution produced by London would have passed above the sampling balloon (Lucas, 1958).

Extreme conditions in London

The general range of values expected at Kew has been discussed earlier in this chapter but we have little or no means of measuring how widespread these conditions were over Greater London until the well-documented smog of 5–9 December 1952. The fog itself will be discussed in Chapter 8; here we are concerned with the pollutants with which it was associated.

Although by no means the worst pollution conditions experienced, at least locally in London, its physiological effects seem to have been unprecedented (Logan, 1953, p. 336) (see Chapter 12). The disaster was without doubt the most serious of its kind in this country for at least 80 years, and probably the worst ever, but there is some consolation that it was followed by increased agitation and legislation against the unnecessary pollution of London's air, leading to the report of a Committee under the Chairmanship of Sir Hugh Beaver (Great Britain, Committee on Air Pollution, 1955), the Clean Air Act of 1956 and, beginning in 1958, the instigation of smoke-control regulations in Greater London (Fig. 26). They had been introduced in the City in 1955.

At the time of this incident, measurements of the mean daily concentrations of smoke and sulphur dioxide were taken at only twelve sites in Greater London. Average daily concentrations of smoke in central areas varied between about 200 and 400 mg/100 m³ on the 6th and 7th, but it was also possible to obtain a reasonably detailed picture of the distribution of sulphur dioxide during the smog from the results of a

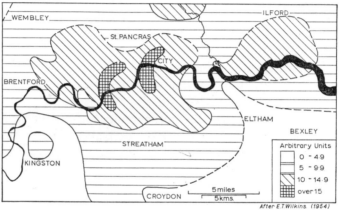

Fig 31 Average sulphur dioxide concentration in London,
5–9 December 1952
(Source: Wilkins, E. T. 1954 'Air pollution aspects of the London
fog of December 1952' *Quart. J. R. Met. Soc.*, London, 80, p. 270)

further 117 instruments which measure the rate of sulphation of a standard surface of lead peroxide over a period of one month. Average concentrations at most sites were increased by 50 per cent or more and the precise increases can be used as a round measure of sulphur dioxide concentrations during the smog period.

Fig. 31 (after Wilkins, 1954, p. 270) shows the approximate pattern of pollution by sulphur dioxide from 5–9 December 1952, based upon these data. There were two areas of maximum pollution: the first covered parts of Westminster, Kensington, Chelsea, Battersea and Lambeth, and the second, Holborn, the City and Southwark. Smaller concentrations lay in strips along the low-lying parts of the Thames and Lea valleys where air movement would be even lighter than elsewhere and the inversion perhaps stronger. But there was remarkably clean air above the more elevated parts of south London, such as Richmond Park and Black Heath, which would be less important as source regions and have stronger air currents mixing with the purer air at higher levels.

As measured at Kew there were 33 per cent of calms during the period; for the remainder of the time the very slight air movements were from the southwest, west and east, all associated with anticyclonic weather and an intense low-level inversion. The fog was observed to extend up to about 500 ft (152 m) and Meetham (1956, pp. 269 and 272) has estimated that the smog covered 450 mi² (1,165 km²), or about three-fifths of Greater London. It probably contained, at its peak, 380 tons of smoke and 800 tons of sulphur dioxide and the fog droplets must have been a 0·4 per cent solution of sulphuric acid!

During the London smog almost exactly ten years later, from 3–7 December 1962, concentrations of smoke reached peak average daily concentrations of over 400 mg/100 m³ in an area about 2·5 mi (4 km) wide from Holborn and St Pancras to the river Lea in Hackney and Poplar. Concentrations were between 300 and 400 mg/100 m³ in a ring from Marylebone in the west to West Ham in the east, and from Wood Green in the north to Deptford in the south. Around this was a zone, roughly coincident with inner suburban, nineteenth-century London, where values ranged from 200 to 300 mg/100 m³, and further out again in the remainder of the suburbs, 100 to 200 mg/100 m³ was typical. The distribution of sulphur dioxide differed only in detail from that of smoke, being highest in the inner areas from Kensington to Hackney where central heating of buildings is common or there is a concentration of industry (Dept. of Sci. and Industr. Res., 1963).

Because of the inadequacy of smoke readings during the December 1952 smog, no valid comparisons can be made with those of December 1962, although calculations based upon the reduction in smoke emission in the intervening years would suggest that the mean smoke concentration may have been one-third or so less in December 1962. Comparisons between the respective concentrations of sulphur dioxide show that almost equal levels were reached, but that they remained for five days in 1952 compared with four days in 1962.

Air pollution is an unwelcome adjunct of urbanization and industrialization and London's atmosphere is grossly polluted, but the vigorous implementation of the Clean Air Act already shows signs of its justification—at least as far as smoke concentrations are concerned; no doubt as controls are applied to more and more areas of London, the air will become cleaner and the city will become less and less the grimy, soot encrusted place with which its name has been associated. One day we may be able, like William Morris, to:

> Forget six counties overhung with smoke,
> Forget the snorting steam and piston stroke,
> Forget the spreading of the hideous town;
> Think rather of the pack-horse on the down,
> And dream of London, small and white and clean,
> The clear Thames bordered by its gardens green.

London will never become smaller, although its growth has been controlled, but it may well become a cleaner and healthier place to live.

5 Radiation and sunshine

We looked o'er London, where men wither and choke,
Roofed in, poor souls, renouncing stars and skies.

Theodore Watts-Dunton

ATMOSPHERIC POLLUTION, a mainly man-made cloud of dust and gases, interposes itself between the ground and the clearer atmosphere above. In so doing it helps to distinguish the climate of London from that of its rural environs by reducing the receipt of solar radiation including sunlight and, indeed, by changing in detail the pattern of the city's heat balance.

Conditions at Kew may be taken again as representative of the general levels of radiation and sunshine and of the pattern of their diurnal, weekly and annual change.

RADIATION AT KEW

Stagg (1950) has made a detailed study of radiation receipt and loss at Kew, only the essential features of which will be given here.

Direct solar radiation

Records of direct solar radiation received on a surface maintained normal to the direction of the sun have been kept at Kew Observatory since July 1932; measurements of the radiation received on a horizontal surface from the sun and sky and from the sky alone were begun in July 1956; and since 1957 a record has been made of net radiation receipt and loss by and from the ground.

Table 35 lists the totals of direct solar radiation at Kew Observatory in gram-calories per square centimetre per minute for all days of the 14 years from 1933–46 between exact hours LAT (Local Apparent Time). (1 gm cal/cm² = 1·16 milliwatts/hr/cm²).

It shows how the average intensities of solar (short-wave) radiation increase sharply after sunrise and decrease equally rapidly near sunset. In summer there is clearly a levelling out of intensities in the middle of the day, caused partly by rates of change in the depth of atmosphere penetrated by radiation with different sun elevations, and partly by the interference of water vapour, dust and smoke which are convected to higher levels during the summer months. There is no such flattening in winter because of the low elevation of the sun and weaker convection.

There is an interesting change from month to month in the time of greatest radiation intensity. In summer, between June and September, the time of maximum intensity is from 1000 to 1100 LAT, that is before convection increases cloud amounts and disperses surface dust and water vapour through the atmosphere, so reducing solar radiation receipts in the early afternoon. In winter and spring, on the other hand, what little difference there is between pairs of morning and afternoon values equidistant from noon

TABLE 35

Average intensity of direct solar radiation, Kew, 1933–46

hour ending (LAT):

	04	05	06	07	08	09	10	11	12
					cal/cm²/min				
Jan					·001	·020	·072	·111	·120
Feb				·001	·021	·085	·143	·184	·199
Mar			·001	·034	·106	·166	·207	·271	·273
Apr		·001	·029	·130	·218	·263	·298	·339	·337
May		·019	·112	·205	·276	·331	·375	·416	·420
June	·001	·054	·162	·258	·330	·382	·411	·428	·425
July	·001	·040	·140	·228	·291	·310	·338	·370	·359
Aug		·003	·063	·166	·244	·314	·344	·387	·379
Sept			·009	·090	·186	·246	·318	·349	·344
Oct				·005	·064	·150	·201	·258	·259
Nov					·003	·049	·095	·133	·155
Dec					·001	·012	·061	·110	·125

	13	14	15	16	17	18	19	20	21
Jan	·124	·103	·064	·024	·001				
Feb	·184	·154	·125	·085	·023	·001			
Mar	·280	261	·232	·190	·107	·028	·001		
Apr	·344	·334	·301	·261	·204	·116	·028	·001	
May	·395	·378	·352	·347	·299	·240	·131	·023	·001
June	·401	·398	·383	·363	·330	·279	·192	·075	·001
July	·340	·337	·328	·308	·277	·230	·148	·037	·001
Aug	·375	·365	·350	·317	·275	·205	·082	·004	
Sept	·338	·315	·280	·240	·184	·089	·006	·001	
Oct	·251	·224	·192	·139	·061	·005			
Nov	·150	·121	·087	·040	·003				
Dec	·123	·097	·057	·016	·001				

Source: Stagg, J. M. 1950 Solar radiation at Kew Observatory. London, Meteorological Office, *Geoph. Mem.*, 11, No. 86, p. 14

is in favour of the latter. The reason for this reversal of summer conditions is probably the partial break-up of a stratiform cloud cover by convective mixing after midday.

Table 36 gives the average intensity of direct solar radiation on days of high radiation (about 8 per cent of all days), that is on days with an unclouded sky and good visibility, generally associated with Polar Maritime air from the northwest. Peak intensities on these days are attained near the time of the sun's greatest elevation.

The highest average radiation intensities for all days (Table 35) occur in May and June in the hours just before noon when they reach 0·42 cal/cm²/min: on the best radiation days (Table 36) the maximum intensity falls about midday in June and is about three times the previous values.

The variation from month to month in the daily totals of direct radiation for various categories of days is given in Table 37.

TABLE 36

Average intensity of direct solar radiation on days of high radiation, Kew, 1933–46

	04	05	06	Hour ending (LAT): 07	08	09	10	11	12
				cal/cm²/min					
Jan					·001	·121	·394	·621	·653
Feb					·104	·396	·642	·817	·836
Mar			·001	·153	·439	·588	·769	·877	·889
Apr			·079	·357	·599	·771	·848	·955	·977
May		·035	·247	·504	·650	·842	1·022	1·124	1·142
June		·110	·340	·592	·745	·876	1·033	1·102	1·129
July		·105	·367	·571	·738	·805	·903	·979	1·006
Aug		·005	·154	·431	·672	·852	·934	1·031	1·007
Sept			·023	·283	·588	·754	·902	1·020	1·037
Oct				·031	·254	·629	·863	·956	·995
Nov					·028	·229	·585	·834	·870
Dec					·010	·139	·464	·652	·734

	13	14	15	16	17	18	19	20	21
Jan	·626	·464	·283	·106	·002				
Feb	·767	·584	·451	·263	·061	·001			
Mar	·939	·838	·792	·643	·445	·139	·001		
Apr	·976	·944	·882	·768	·593	·326	·087	·001	
May	1·133	1·090	1·016	1·007	·867	·650	·408	·087	·003
June	1·093	1·072	1·026	·988	·862	·736	·512	·153	·004
July	·973	·904	·891	·849	·722	·602	·388	·097	·002
Aug	·990	·985	·907	·793	·636	·450	·180	·019	
Sept	·976	·881	·853	·753	·540	·268	·022		
Oct	·821	·821	·692	·565	·247	·023			
Nov	·737	·572	·503	·266	·035				
Dec	·699	·587	·359	·077					

Source: Stagg, J. M. 1950 Solar radiation at Kew Observatory. London, Meteorological Office, *Geoph. Mem.*, 11, No. 86, p. 14

It will be noted how far below the maximum recorded or ceiling values are the totals received on the average day at Kew. The ratio between these two sets of figures varies from 11 per cent in January to 28 per cent in June. Also, although the maximum values in January are 33 per cent of those in June, the mean value for all days in January is only 13 per cent of that for June. The explanation lies mainly in the more complete winter cloud cover. The range of daily values recorded in 14 years is shown in Table 38 which gives the percentage frequency of daily totals in various grades and expresses

TABLE 37

Average daily totals of direct solar radiation for various categories of days, Kew, 1933–46

	Jan	Feb	Mar	Apr	May	June	July	Aug	Sept	Oct	Nov	Dec	Mean
						cal/cm²							
A	38	72	130	192	258	294	245	233	181	108	49	36	154
B	196	295	451	550	701	742	654	603	534	418	279	223	519
C	338	495	679	849	971	1,035	999	895	748	571	379	291	687

A: all days
B: days of high radiation
C: ceiling values

Source: Stagg, J. M. 1950 Solar radiation at Kew Observatory. London, Meteorological Office, *Geoph. Mem.*, II, No. 86, p. 10

the annual cycle in a rather more realistic way. The main features of contrast between winter and summer are clear enough and need no emphasis or explanation.

The total direct solar radiation received at Kew during an average year is about 56,000 cal/cm², ranging between 69,200 (1943) and 47,300 (1936) cal/cm² in the 14 years

TABLE 38

Percentage frequency distribution of daily totals of direct solar radiation, Kew, 1933–46

cal/cm²	Jan	Feb	Mar	Apr	May	June	July	Aug	Sept	Oct	Nov	Dec
						per cent						
< 50	73	60	40	31	22	16	22	21	31	45	69	73
51–100	12	12	14	11	9	10	11	12	14	13	12	12
101–150	7	7	11	10	10	9	11	9	10	14	10	8
151–200	5	8	10	8	7	9	8	10	6	9	4	4
201–300	3	10	9	12	14	15	15	15	14	11	5	3
301–400		3	10	11	13	12	11	14	10	6	< 1	
401–500			4	8	11	8	7	10	8	2	< 1	
501–600			2	5	6	9	7	5	6	1		
601–700			< 1	3	5	6	4	3	1			
701–800				1	2	3	3	1				
801–900				< 1	1	2	1	< 1				
901–950						< 1	< 1					

Source: Stagg, J. M. 1950 Solar radiation at Kew Observatory. London, Meteorological Office, *Geoph. Mem.*, II, No. 86, p. 12

from 1933 to 1946. Of the yearly total the four months from May to August contribute 56 per cent, and the four winter months from November to February only 10 per cent. The lowest recorded monthly receipt was 465 cal/cm² in December 1933 and the highest was 12,263 cal/cm² in May 1943. October has the smallest absolute range of values over the 14 years and February the greatest. Of the summer months, June and August are less variable than July.

Short-wave radiation from sun and sky on a horizontal surface

As previously stated, records of radiation from the sun and sky, and from the sky alone, on a horizontal surface have been taken at Kew Observatory since July 1946. The first 14 months of records were analysed by Stagg (1950, pp. 27–36) but the figures were shown by Blackwell (1954) to be marred in detail by several sources of error. The figures quoted by Stagg for diffuse (sky) radiation were found to need reduction by 16 per cent and the total radiation by 10 per cent of the corrected diffuse values (Blackwell, 1954, Table 1). But the broad features of change and comparison outlined by Stagg remain true.

Mean and extreme monthly and daily values of total radiation (on a horizontal surface) are given in Table 39.

TABLE 39

Average and extreme values of total radiation on a horizontal surface, Kew, 1950–60

Monthly and yearly values

	Jan	Feb	Mar	Apr	May	June	
	milliwatt hours per square centimetre						
Average	1,726	2,939	6,073	9,952	13,298	14,177	
Max	2,085	3,354	7,290	11,292	15,453	17,432	
Min	1,359	2,524	4,741	8,615	10,353	11,559	

	July	Aug	Sept	Oct	Nov	Dec	Yr
Average	13,507	11,366	8,099	4,670	2,179	1,313	89,308
Max	15,719	13,213	9,645	5,759	2,492	1,701	95,881
Min	12,219	9,812	6,680	3,895	1,658	995	82,949

Daily values

	Jan	Feb	Mar	Apr	May	June	
Average	56	105	202	328	433	478	
Max	151	280	440	643	806	807	
Min	4	16	13	35	45	56	

	July	Aug	Sept	Oct	Nov	Dec	Yr
Average	438	359	271	152	73	43	245
Max	784	671	552	345	230	110	807
Min	98	73	29	9	2	4	2

Hourly values

	Jan	Feb	Mar	Apr	May	June	
Max	29	49	66	81	92	96	

	July	Aug	Sept	Oct	Nov	Dec	Yr
Max	107	83	78	55	39	27	107

1 milliwatt hour = 0·861 gram calories

Source of data: London, Meteorological Office tabulations, Form 3265B (MS)

As with the other elements of London's climate, the amount of radiation expected on any individual day or month lies within a broad range, though being so strongly influenced by rhythmic astronomical forces, the margins of fluctuation are closer than for, say, wind speed or rainfall. Table 40 gives the frequencies of daily values of total radiation (on a horizontal surface), by months, for the 6 years 1957–62. In this period, daily values ranged from 1·72 cal/cm² (2 mw hr/cm²) on 26 November 1958 to 693 cal/cm² (806 mw hr/cm²) on 26 May 1957 and 14 June 1962.

TABLE 40

Percentage frequency distribution of daily amounts of total radiation on a horizontal surface, by months, Kew, 1957–62

mw hr/cm²	cal/cm²	Jan	Feb	Mar	Apr	May	June
				per cent			
0– 50	0– 43	47	24	5	1	1	0
51–100	44– 86	46	32	14	3	2	2
101–150	87–129	7	20	16	10	5	1
151–200	130–172		17	12	11	4	3
201–300	173–258		7	29	22	15	10
301–400	259–344			21	22	15	13
401–500	345–430			3	18	20	15
501–600	431–516				12	20	21
601–700	517–602				1	14	18
701–800	603–688					3	15
801–900	689–744					1	2

mw hr/cm²	cal/cm²	July	Aug	Sept	Oct	Nov	Dec	Yr
				per cent				
0– 50	0– 43	0	0	2	9	39	59	16
51–100	44– 86	1	1	5	18	33	35	16
101–150	87–129	2	3	6	17	19	6	9
151–200	130–172	2	10	10	21	7		8
201–300	173–258	13	19	34	30	2		15
301–400	259–344	27	25	31	5			13
401–500	345–430	23	22	11				9
501–600	431–516	22	16	1				8
601–700	517–602	7	4					4
701–800	603–688	3						2
801–900	689–744							<1

Source of data: London, Meteorological Office tabulations, Form 3265B (MS)

Although the general pattern of change is similar to that of direct solar radiation, one notable expected difference is the sharp peak frequency of high total radiation amounts in June compared with May and July. In June there is a chance of about one day in six having a total radiation above 700 mw hr/cm², but this is reduced to about one in thirty in May and July. The highest direct solar radiation on a surface normal to the direction of the sun occurs on days of good visibility with little cloud, but the maxima of total (sun and sky) radiation on a horizontal surface fall, by comparison, on days when the sky is 2–4 oktas (eighths) covered with broken fair-weather cumulus. These clouds reflect a great deal of incident radiation without too seriously reducing the direct solar component which contributes more than 70 per cent of the total. The highest diffuse radiation occurs on days with good visibility and with broken mixed cloud at several levels giving a total cloud cover of about 7 oktas (Stagg, 1950, p. 30). On such days diffuse radiation contributes about 70 per cent of the total radiation but this falls to less than a quarter on days with clear sky and good visibility. On an average summer day, on the other hand, about half the total receipt is by diffuse sky radiation.

Turning to the daily cycle, the main features of the variations of total radiation (for all days) are shown in Table 41. Two points are worthy of note: the contribution of

TABLE 41

Hourly averages of total radiation on a horizontal surface, by months, Kew, 1947–56

	Local Apparent Time							
	04–05	05–06	06–07	07–08	08–09	09–10	10–11	11–12
	milliwatts per square centimetre							
Jan				trace	2·2	6·3	10·3	12·7
Feb			trace	2·0	7·2	12·3	16·7	18·0
Mar		trace	1·9	7·9	13·9	20·4	25·8	29·0
Apr	trace	2·2	9·9	20·5	32·1	39·6	44·3	47·6
May	0·9	5·7	13·6	22·6	31·4	38·2	45·9	46·9
June	2·9	10·2	20·4	30·5	39·8	46·6	52·8	53·8
July	1·9	8·0	16·7	27·4	36·0	43·8	49·2	52·4
Aug	0·1	3·8	12·0	21·9	33·6	41·0	45·1	48·8
Sept		0·3	4·0	12·4	22·0	29·1	35·2	38·5
Oct			0·4	3·7	9·9	15·9	22·4	25·9
Nov				0·4	3·9	8·5	12·9	15·3
Dec					1·2	4·4	8·1	10·1

	12–13	13–14	14–15	15–16	16–17	17–18	18–19	19–20
	milliwatts per square centimetre							
Jan	11·6	8·0	5·7	2·0	trace			
Feb	18·1	16·0	11·6	6·7	1·6	trace		
Mar	28·9	25·0	19·8	13·7	6·9	1·4	trace	
Apr	46·6	42·2	35·4	26·6	17·0	7·6	1·4	trace
May	45·7	44·4	39·5	31·9	23·3	13·7	5·6	0·7
June	54·4	51·6	48·1	39·2	29·9	18·6	9·9	2·5
July	49·7	47·0	40·3	32·7	23·7	15·3	7·1	1·6
Aug	49·1	45·4	37·9	30·7	20·6	11·7	3·6	0·1
Sept	36·9	34·5	28·5	21·0	11·1	3·7	0·1	
Oct	26·5	22·9	16·9	10·4	3·7	0·2		
Nov	15·2	12·2	7·7	2·9	0·2			
Dec	9·9	7·7	4·3	1·0	trace			

1 milliwatt hour = 0·861 gram calories

Source of date: Blackwell, M. J. 1954 Five years continuous recording of total and diffuse solar radiation at Kew Observatory. *Met. Res. Pap.* No. 895, London

direct solar radiation to the total is reduced in the hours immediately around noon, more especially in summer, owing to an increased cloudiness and tubidity of the air; also the direct and diffuse components of the total radiation are roughly complementary, a fluctuation in one being approximately compensated by an opposite change in the other, thus maintining a fairly smooth diurnal cycle in total radiation amounts but with a suggestion of higher values in the forenoon period.

Blackwell (1950, Figs. 12, 13 and 14) also calculated the mean hourly values of total and diffuse radiation at Kew on cloudless and overcast days.

SUNSHINE AT KEW

Bright sunshine at Kew is recorded by the burnt trace of the Campbell Stokes instrument sited on the roof of the Observatory. There is of course a very close relationship between its record and that of radiation receipt, but it has been estimated that the card of the Campbell Stokes recorder does not begin to burn until direct solar radiation reaches about 0·2 cal/cm²/min. However, this is out-balanced by an over-estimation by the recorder when the sunshine is intermittent (Stagg, 1950, p. 11).

Diurnal and annual variations of bright sunshine

Fig. 32 shows the pattern of change in the average length of bright sunshine for each 60 min period ended at exact hours LAT (Local Apparent Time). Totals increase sharply after sunrise and decrease rapidly before sunset. In summer there is a levelling out of intensities in the middle of the day for astronomical reasons and because of increased cloud amounts and a deepening of the haze layer at this time. In winter and spring, sunshine ratios are highest in the hour after noon; in summer, on the other hand, a higher zenithal sun and more active convection (of dust, smoke and water vapour) give a different pattern. In June, July, August and September, temperatures and consequent convection and cloud amounts reach their peak in the early afternoon so that sunshine is reduced then and the mornings are left as the sunniest part of the day. The afternoon reduction is greatest in July, when temperatures are highest, and in this month sunshine rates reach their maximum at about 0900 LAT. June, in fact, records the highest hourly mean value, namely 0·54 hr between 1100 and 1200 LAT. The reduction of midday values in April is difficult to understand although it is obviously linked with increased cloud amounts (see Chapter 9) but its severity may be peculiar to the years analysed. The longer period picture also suggests some falling off in amounts of bright sunshine in the second half of April.

Monthly averages and extremes of bright sunshine are given in Table 42. The month-to-month changes follow a simple broad pattern with average and extreme values in June about five times those in December and January.

Fig. 33 shows the day-to-day variations of mean bright sunshine totals at Kew Observatory excluding the intercalary date, 29 February. The general pattern of change

H

is clear enough, but there are some interesting phases within the longer period cycle of which a levelling off in the curve from 17 April to 2 May is amongst the most notable. It is associated with increased cloud amounts in a period of recurrent stormy weather. Another well marked singularity is the increase in sunshine amounts from 22–24 May,

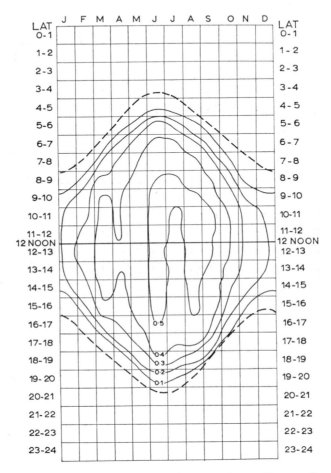

Fig 32 Average hourly totals of bright sunshine at Kew, 1928–37.
Broken lines indicate the times of sunrise and sunset
(Source of data: *Observatories' year book* 1928–37)

a period recognized by Lamb (1950) as one dominated by Anticyclonic and Southerly weather with clear skies. It is separated by rather dull days between 25 and 27 May from another sunny spell from 28–31 May; 28 May has, in fact, the year's equal highest mean number of sunshine hours. In June the bright sunshine curve flattens out, its irregularities bearing a close correspondence to changes in the normal pattern of weather systems. Low mean daily sunshine totals (1881–1950), for instance, occur on 14, 20 and 24 June, and the first two at least correspond with well defined periods of cloudy, cyclonic weather. These are separated by brighter spells, such as those from 15–19 June and 26

June–1 July. From 13–23 July there is a very clear fall in mean sunshine hours before a recovery later in the month, the 4·7 hr average for 23 July being the lowest of any day between 2 May and 1 September. It is associated with a fall in the number of Anticyclonic days which are frequently associated in summer with blue skies broken only by patches of fair-weather cumulus.

In late July and early August mean sunshine values hover around 6 hr per day (which is still only about 40 per cent of the length of daylight) but the 2 days, 15 and 16 August, mark the brilliant end to this mainly sunny three weeks, after which totals fall fairly sharply except for a temporary recovery around 28 and 29 August. The first 2 days in September are frequently overcast with low clouds and rain, and mean daily sunshine amounts are consequently low, namely 4·6 hr.

From early September to the end of the year, sunshine values fall remarkably smoothly, and without the irregularities which so characterize the day-to-day changes of summer. From 20 November to 1 February, totals are very low, most days recording little more than 1 hour (about 12 per cent of the possible amount).

Figs. 34 and 35 show the mean picture at the extremes of the sunshine range. The percentage of days of no sunshine at Kew varies from less than 10 per cent in summer to more than 40 per cent in winter. Between late April and early September there is a chance of less than one in ten that a day will remain overcast with no measurable sunshine, but the expectation rises to about one in two in December and January. Almost the reverse conditions are shown in Fig. 35: 75 per cent of possible bright sunshine is

TABLE 42

Averages and extremes of bright sunshine, by months, Kew, 1937–51

Monthly totals

	Jan	Feb	Mar	Apr hours	May	June
Average	42·8	62·6	110·0	168·4	198·5	219·9
Highest	55·2	106·2	173·0	224·7	247·2	277·4
Lowest	26·2	17·3	59·3	95·9	149·2	144·1

	July	Aug	Sept	Oct hours	Nov	Dec	Yr
Average	192·8	189·6	136·8	95·6	54·7	39·6	1459·7
Highest	251·4	278·5	171·4	115·3	76·6	54·0	1790·5
Lowest	96·2	134·9	56·4	62·1	29·7	20·5	1279·4

Daily mean

Jan	Feb	Mar	Apr	May	June	July hours	Aug	Sept	Oct	Nov	Dec	Year
1·4	2·2	3·5	5·6	6·4	7·0	6·2	6·1	4·6	3·1	1·8	1·3	4·2

Corrections have been made for the years 1942–8

Source: London, Meteorological Office 1951 *Climate of Kew Observatory, 1871–1950*, Appendix p. 5 (Typescript)

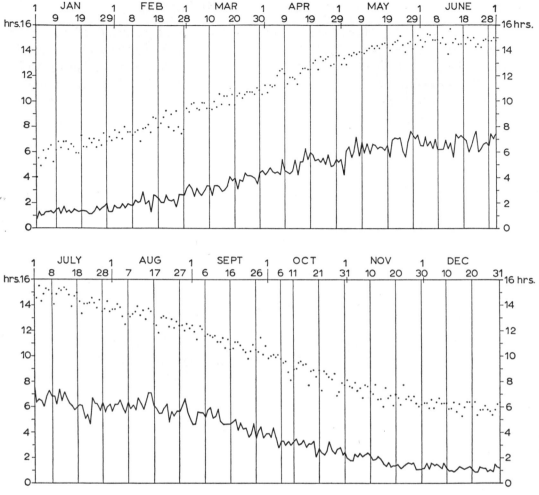

Fig 33 Average and extreme daily sunshine amounts at Kew, 1881–1950.
Extremes are shown by dots
(Source of data: London, Meteorological Office 1951 *Climate of Kew Observatory, 1871–1950*. Typescript with later corrections for 1942–48)

not far from the expected maximum at Kew, remembering the restricted sensitivity of the recording instrument near sunrise and sunset and the reduction of solar radiation by the atmosphere. The maximum recordable sunshine at Kew Observatory on cloudless days in summer is probably less than 96 per cent of the theoretical length of day, with 85 per cent as the corresponding value in winter. The ratios shown in Fig. 35 underline how rare are those memorable days of almost continuous sunshine during daylight hours in winter, 98 per cent of the days in December and January from 1881–1950 failing to record more than 75 per cent of the possible sunshine hours. Such sunny days are most frequent, with an occurrence rate of about one in six, in May, being especially frequent from 6–11 May. The frequency reaches its annual peak, 26 per cent, on 7 May. There are many day-to-day changes in summer as will be seen from Fig. 38; notable amongst these is the period from 20–23 July when frequencies fall to about one in twenty. This is a well-known stormy period with overcast skies, high wind speeds and heavy rain in many years. A week later, the first two days of August and 5–6 August have an equally poor record of sunny days. After this gloomy start, the position improves in the remainder of the month with long sunny days broken only by a rather overcast spell between 20–25 August. There is no doubt, however, that increased cloud amounts in late summer make August days in London far less consistently brilliant than in May. August's high mean sunshine amount is a reflection of spasmodic sunshine from broken skies rather than of cloudless, sunny days which are far more common in May. But May also records more sunless days (Fig. 34) which help to reduce the overall

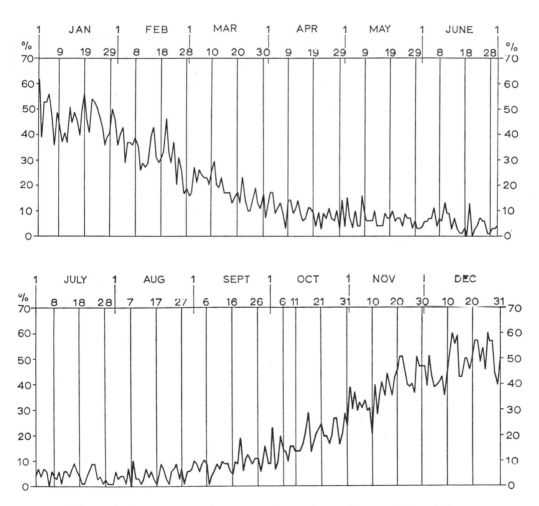

Fig 34 Daily percentage frequency of occasions of no sunshine at Kew, 1881–1950
(Source of data: London, Meteorological Office 1951 *Climate of Kew Observatory*, 1871–1950. Typescript)

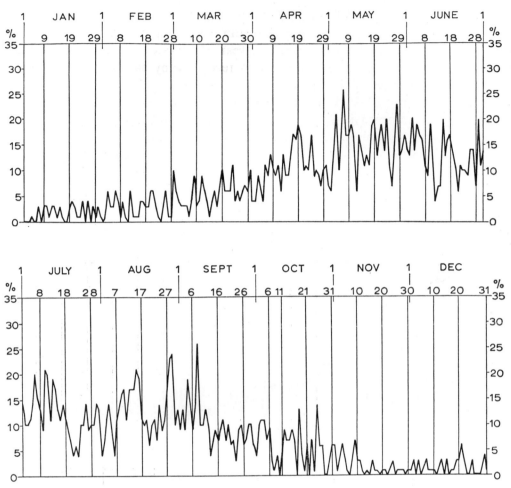

Fig 35 Daily percentage frequency of occasions of more than 75 per cent of possible sunshine at Kew, 1881–1950
(Source of data: London, Meteorological Office 1951 *Climate of Kew Observatory, 1871–1950*. Typescript)

mean number of sunshine hours (Fig. 33). During the last two weeks of September and the first of October there is a sharp decline in the number of bright days with almost continuous sunshine.

The extreme number of hours with bright sunshine recorded between 1881 and 1950 are shown by dots in Fig. 33. Their general line approximates to the changing number of daylight hours but with a larger reduction from this absolute limit in winter than in summer owing to both astronomical and atmospheric (including pollution) reasons. Both Bilham (1938, p. 196) and Marshall (1952, p. 7) make reference to extreme monthly totals of sunshine at Kew, perhaps the most notable of which was the almost sunless month of December 1890 when only 0·3 hr was recorded.

But over a period of years, sunshine amounts in a given month or on a particular day in the year will vary between zero and something approaching the available daylight hours. Table 43 gives some indication how frequencies vary within this obvious range.

TABLE 43

Percentage frequency distribution of daily sunshine amounts, Kew, 1931–60

hours	Jan	Feb	Mar	Apr	May	June	
0·0	42·2	32·6	18·2	8·7	6·2	4·0	
0·1–3·0	36·1	34·3	32·2	26·7	23·5	20·1	
3·1–6·0	17·9	20·5	22·5	21·9	19·6	22·8	
6·1–9·0	3·8	12·6	20·8	21·0	19·7	18·8	
>9·0	0·0	0+	6·3	21·7	31·0	34·3	

hours	July	Aug	Sept	Oct	Nov	Dec	Yr
0·0	4·7	5·1	7·3	17·2	37·5	47·0	19·2
0·1–3·0	24·3	23·2	30·8	37·4	37·0	34·9	30·0
3·1–6·0	21·8	22·5	23·5	25·5	18·1	16·8	21·1
6·1–9·0	20·6	23·8	26·3	18·4	7·4	1·3	16·2
>9·0	29·1	25·4	12·1	1·2	0·0	0·0	13·5

hours	Jan–Mar	Apr–June	July–Sept	Oct–Dec
0·0	31·0	6·3	5·7	33·9
0·1–3·0	34·2	23·4	26·0	36·5
3·1–6·0	20·3	21·4	22 6	20·2
6·1–9·0	12·4	19·8	23·5	9·0
>9·0	2·1	29·0	22·2	0·4

Source of data: London, Meteorological Office, *Monthly weather report* 1931–60

It will be seen that sunless days occur with an average frequency of one day in five, but that this varies from almost one day in two in December to as little as one day in twenty-five in June. Days with more than 9 hr sunshine naturally occur mainly in summer, and in June they are recorded as often as on one day in three. It is also interesting to compare pairs and groups of months on either side of the summer and winter solstices, which for convenience we can regard as falling at the end of June and December respectively. More continuous cloud and more frequent fogs from October to December than from January to March are reflected in a higher percentage frequency of days with 3 hr or less sunshine and a lower frequency of days with more than 6 hr sunshine in the last three months of the year. By contrast, July, August and September have more days with over 6 hr sunshine than April, May or June, probably because of the clearer evenings in September than in any other month at Kew.

RADIATION AND SUNSHINE IN GREATER LONDON

Radiation

It is well known that the amount of solar radiation received at the ground in most cities is below that outside owing to the pollution and fog blankets which so frequently cover them, particularly in winter. Measurements in the five months from November to March of daylight inside and outside a number of British cities show (or showed) losses of from 25 to 55 per cent owing to smoke alone. The losses of ultra-violet radiation are similar. On the gloomier winter days, nine-tenths of all radiation is lost. This reduction in sunlight and ultra-violet radiation was considered by many to be responsible for much general ill-health and a high incidence of tuberculosis and rickets in towns, but whilst this was probably true in the past, the position in recent years has been improved by more frequent travel outside the city and by improved diets.

London, like other cities in Great Britain, suffers a general reduction in the transparency of its air to both incoming and outgoing radiation. The reduction in direct solar radiation due to absorption after scattering or reflection by suspended matter (mainly smoke) on cloudless days at Kew averages 8·5 per cent when the sun's elevation is 30 degrees and 12·8 per cent with an elevation of only 14·3 degrees (based on data given by Stagg, 1950, p. 23). In February and March combined the figures are 9·7 per cent and 16 per cent respectively and in June and July, 6·2 per cent and 8·2 per cent. On days of high total radiation, though not necessarily free from cloud, suspended matter becomes the dominant deflecting agent of direct solar energy in its passage through the atmosphere, accounting with sun elevations of 30 degrees for 46 per cent of the total loss, and with elevations of 14·3 degrees for 39 per cent. The average reduction amounts to 26·5 per cent of the solar constant at solar altitudes of 30 degrees and 28·5 per cent at 14·3 degrees.

The weekly changes in pollution levels might be expected to show in a parallel cycle of mean radiation amounts but the results of analyses are inconclusive (Table 44), for changes in pollution concentrations are submerged by larger and more irregular fluctuations owing to molecular scattering, reflection from and absorption by clouds

TABLE 44

Average amounts of total radiation on a horizontal surface, by days of the week,
Kew, 1957–62

	Sun	Mon	Tues	Wed	Thurs	Fri	Sat
Winter			milliwatt hours per square centimetre				
(Oct–Mar)	111·9	116·4	102·2	96·3	109·5	106·1	112·8
Summer							
(Apr–Sept)	404·9	370·1	379·6	394·9	375·0	393·4	389·9

Source of data: London, Meteorological Office tabulations, Form 3265B (MS)

TABLE 45

Total radiation on a horizontal surface at Kingsway as a percentage of that at Kew,
1959–62

Jan	Feb	Mar	Apr	May	June	July	Aug	Sept	Oct	Nov	Dec	Yr
						per cent						
105	102	99	101	102	102	101	104	104	101	102	105	103

Source of data: London, Meteorological Office tabulations, Form 3265B (MS)

and selective absorption by water vapour. The day-to-day changes of radiation receipt during the week are, however, very similar to, though understandably smaller than, those for sunshine (Table 48) and if they are physically controlled and not accidental occurrences, they are obviously similarly explained.

London's influences upon radiation depend upon the intensity of pollution, the distribution and density of fogs and the form of the ground. Losses will be greatest in central and northeast low-lying parts of the conurbation, especially those areas without smoke control, while higher, more open areas such as Hampstead Heath, Harrow Hill and Black Heath can expect more solar radiation because their air is less polluted and fogs are less frequent. South-facing slopes will also be favoured with more radiation and sunshine than those with a northern aspect. In addition, there are reasons for thinking that in winter especially, southeastern suburbs may receive more early morning sunshine than elsewhere because of a near-surface pollution haze which frequently interferes with the low-angle insolation in other parts of London. Similarly, western and southwestern suburbs may benefit from higher evening values. On the very local scale there will be contrasts between the amount of solar radiation falling on and reflected from different walls of buildings (Stagg, 1950, p. 19), and over open spaces with various aspects and degrees of shading. Net terrestrial radiation will also be affected by the varying amount of available open sky and by back radiation from buildings.

In view of what has been said one would expect the radiation received at Kingsway, in a heavily built-up area of the city centre, to be less than at Kew in a fairly substantial open space (Fig. 5) although the solarimeter at Kingsway is over 100 ft (30·5 m) above ground, more than twice the height of that at Kew and probably above some of the worst pollution which collects near street level. There has, however, been a definite increase in the receipt of solar radiation at Kew since the mid 1950's and it is suggested that this may be the result, in part at least, of a reduction in smoke pollution during this period. But although months when the mean Kingsway values are less than at Kew have become increasingly frequent since 1959, the average receipt of total radiation on a horizontal surface during the four years 1959–62 was slightly higher at Kingsway than at Kew in all months but March (Table 45).

The reduction of radiation at Kingsway since 1959 may be related to additional dust in the local air, as evidenced by deposit-gauge readings of undissolved pollution on the roof of the nearby British Museum. These increased by 28 per cent between 1959 and 1962; the increase may be due to widespread demolition and building work in this part of central London. Higher radiation values at Kingsway than at Kew may be due to less frequent dense fogs here than in the suburbs (see Chapter 8).

It is difficult, because of differences in instrument siting and the comparative brevity of the records, to be absolutely sure that the Kingsway radiation readings show the effect of smoke-control regulations and hence an increased clarity of the air (in spite of more dust), but the signs are hopeful. Sunshine records support this view as will be seen later.

A comparison of total radiation at Rothamsted, 26 mi (67 km) north of London near Harpenden, Hertfordshire, with that at Kew, for the period 1959–62, shows only small, rather inconclusive differences except in January (108 per cent of Kew's total) and February (106 per cent of Kew's total). But again the period of records is too brief to be sure that these are representative differences because of the greater turbidity of Kew's atmosphere.

Sunshine

Reduction in the duration of bright sunshine by London's foggy, polluted atmosphere is more immediately obvious and much more readily analysed than reduction of radiation, for there are several stations within and around London with long sunshine records.

Averages of bright sunshine decrease markedly towards central London (Table 46).

TABLE 46

Averages of bright sunshine, London, 1921–50

	Jan	Feb	Mar	Apr	May	June	July	Aug	Sept	Oct	Nov	Dec	Yr
						hours per day*							
A	1·7	2·5	4·1	5·2	6·4	7·2	6·6	6·2	4·9	3·5	2·1	1·6	4·3
B	1·4	2·2	3·7	4·9	6·3	7·0	6·5	6·0	4·7	3·2	1·7	1·2	4·1
C	1·3	2·1	3·6	4·9	6·3	7·0	6·3	5·9	4·7	3·3	1·7	1·2	4·0
D	1·3	2·0	3·5	4·7	6·1	6·8	6·3	5·9	4·6	3·1	1·6	1·1	4·0
E	0·8	1·6	3·0	4·4	6·0	6·8	6·2	5·6	4·2	2·6	1·3	0·7	3·6

* to the nearest 0·1 hr

A Surrounding country: mean of Rothamsted, Tunbridge Wells
B Outer suburbs: mean of Croydon, Enfield
C Inner, high-level suburbs: Hampstead
D Inner, low-level suburbs: mean of Greenwich, Kew
E Central districts: mean of Bunhill Row, Regent's Park

Source of data: London, Meteorological Office 1953 *Averages of bright sunshine for Great Britain and Northern Ireland 1921–50*. M.O. 572 (H.M.S.O)

The mean daily sunshine, 1921–50, outside London (using Rothamsted and Tunbridge Wells records) was 4·33 hr; at outer suburban stations (Enfield and Croydon) it was 4·07 hr; at the inner, high-level suburban station of Hampstead it was 4·03 hr; at inner, low-lying suburban stations (Greenwich and Kew) it was 3·95 hr; and at central stations (Bunhill Row and Regent's Park) 3·60 hr. The reduction in average bright sunshine amounted to a loss of 16 min per day in the outer suburbs, 18 min at an elevated, inner suburban station, 25 min in the inner, low-lying suburbs and 44 min in the centre. Hampstead, raised above some of the worst pollution and fogs, receives more sunshine than the nearby, low-lying parts of north London.

Sunshine losses vary from month to month as Table 47 shows.

TABLE 47

Average loss of bright sunshine, London, 1921–50

	Jan	Feb	Mar	Apr	May	June	July	Aug	Sept	Oct	Nov	Dec	Yr
					minutes per day								total hours
B	20	19	22	17	8	10	10	9	10	17	22	23	94·7
C	26	24	29	15	8	12	19	17	11	16	23	24	113·5
D	29	31	36	28	16	22	19	14	15	25	32	29	149·8
E	55	56	68	49	26	25	28	32	40	53	47	52	268·9

B Outer suburbs: mean of Croydon, Enfield
C Inner, high-level suburbs: Hampstead
D Inner, low-level suburbs: mean of Greenwich, Kew
E Central districts: mean of Bunhill Row, Regent's Park

Source of data: London, Meteorological Office 1953 *Averages of bright sunshine for Great Britain and Northern Ireland 1921–50*. M.O. 572 (H.M.S.O.)

In the centre, the loss averaged more than three-quarters of an hour per day from October to April but was less than half an hour per day from May to July. The March peak of losses is probably explained by a substantial increase in the average number of early-morning fogs in this month (Fig. 72). Expressed as a percentage of bright sunshine outside London, the month-to-month changes are shown in Fig. 36. In May, June and July, when atmospheric pollution is light throughout London and fogs are rare, even central districts received more than 90 per cent of the extra-metropolitan totals of sunshine and the difference between central and suburban areas was small. In winter the combined effect of a thick pollution screen, frequent fogs and the sun's low elevation drastically reduced the amount of bright sunshine which penetrated to the ground. In December and January, central areas recorded less than half, and suburban areas about three-quarters of the mean sunshine hours in rural areas outside London. The annual loss of bright sunshine in central districts, 268·9 hr, was about three times greater than in the outer suburbs.

An analysis of mean sunshine hours by days of the week (Table 48) appears to show notable differences, more especially between Sundays and Mondays and the remainder of the week. The cause of these contrasts, if more than just chance, might be thought to be linked with changes in the output and dispersal of pollutants. Smoke particles, as we have already seen, remain in the atmosphere for one or two days before deposition, and for this reason we should expect some lag between the cycle of output and their concentration in the atmosphere. Close to the ground the lag will be small, but at higher levels

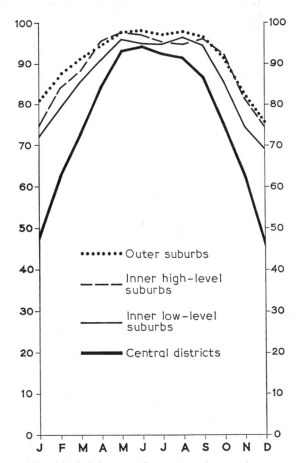

Fig 36 Monthly bright sunshine at London stations as a percentage of that outside London, 1921–50
(Source of data: London, Meteorological Office 1953 *Averages of bright sunshine for Great Britain and Northern Ireland* 1921–50. M.O. 572)

it may be 24 to 48 hr, hence it would not be surprising to find a similar lag between reduced (industrial) output of smoke at weekends and diminished sunshine rates. This, at first sight, seems to explain the winter conditions of Table 48. The values are not, however, statistically significant, for only 69 of the 156 Sundays and 73 of the 156 Mondays in the six winters analysed had values above the weekly mean. The fall in the average number of sunshine hours on Mondays in summer has a slightly higher statistical validity, 92 of the 156 records falling below the summer mean. The only possible cause would seem to be the rapid transport of smoke, formed when furnaces are recharged, to levels of the atmosphere critical for radiation interference, particularly in the first and last hours of daylight.

As with radiation, there is little doubt that the severest reduction in winter sunshine is found in the central–northeast district of London, especially the heavily polluted and foggy areas of the lower Lea valley and the areas from Islington and Finsbury, through

Shoreditch, Bethnal Green and Poplar to East Ham. Losses occur mainly in the hours after sunrise and before sunset in winter when the sun's altitude is low and pollution concentrations are high. Bunhill Row (Finsbury) recorded a mean sunshine value only 48 per cent of the average for Kew and 40 per cent of that for the surrounding country in the thirty Decembers and Januarys from 1921–50 (London, Meteorological Office, 1933).

Bilham (1938, p. 307) has shown an upward trend in the ratio of central London to Kew winter (December and January) sunshine totals from 20 per cent for the period 1881–5 to 52 per cent for the years 1930–5, whilst a revised and extended version of Bilham's diagram suggests that the ratio reached 55 to 60 per cent in 1940–50 (Absalom, 1954, p. 262) but fell to 26 per cent for 1950–5 before recovering to 68 per cent in 1955–60. The ratio for June–July has increased from 84 per cent for 1881–5 to 92 per cent for 1955–60. It would seem that the atmosphere of central London has become generally

TABLE 48

Average number of hours of bright sunshine, by days of the week, Kew, 1957–62

	Sun	Mon	Tues	Weds	Thurs	Fri	Sat	Mean
Winter				hours per day				
(Oct–Mar)	2·7	2·8	2·1	2·2	2·5	2·4	2·5	2·5
Summer								
(Apr–Sept)	6·4	5·5	6·1	6·3	5·9	6·3	6·2	6·1

Source of data: London, Meteorological Office tabulations, Form 3455 (MS)

cleaner during the last 80 years or so, a conclusion supported by Bonacina (1950, p. 91) but hardly progressive or over-comforting in the light of the six years 1950–5. Nevertheless, recent records certainly suggest that smoke-control regulations in the vicinity of Bunhill Row have led to a remarkable increase in sunshine amounts in central areas during the winter months. The ratio of average daily sunshine hours at Bunhill Row to those at Kew in December and January increased from 48 per cent in the six years from 1951–6 (before, that is, the instigation of smoke-control areas) to 76 per cent in the six years 1957–62, following controls. The comparable values for the two summer months, June and July (when pollution levels are low and the relative effect of controls is small), are 92 per cent in both periods. On some days with smog or high fog, London will of course be masked from the sun, whilst all around skies will be clear and the sun shining.

Radiation and sunshine, perhaps the most fundamental of the elements, are also the ones most radically changed by London, differentiating the city from its rural setting and one district from another. But perhaps the past tense should be used for there are grounds for hope that the Clean Air Act is righting some of man's climatic errors, leading to a sunnier as well as a cleaner London. This may well, in its turn, affect temperatures.

6 Temperature

To mention the differing warmths of the day and night, or of the different months of the year, is simply to appeal to the test of feeling. But feeling informs us on these subjects only by a vague comparison with past sensations, the memory of which, when they have been some time past, is very imperfect.

Luke Howard

DIFFERENCES IN TEMPERATURE between central London and nearby rural sites were first measured by Luke Howard (1818) and he was led to remark (Howard, 1820, p.91):

But the temperature of the *city* is not to be considered as that of the *climate*: it partakes too much of an artificial warmth, induced by its structure, by a crowded population and the consumption of great quantities of fuel.

But modifications by the city, though substantial, should sensibly be regarded as lower order variations superimposed upon day-to-day changes which are themselves part of a strong, basic, regional climatic theme. As in previous chapters, conditions at Kew will serve to illustrate the development of this broad climatic melody over different time scales. This will be followed by a discussion of contrasts within and about London. Readings at Kew are of course subject to the controls of the Observatory's location in an extensive open space in suburban London but the patterns of change must be reasonably representative of conditions throughout the conurbation.

Kew Observatory's temperature records have the advantage of length and continuity but unfortunately not of direct comparability with those at most other stations, for the thermometers from which the published records are taken do not have a standard exposure. They are housed in a screen with single louvres and open at the bottom, attached to the north wall of the Observatory. There is an additional flat, single-louvred shield which protects the main screen from direct sunshine when the sun is in the west and not too low. The height of the bulbs of the recording thermometers above the bottom of the screen containing them is 11·8 in. (30 cm) in summer and 14·0 in. (33 cm) in winter. Their height above the artificial mound on which the Observatory stands is approximately 10 ft (3 m); the height above the garden lawn, where the Stevenson Screen, rain gauge and other instruments are sited, is approximately 17·5 ft (5 m). Values of the wet- and dry-bulb thermometers are continuously recorded (photographically).

There are, of course, differences between temperatures in the North Wall Screen and those in the Stevenson Screen which is well exposed and stands at the normal 4 ft (1·2 m) height on a lawn about 50 yd (45·7 m) south of the Observatory. The bulbs of the thermometers are about 13 ft (4 m) lower than those in the North Wall Screen.

Drummond (1943, p. 154) showed that the annual absolute minimum temperature from 1914 to 1943 registered by the photothermograph in the North Wall Screen was, on average, higher by about 1·7°C (3°F) than the temperature in the Stevenson Screen. The greatest differences occurred in December, the largest being 3·9°C (7°F) in 1942. A comparison by the author of maximum and minimum temperatures for each day of the three years 1958–60 shows the following pattern of differences:

TABLE 49

Average differences between maximum and minimum temperatures in the North Wall and Stevenson Screens, Kew, 1958–60

	Jan	Feb	Mar	Apr	May	June	July	Aug	Sept	Oct	Nov	Dec
Maximum				(higher in the Stevenson Screen)								
°C	0·4	0·6	0·5	0·5	0·4	0·3	0·5	0·4	0·7	0·6	0·4	0·4
°F	0·8	1·0	0·9	0·9	0·7	0·5	0·9	0·8	1·3	1·1	0·8	0·8
Minimum				(higher in the North Wall Screen)								
°C	1·2	1·0	0·8	0·8	0·7	0·9	0·8	0·8	0·6	0·8	1·1	0·9
°F	2·2	1·8	1·5	1·4	1·2	1·6	1·5	1·5	1·1	1·4	1·9	1·7

Source of data: Kew Observatory records (MS)

Maximum temperatures in the Stevenson Screen are, on average, higher than those in the North Wall Screen although on some days, more common in summer than winter, conditions are reversed. The greatest difference on any one day was 2·4°C (4·3°F) but differences of more than 1·7°C (3°F) occurred in all months, with a tendency to more frequent high values in autumn than in spring and summer. Minimum temperatures were nearly always higher in the North Wall Screen with far fewer occasions when conditions were reversed compared with maximum temperatures. There was also a more marked annual range of differences with higher averages in the winter months. The greatest single difference in minimum temperatures was 3·3°C (5·9°F), apart from some outstandingly big differences of as much as 11·1°C (20°F) which comparison with nearby stations showed to be accidental errors or the result of differences in the times of reading.

The reversal of daytime and night-time differences may seem, at first sight, surprising. The lower maximum temperatures in the North Wall Screen are partly a result of its greater height but investigations of lapse rates near the ground in southeast England (Best et al., 1952, pp. 10–11) suggest that this is not the whole explanation, more particularly in winter. The difference is also explained by north wall shading and by contrasts in the thermal lag of buildings and vegetation-covered soils, the latter warming more quickly during the early part of the day (this particular contrast is also important in general comparisons between temperatures inside and outside London and is discussed in the second half of this chapter).

Differences between minimum temperatures in the two screens are again the result, in part, of height differences during night-time inversions but, as before, this leaves considerable unexplained anomaly. This is related to the position of the North Wall Screen, which is attached to the wall of the Observatory, and like London as a whole, is artificially heated in winter and conserves solar energy in its fabric by day which it slowly releases during the night.

Differences in maximum temperatures are generally small, but those recorded in the North Wall Screen at Kew are about 0·3°C (0·5°F) below what one would normally expect in London's suburbs, whilst minimum temperatures are a little above those for its area and closer to those experienced nearer the centre. The recorded mean diurnal range is also below that of comparable open spaces at its distance from central London, but for most of our immediate purposes the unusual exposure of the North Wall Screen is of small consequence.

AIR TEMPERATURE AT KEW

Temperatures at Kew Observatory have been studied many times but it is important to set out the main thermal characteristics of the London area before embarking on an investigation of variations within the city. The majority of previous investigations have been concerned either with periodic changes in the general level of London temperatures (Booth, 1957; Drummond, 1943; Drummond, 1946; Hawke, 1948; Lamb, 1963; Lewis, 1947; Manley, 1961, 1963a; Poulter, 1962; Rogers, 1960; Smith, 1956) or with the validity of singularities in the annual cycle (Brooks and Mirrlees, 1930; Craddock, 1963; Gilchrist, 1956; Marshall, 1952). The present analysis sets out merely to establish the facts about what might be called the 'expected' temperatures at Kew for these are the foundations upon which the occurrence and intensity of London's heat-island, the ever changing mass of warm air over the city, are built.

Diurnal changes

Fig. 37 shows the average temperatures at exact hours GMT for the 20 years 1937–56. Apart from the more obvious features, a number of points are worthy of mention:

1 The lowest mean temperature, 2·7°C (36·9°F), occurs around dawn in February, and the highest, 20·4°C (68·7°F), falls between 1500 and 1600 GMT in both July and August.
2 The highest temperatures occur about 2 hr after noon from November to January but the lag increases to 4 hr in July. (This may be related to the site of the Screen.)
3 Minimum temperatures occur fairly consistently shortly before dawn following a sharp drop in temperatures after sunset (especially in summer) and a more gentle fall during the remainder of the night. In winter, temperatures are almost constant for several hours before dawn.
4 The mean diurnal temperature range, it will be noted, is very nearly doubled between December and May. But the diurnal temperature range is as variable as the cloud

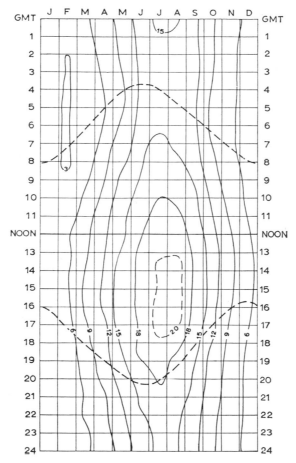

Fig 37 Average hourly temperature at Kew, 1937–56. The two
unnumbered broken lines indicate the times of sunrise and
sunset

(Source of data: *Observatories' year book* 1937–56)

amounts to which it is closely linked and although the general tendency is towards
larger ranges in summer, substantial differences can occur on any day when conditions are suitable; which means, in the first instance, when skies are clear. This is
demonstrated in Table 50 which is based upon values of daily maximum and
minimum temperatures (0000–2400 GMT) at Kew Observatory.

In December and January one day in about seven has a remarkably even temperature
regime, there being less than 2·5°C (4·4°F) difference between dawn and afternoon
temperatures and very few days, about one per month only, have a range of 9·5°C (17°F)
or more. In June and July, on the other hand, only one day in a hundred has a temperature range of less than 2·5°C (4·4°F) and as many as two days in five have a range of
9·5°C (17°F) or more.

I

TABLE 50

Percentage frequency distribution of the diurnal temperature range, Kew, 1921–50

Range °C	°F	Jan	Feb	Mar	Apr	May	June
				per cent			
0·0– 0·4	0·0– 0·7						
0·5– 1·4	0·8– 2·5	2·4	1·7	0·2	0·1		
1·5– 2·4	2·6– 4·3	11·1	7·4	3·0	1·1	0·3	0·4
2·5– 3·4	4·4– 6·1	15·7	12·0	5·9	2·7	1·9	1·7
3·5– 4·4	6·2– 7·9	17·7	19·5	9·7	4·7	3·0	2·9
4·5– 5·4	8·0– 9·7	18·4	14·9	13·7	8·9	4·9	4·9
5·5– 6·4	9·8–11·5	13·7	13·5	16·0	14·7	8·1	9·5
6·5– 7·4	11·6–13·3	8·1	10·6	13·9	15·7	13·2	12·7
7·5– 8·4	13·4–15·1	6·5	8·5	10·5	13·1	13·7	14·0
8·5– 9·4	15·2–16·9	3·7	4·6	7·4	10·5	10·8	12·3
9·5–10·4	17·0–18·7	1·4	3·0	6·5	8·1	10·6	11·6
10·5–11·4	18·8–20·5	0·6	2·1	4·5	6·3	9·5	8·0
11·5–12·4	20·6–22·3	0·2	0·9	2·5	4·7	8·8	6·9
12·5–13·4	22·4–24·1	0·3	0·7	2·1	4·3	5·0	5·7
13·5–14·4	24·2–25·9	0·1	0·1	1·4	2·7	4·4	3·8
14·5–15·4	26·0–27·7	0·1	0·1	1·0	1·3	3·4	2·9
15·5–16·4	27·8–29·5	0·1	0·2	0·7	0·7	1·5	1·7
16·5–17·4	29·6–31·3			0·5	0·7	0·6	0·7
17·5–18·4	31·4–33·1			0·3	0·1	0·3	0·3
18·5–19·4	33·2–34·9			0·3	0·1	0·1	0·1
19·5–20·4	35·0–36·7			0·1			
mean range °C		4·9	5·5	7·1	8·1	9·3	9·1
°F		8·8	9·9	12·8	14·6	16·8	16·4

Range °C	°F	July	Aug	Sept	Oct	Nov	Dec	Yr
				per cent				
0·0– 0·4	0·0– 0·7							0·0
0·5– 1·4	0·8– 2·5				0·2	1·5	2·9	0·7
1·5– 2·4	2·6– 4·3	0·5	0·6	0·7	2·4	6·3	11·5	3·8
2·5– 3·4	4·4– 6·1	1·3	1·0	2·2	4·5	11·7	17·7	6·5
3·5– 4·4	6·2– 7·9	3·7	3·2	4·9	9·7	16·5	18·1	9·4
4·5– 5·4	8·0– 9·7	5·7	6·2	9·7	14·1	16·1	18·9	11·3
5·5– 6·4	9·8–11·5	11·3	11·3	12·4	14·5	14·6	11·2	12·5
6·5– 7·4	11·6–13·3	14·2	15·2	15·5	14·2	12·6	8·1	12·8
7·5– 8·4	13·4–15·1	14·3	14·3	15·4	13·0	7·5	5·4	11·4
8·5– 9·4	15·2–16·9	10·5	12·8	11·1	8·5	5·9	3·0	8·4
9·5–10·4	17·0–18·7	10·1	9·6	8·8	6·7	4·1	2·1	6·8
10·5–11·4	18·8–20·5	8·5	7·4	5·9	5·2	2·2	0·7	5·1
11·5–12·4	20·6–22·3	6·8	5·8	4·3	2·9	0·5	0·4	3·7
12·5–13·4	22·4–24·1	5·1	5·4	3·3	2·0	0·3	0·1	2·9
13·5–14·4	24·2–25·9	3·7	3·2	2·3	1·0	0·1		1·9
14·5–15·4	26·0–27·7	1·8	1·8	1·4	0·8		0·1	1·2
15·5–16·4	27·8–29·5	1·5	1·2	0·7	0·3			0·7
16·5–17·4	29·6–31·3	0·9	0·5	0·7			0·1	0·4
17·5–18·4	31·4–33·1	0·1	0·2	0·5	0·1			0·2
18·5–19·4	33·2–34·9	0·1	0·1	0·1	0·1		0·1	0·1
19·5–20·4	35·0–36·7	0·1		0·1				0·1
Mean range °C		8·9	8·7	8·1	7·1	5·6	4·8	7·3
°F		16·0	15·6	14·6	12·8	10·1	8·7	13·2

Source: Shellard, H. C. and Brown, P. R. 1961 Frequency distribution of the daily range of temperature at Kew Observatory and London Airport. London, Meteorological Office *Clim. Mem.*, No. 28 (Typescript)

Seasonal changes

The broad pattern of change, based upon monthly averages, is simple enough. For the 80 years 1871–1950, values (calculated to the nearest °F) are given in Table 51.

TABLE 51

Average and extreme mean monthly temperatures, Kew, 1871–1950
(0000–2400 hr)

	Jan	Feb	Mar	Apr	May	June	July	Aug	Sept	Oct	Nov	Dec
Average												
Maximum												
°C	6·7	7·2	9·4	12·8	16·7	20·0	21·7	21·1	18·3	13·9	9·4	7·2
°F	44	45	49	55	62	68	71	70	65	57	49	45
Minimum												
°C	1·7	1·7	2·8	4·4	7·2	10·6	12·8	12·2	10·0	6·7	3·9	2·2
°F	35	35	37	40	45	51	55	54	50	44	39	36
Mean												
°C	3·9	4·4	6·1	8·9	12·2	15·0	17·2	16·7	14·4	10·0	6·7	4·4
°F	39	40	43	48	54	59	63	62	58	50	44	40

	Jan	Feb	Mar	Apr	May	June	July	Aug	Sep	Oct	Nov	Dec
Highest												
Maximum												
°C	10·0	10·6	14·4	16·7	20·0	22·8	25·6	25·6	22·8	18·9	12·8	10·6
°F	50	51	58	62	68	73	78	78	73	66	55	51
Minimum												
°C	5·0	5·0	5·0	7·2	9·4	12·8	15·0	15·0	13·9	9·4	7·2	6·7
°F	41	41	41	45	49	55	59	59	57	49	45	44
Mean												
°C	7·8	7·8	9·4	11·7	14·4	17·2	20·0	20·0	17·8	13·3	10·0	8·3
°F	46	46	49	53	58	63	68	68	64	56	50	47
Lowest												
Maximum												
°C	1·7	0·6	6·1	10·0	13·9	16·1	18·3	17·8	15·6	10·6	6·1	0·6
		0·6 (1963)										
°F	35	33	43	50	57	61	65	64	60	51	43	33
	33	(1963)										
Minimum												
°C	−2·8	−4·4	−1·1	2·2	5·0	8·9	10·6	10·0	7·8	2·8	0·6	−3·9
°F	27	24	30	36	41	48	51	50	46	37	33	25
Mean												
°C	−0·5	−1·7	2·8	6·1	9·4	12·8	14·4	14·4	11·7	7·2	3·9	1·7
°F	31	29	37	43	49	55	58	58	53	45	39	29
	30	(1963)										

Source: London, Meteorological Office 1951 *Climate of Kew Observatory, 1871–1950* (Typescript)

It will be noticed that whilst July has the highest average maximum, minimum and mean temperatures, January is not consistently the coldest month, for February has a lower average minimum temperature. Indeed, in an apparently increasing number of winters, the lowest mean monthly temperature at Kew has fallen in February. Smith (1956, p. 27) drew attention to this feature, pointing out changes in the particular month which provides Londoners with their coldest weather. From 1871–1900, January was clearly in the lead with thirteen occasions, December was second with nine and February third with only five. The remaining three were in March and November. From 1901–30, January was the coldest in ten years, February in nine; they shared honours in one year whilst December was third with seven. Continuing this analysis for the period 1931–60, February still rivals January as London's coldest month for it has

TABLE 52

Mean monthly temperatures, Kew, 1931–60

	Jan	Feb	Mar	Apr	May	June	July	Aug	Sept	Oct	Nov	Dec
Maximum												
°C	6·4	7·1	10·1	13·2	16·9	20·3	21·8	21·4	18·5	14·1	9·9	7·4
°F	43·5	44·8	50·2	55·8	62·4	68·5	71·2	70·5	65·3	57·4	49·8	45·3
Minimum												
°C	1·9	1·8	3·1	5·3	8·0	11·4	13·4	13·1	11·0	7·5	4·8	3·0
°F	35·4	35·2	37·6	41·5	46·4	52·5	56·1	55·6	51·8	45·5	40·6	37·4
Mean												
°C	4·2	4·4	6·6	9·3	12·5	15·9	17·6	17·2	14·8	10·8	7·3	5·2
°F	39·6	39·9	43·9	48·7	54·5	60·6	63·7	63·0	58·6	51·4	45·1	41·4

Source: London, Meteorological Office 1963a *Averages of temperature for Great Britain and Northern Ireland, 1931–60.* M.O. 735 (H.M.S.O.)

been so in 11 of the 30 years compared with January's 13, December's five and March's one. Whether the practice of late winters will continue is as uncertain as the fluctuations of temperature from year to year and from decade to decade. They are linked with circulation change which, after warmer winters in the first four decades of this century, have given more severe winters since about 1940 (Lamb, 1963).

Mean monthly values, though useful, necessarily provide only a broad indication of the temperature characteristics of their period. Being statistical abstractions of hourly, daily and year-to-year changes, they have obvious limitations. For this reason, Table 53 has been prepared from daily values during a recent 20-year period to provide some indication of the range of daily temperatures within each month. In all but two months, the average (Table 52) lies within the modal grade (Table 53), but about this there is a substantial scatter of values.

One notable feature is the higher average frequency of maxima below freezing in February compared with January (a feature which remains true even when the winter of 1963 is included) and this relates to what has been said about winter's coldest month. Also notable in Table 53 is the frequency of very warm nights in August, probably

TABLE 53

Maximum and minimum temperatures, average and extreme frequencies, Kew, 1943–62

Average

°C	°F	Maximum					
		Jan	Feb	Mar	Apr	May	June
		number of days					
< 0·1	<32·1	0·8	1·5	0+			
0·1– 5·0	32·1–41·0	9·7	7·4	3·7			
5·1– 10·0	41·1–50·0	15·5	11·7	11·3	4·4	0·9	
10·1– 15·0	50·1–59·0	5·0	7·3	14·0	16·9	9·5	2·3
15·1– 20·0	59·1–68·0		0·1	2·0	7·6	14·9	14·1
20·1– 25·0	68·1–77·0			0·1	1·2	5·0	10·6
25·1– 30·0	77·1–86·0					0·8	2·6
> 30·0	> 86·0					0+	0·4

°C	°F	July	Aug	Sept	Oct	Nov	Dec
<0·1	<32·1						0·2
0·1– 5·0	32·1–41·0					2·1	7·9
5·1– 10·0	41·1–50·0			0·2	2·6	15·6	16·3
10·1– 15·0	50·1–59·0	1·0	1·2	3·5	16·7	11·6	6·5
15·1– 20·0	59·1–68·0	11·5	13·0	18·7	10·6	0·7	0·1
20·1– 25·0	68·1–77·0	13·1	13·3	7·2	1·1		
25·1– 30·0	77·1–86·0	5·0	3·3	0·4	0+		
> 30·0	> 86·0	0·4	0·3				

°C	°F	Minimum					
		Jan	Feb	Mar	Apr	May	June
		number of days					
< −14·9	< 5·1						
−14·9––10·0	5·1–14·0		0·1	0+			
− 9·9–− 5·0	14·1–23·0	0·9	1·4	0·1			
− 4·9– 0·0	23·1–32·0	8·4	7·6	6·3	1·0	0+	
0·1– 5·0	32·1–41·0	15·0	12·8	15·5	13·3	5·0	0·5
5·1– 10·0	41·1–50·0	6·5	6·0	8·8	14·7	18·4	9·8
10·1– 15·0	50·1–59·0	0·2	0·1	0·3	1·0	7·4	17·9
> 15·0	> 59·0					0·2	1·8

°C	°F	July	Aug	Sept	Oct	Nov	Dec
< −14·9	<5·1						
−14·9––10·0	5·1–14·0						
− 9·9–− 5·0	14·1–23·0					0·2	0·4
− 4·9– 0·0	23·1–32·0	0+		0·2	0·7	3·1	6·9
0·1– 5·0	32·1–41·0	0·2	0·1	1·3	6·3	11·8	15·0
5·1– 10·0	41·1–50·0	2·9	3·8	9·7	15·8	13·6	8·2
10·1– 15·0	50·1–59·0	22·0	21·2	16·6	8·1	1·3	0·5
> 15·0	> 59·0	2·9	5·9	2·3	0·1		

Table 53—*contd.*

Extreme

Maximum

°C	°F	Jan	Feb	Mar	Apr	May	June
		greatest number of days in one month					
< 0·1	<32·1	4(13)	13	1			
0·1– 5·0	32·1–41·0	20	20	12			
5·1– 10·0	41·1–50·0	22	26	21	14	6	
10·1– 15·0	50·1–59·0	10	16	27	24	18	16
15·1– 20·0	59·1–68·0		1	6	15	22	22
20·1– 25·0	68·1–77·0			1	8	10	16
25·1– 30·0	77·1–86·0					4	15
> 30·0	> 86·0					1	6

°C	°F	July	Aug	Sept	Oct	Nov	Dec
< 0·1–	<32·1						1
0·1– 5·0	32·1–41·0					8	24
5·1– 10·0	41·1–50·0			3	7	28	26
10·1– 15·0	50·1–59·0	14	17	21	28	25	15
15·1– 20·0	59·1–68·0	19	27	27	22	3	1
20·1– 25·0	68·1–77·0	20	21	23	8		
25·1– 30·0	77·1–86·0	10	14	4	1		
> 30·0	> 86·0	4	2				

Minimum

°C	°F	Jan	Feb	Mar	Apr	May	June
		greatest number of days in one month					
< −14·9	5·1						
−14·9–−10·0	5·1–14·0	(8)	3	1			
− 9·9–− 5·0	14·1–23·0	4(16)	8	1			
− 4·9– 0·0	23·1–32·0	17	23	19	15	1	
0·1– 5·0	32·1–41·0	10	24	24	27	17	4
5·1– 10·0	41·1–50·0	14	19	20	26	24	21
10·1– 15·0	50·1–59·0	3	2	3	5	16	24
> 15·0	> 59·0					1	4

°C	°F	July	Aug	Sept	Oct	Nov	Dec
< −14·9	<5·1						
−14·9–−10·0	5·1–14·0						
− 9·9–− 5·0	14·1–23·0					2	4
− 4·9– 0·0	23·1–32·0	1		4	4	8	18
0·1– 5·0	32·1–41·0	4	3	12	12	19	24
5·1– 10·0	41·1–50·0	22	19	18	23	21	20
10·1– 15·0	50·1–59·0	30	28	24	18	4	3
> 15·0	> 59·0	15	15	12	2		

figures in brackets refer to 1963

Source of data: London, Meteorological Office *Observatories' year book* 1943–56; London, Meteorological Office *Monthly weather report*, 1957–63

associated with some tendency to higher night-time cloud amounts, as well as the intensity of London's heat-island at this time of the year. Maximum temperatures rising to more than 25·0°C (77°F) are quite common, occurring on about one day in six in July and about one day in ten in June; but equally, the temperature fails to rise above 15°C (59°F) on about one day in July and on two days each June. Temperatures above 30°C (86°F) are rare even in July, but we can expect one such day in either June or July in four years out of five.

The second half of Table 53 gives the greatest number of days in any one month, over a period of twenty years, with temperatures in each of the stated grades. In the majority of cases the lowest was zero, except for the modal frequency in each month where it was most commonly between five and ten days. Figures for January and February 1963 are given for comparison. Again the very exceptional number of warm nights in late summer and autumn is noticeable and is no doubt related to the thermal lag of the Observatory wall and the intensity of London's heat-island in these months, a feature studied later in this chapter.

Day-to-day variations of average maximum, minimum and mean temperatures are shown in Figs. 38, 39 and 40. In all cases 29 February has been excluded from the analysis. Fig. 38 of average and extreme daily maximum temperatures is extremely simple in its first order variation from high values in summer to low in winter. The average is, however, the mathematical abstraction of considerable year-to-year changes in values, the limits of which, in the 80 years analysed, are shown by pairs of dots for each day of the year. As evidence of this variability, the highest temperatures recorded on the warmest winter days roughly equal the lowest maximum temperatures in summer. The absolute range of maximum temperatures is from −5·4°C (22·2°F) on 5 January 1894, to 34·4°C (93·9°F) on 9 August 1911; Greenwich recorded 37·8°C (100·0°F) (in the Glaisher Stand) on this day but the difference above Kew is surprisingly large. A maximum temperature of 35·6°C (96·0°F) was recorded at Camden Square on 29 June 1957 and Marshall (1952) gives other extremes of maximum temperature in the London area between 1941 and 1949. Surface temperatures (not only of the soil but of roads and buildings) on very cold and very warm days and nights will, in general, be very much more extreme than those of the air. For instance, during the hot spell of August 1911, temperatures of 44·4°C (112°F) were recorded on iron railings exposed to the sun (Dight, 1934, p. 116) and very low temperatures have been recorded on the conductor rails of the exposed sections of the London Transport Underground network (London Transport Executive, 1959).

It is also interesting to note (Fig. 38) that from 1871–1950, all days between 11 December and 24 February except 26 December and 3 February have recorded at least one day when the temperature never rose above freezing point. Freezing conditions both by day and night occurred on one day or more during only four of the thirty-six Decembers from 1909–44, but since then there have been six such months in the 18 years up to and including 1962. In January the temperature has remained at or below freezing on at least one day of the month during five of the 20 years 1943–62. In January 1917 there were eleven such days when the temperature did not rise above 0°C (32°F); in 1947

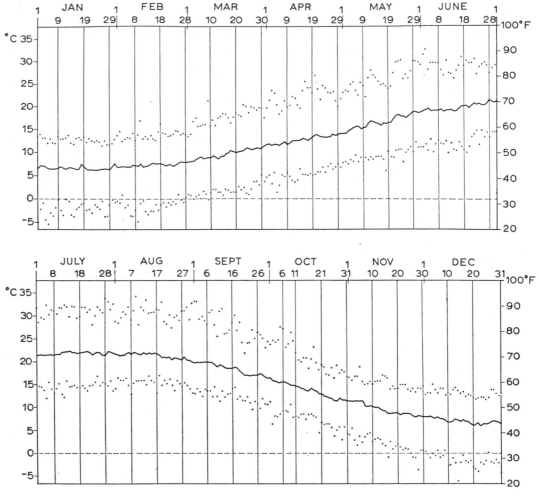

Fig 38 Average and extreme daily maximum temperatures at Kew, 1871–1950.
Extremes are shown by dots
(Source of data: London, Meteorological Office 1951 *Climate of Kew Obser-vatory*, 1871–1950. Typescript)

there were eight, and in 1963 there were 13, nine of which were consecutive (17–25th), and this was the highest total since records began at Kew. Between 1943 and 1962, February recorded days with temperatures never rising above 0°C in the same number of years as January, i.e. five, but the total number of days, 30, was double that of January owing to the very high figures of 13 in 1947 (eight of which were consecutive) and 11 in 1956. In February 1963 there were only two such days although on 25 days the temperature failed to rise above 5°C (41°F). Air frost throughout a whole day has occurred in about one March in ten on the average of the last 100 years, mostly in the early part of the month. More recently the recurrence interval has almost doubled (Table 53) and in 1963 there was not a single instance. The frequency distributions of other daily maxima are listed in Table 53.

Lowndes (1963) has studied, for the period 1935–59, the frequency of cold spells at Kew, defined as a period of four or more consecutive days with the maximum temperature on each day below normal and with the average maximum temperature over the period 3°F (1·7°C) lower. The average number of such spells ranged from 1·0 in February, September and November, to 1·6 in May and July. The average number of cold-spell days per month ranged from 7 in both October and November to from 11 to 13 in January, February, May, June, July and August. Nearly half the spells were of 4 to 6 days duration; 76 per cent were of 4 to 10 days, 20 per cent were of 11 to 21 days, and 4 per cent were 22 days or more in length. Spells tended to last longest in January (average 12 days) and February (average 13 days), the other months showing no marked differences, their averages varying from 7 to 9 days. The maximum length of spell was 56 days in 1947.

Turning to the graph (Fig. 39) of average and extreme minimum temperatures, it is

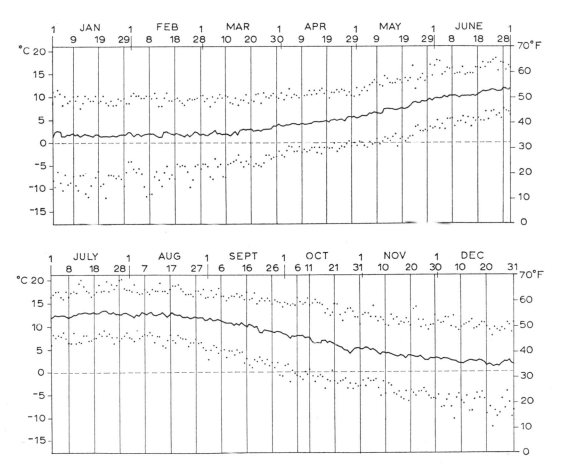

Fig 39 Average and extreme daily minimum temperatures at Kew, 1871–1950.
Extremes are shown by dots
(Source of data: London, Meteorological Office 1951 *Climate of Kew Observatory*, 1871–1950. Typescript)

notable how small are the changes from early December to the middle of March, but how much greater are the winter than summer ranges of individual values about the long period mean. This contrast is more pronounced than with maximum temperatures partly because of the greater relative importance of changes in cloud amounts in the night-time heat balance. In consequence, the warmest December and January nights from 1871–1950 have roughly the same temperatures as the mean for June and September and about equal the coolest nights in July and August. From 9 December to 15 March, mean minima hover around 2°C (3–4°F), and from mid–July to mid–August they are generally about 13°C (55–56°F). But whilst the mean daily minima during winter are a little above freezing point, there are, of course, many occasions with night-time air frost. Table 53 shows the frequency of such occasions in each month during the last 20 years. The highest recorded frequency of night frosts in January at Kew Observatory was 27 nights in 1897 (Marshall, 1952, p. 8); there were 24 in January 1963. In February the highest was 26 nights in 1947; in 1956 there were 24 and in 1963 there were 20. In March there were 19 such nights in 1955 and five in 1963; in October, 12 nights in 1888; in November, 17 nights in 1871; and in December, 27 nights in 1890 (Marshall, 1952, pp. 26, 28 and 30).

The dates of the first and last screen frosts (being defined by a temperature of 0°C (32°F) or less) are very variable, as might be expected. At Kew, the mean date of the first screen frost is 5 November and of the last, 7 April (Applegate, 1960, p. 2), but in one-fifth of the years 1841–1949 the last air frost at either Greenwich or Kew occurred in the first week in May. In 1867, it was as late as 24 May (Marshall, 1952, p. 16) although in the period 1871–1950, analysed in Fig. 39, the latest night frost occurred on 17 May (1935). Similarly, the first night frost of autumn has fallen as early as 29 September but autumn frosts are rare before the middle of October.

It is an interesting commentary on the inconstancy of the British climate that in January 1963, on six days of the month, 12th, 13th, 19th, 23rd, 24th and 25th, the lowest temperature record for each of these days at Kew Observatory was broken. The frequency distribution of absolute monthly minimum temperatures at Kew during the period 1854–1952 (Table 54) has been calculated by Drummond (1943, p. 27). Thus about once in 25 years, assuming the period is representative, Kew will record one night in December and one in February with a temperature falling below − 9·4°C (15°F); in January the average recurrence interval is 13 years. A single night with a minimum temperature below − 6·7°C (20°F) is likely to occur once in five years in December, once in four years in January, and once in 10 years in February.

At this juncture we should recall the somewhat artificially high minimum air temperatures recorded in the North Wall Screen at Kew, from which all the above figures have been taken. The anomalies are highest, as we have seen, on winter nights; in January 1963, the coldest at Kew since records began, the mean minimum temperature in the North Wall Screen was −2·7°C (27·1°F), or 1·3°C (2·3°F) warmer than in the standard Stevenson Screen. Part of this difference results from the dissimilarity in screen heights but the contrast of site, more particularly the proximity of the North Wall Screen thermometers to the Observatory, is also critical. But for these same reasons, the effects

TABLE 54

Percentage frequency of the absolute minimum temperature for each winter month,
Kew, 1854–1942

°C	−17·8 to −15·6	−15·0 to −12·8	−12·2 to −10·0	−9·4 to −7·2	−6·7 to −4·4	> −4·4
°F	0 to 4	5 to 9	10 to 14	15 to 19	20 to 24	> 24
			per cent			
Dec	0	1	3	13	29	54
Jan	1	1	6	16	36	40
Feb	0	0	4	6	36	54

Source: Drummond, A. J. 1943 Cold winters at Kew Observatory, 1783–1942. *Quart, J. R. Met. Soc.*, London, 69, p. 27

of the rather open situation of the Observatory are partly compensated and (published) minimum temperatures are only a little higher than in the neighbouring built-up areas of suburban London.

Mean temperatures at Kew are the average of hourly readings to tenths of a degree Fahrenheit, and they provide a useful summary of the overall thermal conditions. At the lower end of the annual temperature scale, Belasco (1951) made an interesting study of the frequency of freezing days at a number of stations including Kew. A freezing day was defined as a day with a mean temperature below 32·5°F (0·28°C). As part of this study, a table was prepared (Belasco, 1951, p. 215) of the frequency of such days expressed as the number of winters in ten with at least a specified number of freezing days (Table 55).

TABLE 55

Number of winters (October–April) in ten with at least a specified number of freezing days,
Kew, 1878–1950

number of freezing days

1	5	10	15	20	25	30	35	40	45	50
9·4	7·2	4·9	2·9	1·8	1·7	1·3	0·6	0·3	0·0	0·0

Source: Belasco, J. E. 1951 Freezing days in Great Britain. *Met. Mag.*, London, 80, p. 215

This shows that there is (or more accurately, was) an even chance each winter of at least ten freezing days at Kew. The greatest number of freezing days fall in January, followed by February, December, March and November in that order (Brown, 1962, p. 2). In the winter of 1962–3 there were 34 freezing days, 21 of which were in January and 10 in February. This severity, in Belasco's analysis, has an average recurrence interval of about 14 years. This is not, of course, a rigid periodicity and in any case cannot be strictly interpreted except in the light of changing climates.

About half the freezing days are associated with Polar continental air from Europe, about a third with Polar air near the centres of anticyclones and the remainder with direct Polar air (Belasco, 1951, p. 224). Cottis and Groom (1958, pp. 2 and 3) have shown, for London Airport, that cold spells of weather are most frequently associated with northeasterly surface winds around a slow moving or stationary high pressure from Scandinavia and northeast Europe to Scotland and Iceland (such as occurred for long spells during the winter of 1962–3). Similar results were obtained by Lowndes (1963).

The graph of mean temperatures (Fig. 40), whilst of less immediate use as an indication of actual conditions (Marshall, 1954) gives a convenient expression of the general day-to-day trends. As such, this measure has been used by a number of workers in investigations of long-period climatic trends and singularities.

It is a matter of common experience that our weather tends to occur in spells of warm or cold, fine or rainy days. Some people, perhaps the best known being Dr

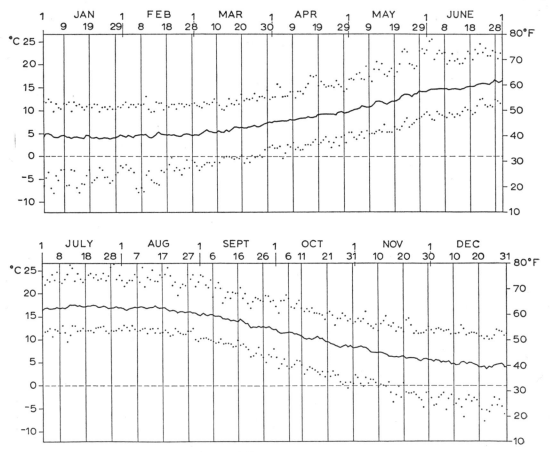

Fig 40 Average and extreme daily mean temperatures at Kew, 1871–1950.
Extremes are shown by dots
(Source of data: London, Meteorological Office 1951 *Climate of Kew Observatory*, 1871–1950. Typescript)

Alexander Buchan (1869) who worked on mid-nineteenth century Scottish temperature records, have suggested that these spells are not entirely haphazard in their occurrence but exhibit a tendency to cluster around certain particular days. Buchan isolated (for Scotland) the following warm and cold periods:

Warm periods		*Cold periods*	
1	12–15 July	1	7–14 February
2	12–15 August	2	11–14 April
3	3–14 December	3	9–14 May
		4	29 June–4 July
		5	6–11 August
		6	6–13 November

Many people have falsely assumed that these findings apply equally to London and elsewhere and some are still reluctant to discard them. There have been at least two notable studies of London temperatures with these ideas in mind.

Brooks and Mirrlees (1930) analysed 5-day smoothed mean temperatures for the periods 1871–1900 and 1901–29. The same technique, applied to the maximum, minimum and mean temperatures, 1871–1950, has been used to produce Fig. 41. The changes are obviously small and Brooks and Mirrlees showed that of all the apparent warm and cold spells shown by positive and negative departures from the period trend values, only an occasionally cool period from 30 July to 3 August was statistically valid, there being a three-to-one chance that the temperature at Kew will be lower than normal between these two dates. The only other positive finding was a tendency for the summer rise of mean temperature to cease towards the end of July and to be followed until autumn by a period of variable temperatures. The progressive fall in temperature sets in about the middle of August. But of Buchan's warm and cold spells, none was proven for London, and the authors conclude (Brooks and Mirrlees, 1930, p. 384) that 'while Buchan's cold and warm spells were probably true for Scotland in the 1860's, they are certainly not true for London in the twentieth century'.

Later, Marshall (1952, pp. 54–58) analysed Greenwich (1841–73) and Kew (1874–1940) records for the number of occasions in each 5-day period when the mean maximum temperature differed from the average by 2·0°F (1·1°C) or more and 5·0°F (2·8°C) or more. Again, the existence of precisely defined and statistically valid warm or cold spells was disproved but a number of interesting features were noted, more particularly:

1 Cold spells are most frequent in winter with a minimum about September. The warm spells have a maximum frequency in summer and a minimum about October.
2 The cold snaps of early and late May, though not falling between well-defined dates, might indicate a genuine liability to cold spells between late April and mid-May, and between then and early June. These are also reflected in very variable mean temperatures during May (Fig. 40).
3 The frequent warm spells and infrequent cold spells during the first part of September.

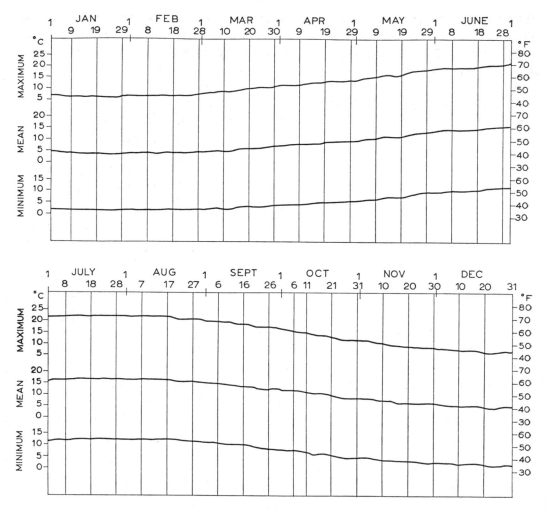

Fig 41 Smoothed mean daily maximum, minimum and mean temperatures at
Kew, 1871–1950. (5-year moving mean)
(Source of data: London, Meteorological Office 1951 *Climate of Kew Observatory, 1871–1950*. Typescript)

4   Late October and mid-November are frequently subject to rather cold spells separated by an interlude of warmer weather.
5   The cold spells of late December have been pronounced over the past 100 years as a whole but their recurrence interval has been rather irregular.

More recently, Craddock (1963) has also disproved the existence of statistically significant departures of 5-day mean temperatures at Kew from the period mean.

Hawke (1941), on the other hand, made an analysis of the anomalies between mean temperatures at Greenwich Observatory for each separate day of the years 1841–1936, believing that the smoothing techniques used by Brooks and Mirrlees (1930) confused the issue. His results were much more positive. In the 96 years analysed, there were three times as many 'warm' days and nine times as many 'cold' days (in both cases differing by 10·0°F (5·6°C) from the smoothed mean value) from 1 December to 28 February as there were from 1 June to 31 August. This highlights the variability of London's winter temperatures. August had only three 'cold' days and no 'very cold' days (cooler by 15·0°F (8·3°C) than the smoothed mean value) but recorded 82 'warm' and 12 'very warm' (15·0°F (8·3°C) warmer than the smoothed mean value) days. 'Cold' days were very rare from the second half of June to the end of September. There was also found to be a very high frequency of 'warm' days from 27 December to 5 January but in this same period 76 'cold' days and 18 'very cold' days occurred. This, as we have already noted, is a time of wide positive and negative departures from the smoothed mean, associated with sequences of depressions and ridges moving into Europe. One day in five from 27 December to 5 January in London is likely to have a mean temperature in excess or deficit of the smoothed average by at least 10·0°F (5·6°C). This contrasts with an average of one day in 13 for the year as a whole and at the other extreme, one day in 51 for 18–27 September, although this period of settled temperature characteristics is frequently divided between an Anticyclonic first half and a Cyclonic second.

Concerning the possible occurrence of cold and warm spells in the London data coincident with those defined by Buchan for Scotland, Hawke's analysis certainly seems to support a short period of markedly lower temperatures in the second week in February (see also Figs. 38, 39 and 40), and this probably occurs when ice in the Baltic extends and intensifies the stability of anticyclones over northern Europe with an influx of cold easterly or northeasterly winds in southeast England. The idea of singularities (one may even regard them as micro-seasons) in the annual cycle of temperature is peculiarly attractive, but the bulk of evidence seems to show that the most constant feature of London's climate is its inconstancy. For this reason I will do no more than point a figurative finger at the temporary but decided halt in the rise of temperatures in mid-May, and at the higher temperatures of mid-December (Fig. 41).

The very large range of extreme daily mean temperatures from 1871–1950 is shown by dots in Fig. 40. An analysis of the standard deviation of the mean daily temperature at Kew for each day from 1900–50 (Craddock, 1957, p. 354) shows very disturbed conditions, with large deviations, from 13 March to 15 June, a period of progressively less disturbed conditions during summer from 16 June to 14 September, a period of year-to-year uniformity from 15 September to 9 October followed by a disturbed temperature regime until 3 December and another relatively undisturbed period from 4 December to 12 March.

A number of investigators, using Kew temperatures, have directed their attention to the persistence of cold and warm spells and their bearing upon conditions in the following days and weeks. If such tendencies exist, they could provide a most useful forecasting tool. There is of course a strong lay opinion (or sometimes a pious hope) that the much maligned 'law of averages' will assure future happy atonement for the poor weather of the past, or that the present fine weather will have to be 'paid for' later. But the facts show, if anything, that such ideas are the reverse of truth (Brazell, 1963). In London, for instance, with the exception of October and November and to a lesser degree May and December, there is more chance that a month will be above average in temperature if the previous month was above average than the reverse. This is especially true of January, June and September but the relationship is reversed in December which shows lower temperatures than average after a warm November. The reasons for this anomaly are not clear (Smith, 1957). Similar conclusions were reached by McIntosh (1955) who showed in an analysis of London temperatures from 1841–1953 that there was a definite tendency for warm and cold spells to follow months of the same temperature anomaly as the type of spell, and that the following months are similarly affected. The length of this after-effect is uncertain. Craddock (1963, pp. 465 and 468), working in a related field, found little effect after 30 days or so, while Mc-Intosh's work suggested sympathetic repercussions extending over more than six months (McIntosh, 1955, p. 371). Following this after-effect, values normally return to the long-period average, there being no apparent tendency for subsequent compensatory changes. The most notable period of temperature anomaly persistence would seem to be 14 August to 12 September with the period 25 June to 19 July also showing a tendency towards a consistent temperature regime. Interestingly enough, this tendency is not shared, in London, by the intervening period from 20 July to 13 August. The general picture which emerges is that in winter the temperature regime shows a 'tendency to self perpetuation' (Craddock, 1963, p. 468) while in spring and for a short time in autumn the reversion from some positive or negative anomaly to normal conditions takes place in from 10 to 20 days. In summer there are two well-marked but clearly separated periods when differences tend to be perpetuated.

Soil temperatures and ground frost at Kew

Soil temperatures at depths of 1 ft (30 cm) and 4 ft (122 cm) have been taken at Kew Observatory since 1906. The soil is a light sandy loam above river gravel and is grassed· Given opposite are the normal and extreme monthly values for the period 1921–50. The values are based upon 0900 GMT readings but it must be stressed that soil temperatures are peculiarly sensitive to immediate site conditions, especially soil type and profile, and drainage; they should not be extrapolated to other areas without qualification. Observations from stations only a few hundred yards apart may show very different soil temperatures despite an equality of air temperature (London, Meteorological Office, 1960, p. 8) and large differences are particularly common in London and other cities where there is a variety of relief, aspect and shading and where there have been considerable soil disturbances.

The diurnal range of readings at a depth of 1 ft often amounts to 2·8°C (5°F) in summer but with a time lag behind air temperature of 4–5 hr; at 4 ft, the diurnal range is negligible. The annual variation, on the other hand, is quite large, even at 4 ft. It is difficult to compare soil and air temperature ranges at Kew because of the anomalous exposure of the air thermometers, but the mean annual range at 1 ft is, in fact, slightly

TABLE 56

Averages and extremes of earth temperature, Kew, 1921–50

1 ft

	Jan	Feb	Mar	Apr	May	June	July	Aug	Sept	Oct	Nov	Dec
Average												
°C	4·2	4·2	5·6	8·8	12·4	15·9	17·8	17·4	15·2	11·4	7·4	5·0
°F	39·6	39·6	42·0	47·8	54·3	60·7	64·0	63·4	59·4	52·5	45·4	41·0
Maximum												
Monthly mean												
°C	6·7	6·7	7·4	10·6	13·9	17·4	19·8	19·3	17·3	13·8	9·8	8·0
°F	44·1	44·1	45·3	51·1	57·0	63·3	67·6	66·7	63·1	56·8	49·6	46·4
Absolute												
°C	8·5	8·6	10·6	13·3	18·2	20·4	22·0	21·9	20·1	15·9	12·5	10·2
°F	47·3	47·5	51·1	55·9	64·8	68·9	71·6	71·4	68·2	60·6	54·5	50·4
Minimum												
Monthly mean												
°C	0·6	0·7	2·9	6·7	9·8	13·3	15·5	15·7	13·4	9·7	5·2	2·1
°F	33·1	33·3	37·2	44·1	49·6	55·9	59·9	60·3	56·1	49·5	41·4	35·8
Absolute												
°C	−0·4	0·0	0·1	3·7	7·3	10·9	13·9	13·5	11·0	5·2	2·1	1·0
°F	31·3	32·0	32·2	38·7	45·1	51·6	57·0	56·3	51·8	41·4	35·8	33·8

4 ft

	Jan	Feb	Mar	Apr	May	June	July	Aug	Sept	Oct	Nov	Dec
Average												
°C	6·8	6·3	6·6	8·3	10·5	13·1	15·1	15·8	15·2	13·2	10·5	8·2
°F	44·3	43·3	43·8	47·0	50·9	55·6	59·1	60·4	59·4	55·8	50·9	46·7
Maximum												
Monthly mean												
°C	8·2	7·3	7·9	9·6	11·6	14·1	16·0	17·0	16·5	15·1	11·5	9·7
°F	46·8	45·1	46·2	49·3	52·9	57·4	60·8	62·6	61·7	59·2	52·7	49·5
Absolute												
°C	9·1	8·0	8·8	10·7	12·8	15·1	16·9	17·5	17·0	15·9	12·9	10·5
°F	48·4	46·4	47·8	51·3	55·0	59·2	62·4	63·5	62·6	60·6	55·2	50·9
Minimum												
Monthly mean												
°C	5·4	4·0	4·2	6·8	8·9	11·5	13·6	14·4	13·7	12·1	9·0	6·4
°F	41·7	39·2	39·6	44·2	48·0	52·7	56·5	57·9	56·7	53·8	48·2	43·5
Absolute												
°C	4·0	3·7*	3·3	6·0	7·3	10·2	12·4	14·2	13·1	10·2	7·2	5·8
°F	39·2	38·7*	37·9	42·8	45·1	50·4	54·3	57·6	55·6	50·4	45·0	42·4

*3·4°C (38·1°F), 1963

Source: London, Meteorological Office 1960 *Averages of earth temperature for the British Isles*. M.O. 665 (H.M.S.O.)

larger than that in the North Wall Screen but probably 80–90 per cent of that in the standard Stevenson Screen. At a depth of 4 ft the range of soil temperature is most likely 45–65 per cent of the air range. The lag of soil temperature behind the annual waves of air temperature is generally from 6–12 days at 1 ft, increasing to 25–45 days at 4 ft (London, Meteorological Office, 1960, p. 6). This means (Table 56) that the highest temperatures are reached in August and are least in February at this lower depth. On heavier soils, such as those on London Clay, the lag is greater, extending into September and March respectively.

For ground frost, defined as a grass minimum temperature of −0·9°C (30·4°F) or less, the mean annual frequency (1906–50) at Kew Observatory is 92·7 days (London, Meteorological Office, 1951, Appendix, p. 5), though this is probably eight or so below the average for the past 100 years because of the generally warmer period during the first four decades of the twentieth century. Table 57 gives the mean and extreme monthly totals of days with ground frost at Kew.

TABLE 57

Number of days with ground frost, Kew, 1906–50

	Jan	Feb	Mar	Apr	May	June	July	Aug	Sept	Oct	Nov	Dec	Yr
Mean	15	15	15	11	4	1	0	0+	1	6	11	13	92
Highest	26	25	26	20	13	3	0	1	6	19	20	24	127

Source: London, Meteorological Office 1951 *Climate of Kew Observatory, 1871–1950*, p. 34 (Typescript)

TABLE 58

Lowest grass minimum temperature, Kew, 1895–1950

	Jan	Feb	Mar	Apr	May	June
°C	−16·1	−17·8	−15·6	−11·1	−9·4	−3·3
°F	3	0	4	12	15	26

	July	Aug	Sept	Oct	Nov	Dec
°C	−0·5	−2·2	−7·3	−9·4	−11·1	−14·4
°F	31	28	19	15	12	6

Source: London, Meteorological Office 1951 *Climate of Kew Observatory, 1871–1950*, p. 32 (Typescript)

It will be noted that ground frost is very exceptional in August (that it has occurred at all is very remarkable) and was not recorded in any of the 45 Julys from 1906–50, although even this month has recorded a grass minimum below 0°C (32°F) (Table 58). The latest ground frost, 1906–50, at Kew was on 27 June (1919) and the earliest on 24 August (1940).

TEMPERATURES WITHIN GREATER LONDON

That central areas of London are warmer than suburban or surrounding districts is a matter of common experience. Luke Howard was the first to make a quantitative analysis of the contrast. His thermometer exposures were anomalous by present standards but his studies of the differences between temperatures within and beyond the city margin were based upon a series of measures taken at 'the Apartments of the Royal Society by order of the President and Council' (Howard, 1820, p. 91) and successive sites in what is now northeast London but was, in the early nineteenth century, open country. Unfortunately, his exposures varied and were far from standard—at Plaistow, in 1809 a village 4 miles (6·4 km) east of London, the thermometer hung beneath a laurel bush, and at Tottenham, where readings were taken between 1813 and 1816, the thermometer was 10 ft (3 m) above ground on the north wall of a house; but in spite of these drawbacks, Luke Howard's account is monumental. Even today there is uncertainty about the details of exposure needed for values representative of the station vicinity, and it is by no means easy to decide which, if any, areas are typical of London's morphology and climate. The complexity of the urban landscape with its kaleidoscope of roads, houses, offices, shops, factories and open spaces, is reflected in an equally complex pattern of local climates which differ, in the limit, between two sides of a street. One has to choose a scale of investigation and adjust, largely empirically, the intensity and form of one's observations to conform with this scale.

The broad nature of temperatures within and around London can be seen in a comparison of average maximum, minimum and mean temperatures at central, suburban and country stations for the period 1931–60 (Table 59).

TABLE 59

Average annual temperatures, London, 1931–60

	Mean height		Maximum		Minimum		Mean	
	ft	m	°C	°F	°C	°F	°C	°F
Surrounding country	287	87·5	13·7	56·6	5·5	41·9	9·6	49·2
Margins, high-level	473	144·2	13·4	56·1	6·2	43·1	9·8	49·6
Suburbs, high-level	450	137·2	13·4	56·1	5·9	42·6	9·7	49·4
low-level	203	61·9	14·2	57·5	6·4	43·5	10·3	50·5
Central districts	87	26·5	14·6	58·2	7·4	45·3	11·0	51·8
Kew								
Observatory (00–24 hr)	18	5·5	13·9	57·0	7·0	44·6	10·5	50·9

Surrounding country: mean of Rothamsted, St Albans, Tunbridge Wells, Wisley
Margins, high-level: Addington
Suburbs, high-level: Hampstead; low-level: mean of Bromley, Croydon, Wealdstone
Central districts: mean of Camden Square, Kensington Palace, Regent's Park (1933–60), Westminster (St James's Park)

Source of data: London, Meteorological Office 1963a *Averages of temperature for Great Britain and Northern Ireland 1931–60*. M.O. 735 (H.M.S.O.)

Central districts had average temperatures greater than those of the suburbs and appreciably above country stations outside London. Contrasts between maximum temperatures were small, amounting to an annual average of 0·9°C (1·6°F). The lower temperatures in the higher parts of the suburbs (illustrated by the Hampstead record) and margins (illustrated by Addington) reflects the importance of height during the rapid lapse conditions of daytime, especially in summer (Best et al., 1952, pp. 9–11). People living in Hampstead, Harrow on the Hill, Upper Sydenham and on the flanks of Shooters Hill can expect much cooler daytime temperatures than occur in the streets and parks of the tightly packed suburbs which have flooded around these upstanding islands of less compact urban development. By night, the contrasts between London and its rural envelope are more marked, with an overall average annual difference in temperature of 1·9°C (3·4°F) between the centre and outside. The 'low-level' suburbs are warmer on average by 0·9°C (1·6°F) than the rural parts of southeast England, but at Hampstead, and presumably at similar sites elsewhere in London, the difference is only 0·4°C (0·7°F). The slightly higher night-time temperatures at Addington, on the southern margins of London (Fig. 5), are no doubt attributable to the height of the station related to the mean level of the nocturnal inversion. Little need be said about differences in mean temperatures since these are the average of maximum and minimum values and generalize their separate forms. For comparison, temperatures at Kew Observatory are also given in Table 59. As might be expected from its open position and unusual screen site, maximum temperatures are lower than in the more built-up parts of the immediate suburbs, probably by about 0·5°C (0·9°F), and night-time temperatures are higher by about 0·8°C (1·4°F). The latter is a compromise between higher temperatures due to the position of the North Wall Screen and lower temperatures resulting from the Observatory's setting in the Old Deer Park.

But the picture presented by Table 59 is not, of course, a rigid one to be applied under all conditions. In the first instance there is, in central London, a clearly marked cycle of heat-island intensity which is shown in Table 60 even by the coarse tool of monthly averages.

The wave of high mean values in spring, summer and autumn in central London, similar to that described by Balchin and Pye in Bath (1940–50, p. 6), Manley in Manchester (1944, pp. 254–7) and Parry in Reading (1956a, pp. 47–8) is all the more interesting since it is much less noticeable in the suburbs (Table 60). Many North American and European interior cities show no such seasonal differences (Mitchell, 1961, p. 229; Sundborg, 1951, p. 88; Landsberg, 1956, pp. 30–1, Steinhauser et al., 1957, p. 119). These differences between cities are probably due not only to contrasts in their morphology but also to differences in the general climates of their regions, more particularly in relation to seasonal changes in wind speeds, cloud amounts, and the incidence of surface inversions. The dissimilar response of central and suburban areas of London is probably related to the more important contribution of low-level (combustion) heat sources in suburban areas in winter, the lower building densities, and the frequent, thick suburban fogs (see Chapter 8) which reduce radiation heat losses from these areas (and release latent heat when the fogs are formed).

TABLE 60

Differences in temperature between central and suburban London and the surrounding country areas, 1931–60

	Jan	Feb	Mar	Apr	May	June	July	Aug	Sept	Oct	Nov	Dec
						Differences						

Central London

Maximum

	Jan	Feb	Mar	Apr	May	June	July	Aug	Sept	Oct	Nov	Dec
°C	0·7	0·8	0·7	0·9	1·0	1·2	1·0	0·9	1·0	0·9	0·8	0·7
°F	1·2	1·4	1·2	1·6	1·8	2·1	1·8	1·6	1·8	1·6	1·4	1·2

Minimum

°C	1·7	1·6	1·9	2·0	2·0	2·1	2·1	2·0	1·9	1·9	1·8	1·8
°F	3·0	2·8	3·4	3·6	3·6	3·7	3·7	3·6	3·4	3·4	3·2	3·2

Mean

°C	1·2	1·2	1·3	1·5	1·5	1·7	1·6	1·5	1·5	1·4	1·3	1·3
°F	2·1	2·1	2·3	2·6	2·7	2·9	2·8	2·6	2·6	2·5	2·3	2·2

Suburbs: high-level

Maximum

°C	−0·4	−0·3	−0·5	−0·3	−0·5	−0·2	−0·3	−0·2	−0·4	−0·3	−0·3	−0·3
°F	−0·8	−0·6	−0·9	−0·6	−0·9	−0·4	−0·6	−0·4	−0·8	−0·6	−0·6	−0·6

Minimum

°C	0·2	0·1	0·5	0·5	0·6	0·5	0·5	0·6	0·6	0·6	0·5	0·4
°F	0·4	0·2	0·9	0·9	1·0	0·9	0·9	1·0	1·0	1·0	0·9	0·8

Mean

°C	−0·1	−0·1	0·0	0·0	0·1	0·1	−0·1	0·1	0·1	0·2	0·1	0·0
°F	−0·2	−0·2	0·0	0·0	0·2	0·2	−0·2	0·2	0·2	0·3	0·2	0·0

Suburbs: low-level

Maximum

°C	0·4	0·5	0·4	0·5	0·4	0·7	0·6	0·6	0·5	0·6	0·5	0·4
°F	0·8	0·9	0·8	0·9	0·8	1·2	1·0	1·0	0·9	1·0	0·9	0·8

Minimum

°C	0·9	0·8	1·0	1·0	1·0	1·0	1·0	0·9	0·9	0·9	1·1	1·1
°F	1·6	1·4	1·8	1·8	1·8	1·8	1·8	1·6	1·6	1·6	1·9	1·9

Mean

°C	0·7	0·6	0·7	0·7	0·7	0·8	0·8	0·7	0·7	0·8	0·8	0·7
°F	1·2	1·0	1·2	1·2	1·2	1·4	1·4	1·2	1·2	1·4	1·4	1·2

Central London: mean of Camden Square, Kensington Palace, Regent's Park (1933–60), Westminster (St James's Park)
Suburbs, high-level: Hampstead; low-level: mean of Bromley, Croydon, Wealdstone
Surrounding country: mean of Rothamsted, St Albans, Tunbridge Wells, Wisley

Source of data: London, Meteorological Office 1963a *Averages of temperature for Great Britain and Northern Ireland 1931–60*. M.O. 735 (H.M.S.O.)

Monthly averages of maximum temperatures at Hampstead, perhaps typical of the more elevated parts of London, are below those at rural sites immediately outside in all months, owing no doubt to differences in height (about 160 ft (48·8 m)) at times when the heat-island is weak. By night, Hampstead is warmer because of its urban site and the form of the ground, but by only a small margin in January and February (Table 60) when wind speeds are high and heat-islands are weak and shallow.

The small amounts by which the maximum temperatures in London exceed those in the open country may seem surprising to people who have suffered the heat of summer in the city and look forward to returning to the seemingly much cooler Green Belt dormitory settlements. There are two points to remember in addition to the rapid fall of temperature during the evening. First, the generally lighter winds in the streets of London reduce convective and evaporative cooling of the skin. Second, there is a great deal of reflected solar radiation into the streets by the walls of buildings which will also have high surface temperatures, probably 11·0–16·7°C (20–30°F) above air temperature (Lacy, 1956, p. 533). In the countryside around London, wind speeds are generally higher and the radiant temperature of the vegetation will be closer to air temperature; here the body is more easily cooled by convection, evaporation and radiation.

A feature common to all cities is the higher temperature differences by night. Fig. 42, based upon 14,600 records, shows the differences in maximum and minimum temperatures, Kensington-Wisley, for the 10 years 1951–60 and indicates the distribution of anomalies appropriate to the centre of London. Fig. 43 for Bromley-Wisley is indicative of general suburban levels of heat-island intensity, and Fig. 44 (Hampstead-Wisley) of conditions in the more elevated areas. In all three cases, differences in maximum

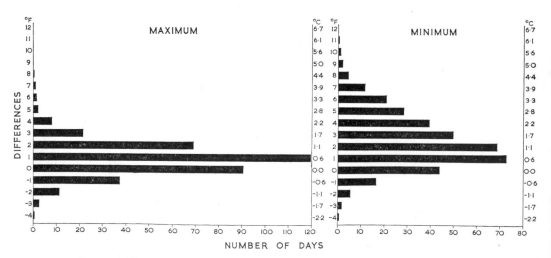

Fig 42 Differences in daily maximum and minimum temperatures, Kensington–Wisley, 1951–60: annual averages
(Source of data: London, Meteorological Office Monthly return of daily observations, Forms F3203 and F3208)

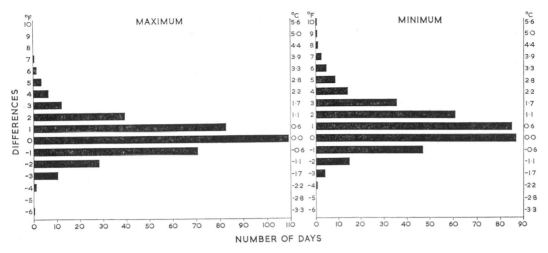

Fig 43 Differences in daily maximum and minimum temperatures, Bromley–
Wisley, 1951–60: annual averages
(Source of data: London, Meteorological Office Monthly return of daily
observations, Forms F3203 and F3208)

temperatures are small, being most frequently 0·6°C (1°F) at Kensington, 0·0°C (0·0°F)
at Bromley and −0·6°C (−1°F) at Hampstead. The highest recorded difference in
maximum temperatures was 3·9°C (7°F) at Bromley, 6·1°C (11°F) at Hampstead (surprisingly large and perhaps an error in reading) and 4·4°C (8°F) at Kensington. There
were, it will be noted, many days when the maximum temperature at Hampstead was
below that outside London; indeed, such occasions comprised about 75 per cent of
the records. At Bromley the corresponding figure was 30 per cent and at Kensington,
14 per cent. The very much higher numbers at Hampstead, lowering the mean monthly
maximum temperatures below those for Wisley, are explained primarily in terms of
the station's elevation but here and at Bromley and Kensington, other factors bring
about these reversals of normal conditions, and their replacement by an urban 'cold-
island'. Many such instances are related to the passage of fronts (Marshall, 1950) or
changes in local cloud amounts, perhaps for very short periods on a generally cloudy
day, or to contrasts of pollution and fog densities. There are also days when a more
rapid increase of temperatures in the open country compared with the city (where
temperatures rise more slowly owing to contrasts between the thermal properties of
buildings and soils and vegetation) is sufficient to reverse normal conditions by making
the city cooler than its environs. Differences in pollution and fog densities between
central, suburban and country areas are also important. Negative anomalies or, as I
propose to call them, urban cold-islands, develop most frequently when regional
temperatures are rising, often occurring in groups of several days. When fogs are dense
in London, as from October to March, these daytime cold-islands may attain quite
extraordinary proportions. For instance, during the severe smog of December 1952,
temperatures in Greater London on the 6th, the coldest day, did not exceed 0°C (32°F)

except in higher areas like Hampstead, 450 ft (137·2 m), which were above the densest fog; here maximum temperatures were about 4·4°C (40°F). There was of course a low level inversion at this time (Absalom, 1954, p. 263) but similar temperatures were also reached at lower stations outside the main smog area.

Contrasts deriving from differences in the thermal responses of bricks and mortar on the one hand and soils and vegetation on the other will be less evident in the narrow streets of densely built-up areas, for here solar radiation will be reflected by the walls of buildings and, usually, air temperatures will be higher than in more open sites such

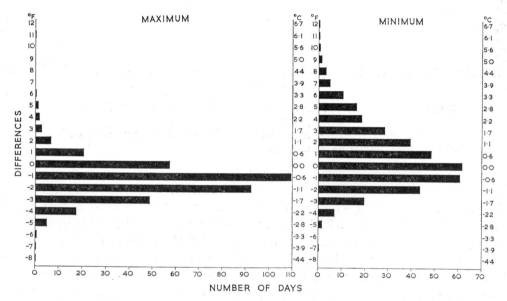

Fig 44 Differences in daily maximum and minimum temperatures, Hampstead–Wisley, 1951–60: annual averages
(Source of data: London, Meteorological Office Monthly return of daily observations, Forms F3203 and F3208)

as the parks and larger squares. These may very well be no warmer, perhaps cooler, than the nearby countryside.

The right-hand histograms in Figs. 42, 43 and 44 illustrate the normally more intense heat-islands which develop by night. Differences in minimum temperatures at Kensington and Wisley were most frequently 0·6°C (1°F), varying between 6·1°C (11°F) and −2·2°C (−4°F). Between Bromley and Wisley the modal difference was 0·0°C (0°F) and varied between −2·2°C (−4°F) and 5·6°C (10°F). The corresponding figures for Hampstead were: mode, 0·0°C (0°F); negative extreme, −3·9°C (−7°F); positive extreme, 6·7°C (12°F). The slightly higher positive extreme intensity of heat-islands at Hampstead than at Kensington resulted on the two occasions indicated in Fig. 44, because Hampstead lay near the level of a particularly strong inversion.

It seems likely that the site of the Wisley station, near the wide, marshy floodplain of the Wey, is responsible for higher night-time and daytime temperatures compared with most of London's rural margins. The average temperatures are compared in Table 61.

TABLE 61

Averages of temperature at stations around London, 1931–60

	Maximum		Minimum		Mean	
	°C	°F	°C	°F	°C	°F
January						
Wisley						
105 ft (32·0 m)	6·6	43·8	0·9	33·6	3·7	38·6
St Albans						
272 ft (82·9 m)	6·0	42·8	0·0	32·0	3·0	37·4
Tunbridge Wells	6·1	43·0	0·0	32·0	3·1	37·5
351 ft (107·0 m)						
July						
Wisley	22·1	71·7	12·0	53·6	17·1	62·7
St Albans	21·5	70·7	11·4	52·5	16·5	61·7
Tunbridge Wells	21·6	70·8	11·6	52·8	16·6	61·8

Source of data: London, Meteorological Office 1963a *Averages of temperature for Great Britain and Northern Ireland 1931–60*. M.O. 735 (H.M.S.O.)

But Wisley is much closer to London than either St Albans or Tunbridge Wells and its altitude is more typical of the city. For these reasons, it has been selected for comparative studies of the intensity of London's heat-island, although one might expect the values given in Figs. 42, 43 and 44 to be increased slightly if figures were available for other stations just beyond the urban margin. One such station operated between 1953 and 1959 at Bayfordbury, Hertfordshire, and gave what were probably more representative temperatures of the immediate rural areas around London. In 1959 the median minimum temperature contrast between Kensington and Wisley was 1·7°C (3°F), but between Kensington and Bayfordbury it was 2·2°C (4°F) and reached 8·9°C (16°F) on one night (Chandler, 1961a, p. 299; 1962a, p. 288).

One may equally question the representativeness of the Kensington Palace records for central London. Bilham (1938, p. 308) used Westminster (St James's Park) which had an average minimum temperature, 1931–50, 0·3°C (0·5°F) higher than at Kensington Palace, ranging from zero in February to 0·4°C (0·7°F) from August to October inclusive. These contrasts are very remarkable and are not easy to understand, although the standard of Westminster records is not as high as from Kensington Palace. Both stations must, of course, be affected by their park setting and temperature traverses along the northern edge and across the centre of Hyde Park suggest that the readings in the Kensington Palace Screen (near the western margins of the open space of Kensington Gardens and Hyde Park) might average about 0·3°C (0·5°F) lower than in the nearby built-up areas. This difference may reach 1·7°C (3·0°F) on a few occasions of calm, clear nights in summer and autumn. The station's position in relation to the Gardens and Park will help to limit these differences because of the prevailing westerly

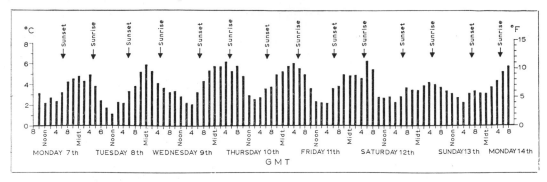

Fig 45 Two-hourly differences in temperature, Westminster–Wisley, 7–14
September 1959
(Source of data: Thermograms at the Westminster (St James's Park) and
Wisley stations)

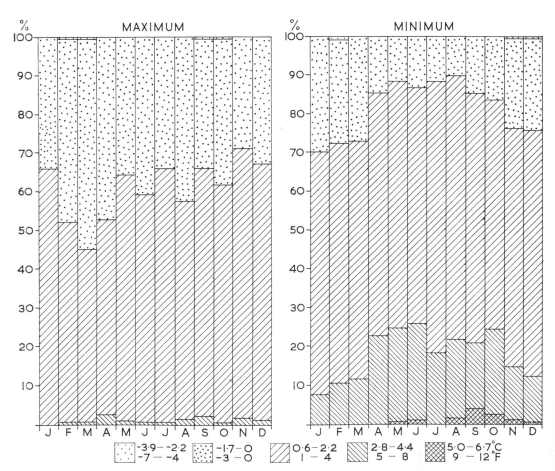

Fig 46 Differences in daily maximum and minimum temperatures, Kensington–Wisley, by months, 1951–60
(Source of data: London, Meteorological Office Monthly return of daily
observations, Forms F3203 and F3208)

winds which will carry warmer air across the margins of the open space, but there is no doubt that even small shifts of site will lead to surprisingly large temperature changes (Glasspoole, 1959, p. 65). Usually, temperatures in city streets (sampled by the temperature traverses) will be higher by day than in parks and similar open spaces, but in certain circumstances cold night air may pond between buildings and by day, solar radiation may be reflected into the area. This might have been the case at the old station of Camden Square (Glasspoole, 1959, p. 65). But in actual fact, neither Kensington Palace nor Westminster lies in the mean peak area of London's heat-island, for a group of new climatological stations (established for the London Climatological Survey) in the Islington, Stoke Newington and Hackney districts, 5 mi (8 km) to the northeast, had a mean minimum temperature for 1959, 0·2°C (0·3°F) higher than at Westminster and 0·4°C (0·7°F) higher than at Kensington Palace. It is obvious that no pair of stations, one inside and one outside London, are perfect for the analysis of

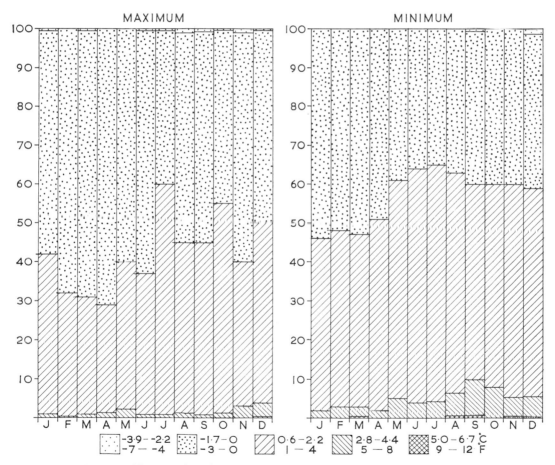

Fig 47 Differences in daily maximum and minimum temperatures, Bromley–Wisley, by months, 1951–60
(Source of data: London, Meteorological Office Monthly return of daily observations, Forms F3203 and F3208)

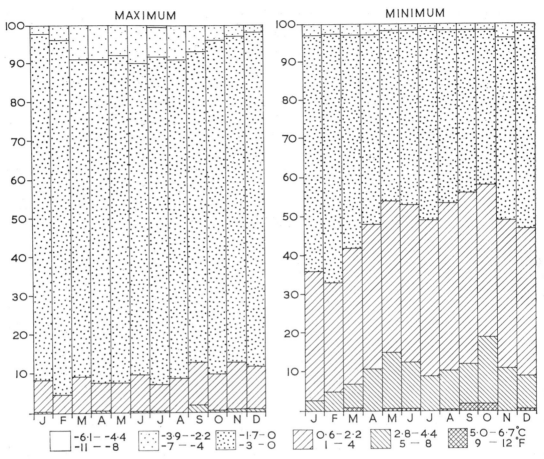

Fig 48 Differences in daily maximum and minimum temperatures, Hampstead–Wisley, 1951–60
(Source of data: London, Meteorological Office Monthly return of daily observations, Forms F3203 and F3208)

London's heat-island but, for the reasons mentioned and because of the length of their records, Kensington Palace and Wisley have been selected for most purposes.

For hour-by-hour analysis, the only central station with a thermograph is Westminster (St James's Park) and Fig. 45 shows a comparison of two-hourly readings here and at Wisley between 7–14 September 1959. The greatest temperature contrast occurs most commonly one or two hours before dawn, after which the value decreases to a minimum in the mid-afternoon. (Analysis by days of the week shows no significant contrasts.)

Temperature differences at Kensington, Bromley and Hampstead (representing central, low-level and high-level suburban areas respectively) with those at Wisley, graded and by months, are illustrated in Figs. 46, 47 and 48. Differences in maximum temperatures show, in all cases, only a weak summer peak and spring trough in values and in all months but November, more than 30 per cent of the days give zero or negative differences. In February, March, April, June and August, more than 40 per cent of the days have negative anomalies. Differences in daily minimum temperatures at Kensington and Wisley (Fig. 46) were greatest in summer and early autumn and least in winter and early spring. Contrasts of 2·8°C (5°F) or more occurred on nearly 23 per cent of the nights from April to October inclusive but on only 11 per cent of the nights from November to March. About one night in five in September gives temperatures in the centre of London warmer by 5°C (9°F) or more. Between Bromley and Wisley, differences in minimum temperatures show a much smaller seasonal change, a feature commented upon earlier. At Hampstead, night-time heat-islands are strongest in autumn but with a secondary peak in May. We have already seen that temperatures at Hampstead are closely controlled by the height of the station and the generally open character of the local urban development. Heat-islands here are strongest when inversions reach above 450 ft (137 m), the height of the station. Some of the deepest inversions occur in autumn and this helps to explain the seasonal preference for the more intense heat-islands at this time of the year.

London's heat-island is far from static. Not only are there diurnal and seasonal pulses in its intensity (and thereby in its areal form) but also changes resulting from differences in the general synoptic situation. These will be illustrated in the following section.

Spatial and sectional forms of London's heat-island

Fig. 49 shows a fairly typical pattern of maximum daily temperature in London, though this particular daytime heat-island was unusually strong. Here, as in all subsequent distribution maps, continuous lines are used only where they can be located with precision; elsewhere, where records are sparser, broken lines indicate uncertainty, not usually in the general run of the isotherms but in their precise location. Even in these cases, however, the margins of possible error are commonly small.

On Wednesday, 3 June 1959, England lay near the centre of a col between an anticyclone over Germany and an extensive Azores 'high'. Pressure fell northward to a deep depression over Iceland and southward to a much shallower depression over North Africa. The day was sunny, never more than half the sky being obscured by cumulus clouds which were of no great vertical development. Winds of about 5·4 m/sec (12·0 mi/hr), recorded at London Airport on the western fringe of the city, backed from northwest to southwest during the morning and remained almost constant in direction for the remainder of the day. Fig. 50 is of a traverse along the Lea valley during the morning and early afternoon of that day and the most outstanding feature is the changing complexity of air temperatures during the period of traverse from 0905 GMT to 1254 GMT. The intricate and changing distribution of warm and cool pockets of air along the line of traverse is a reflection not only of the cellular urban morphology but also of thermals rising spasmodically from perhaps temporary areas of warming. Cloud shadows also complicated the picture.

Maximum temperatures for the same day as the traverse are shown in Fig. 50. One cannot be absolutely certain that this is a picture at any one instant, although thermo-

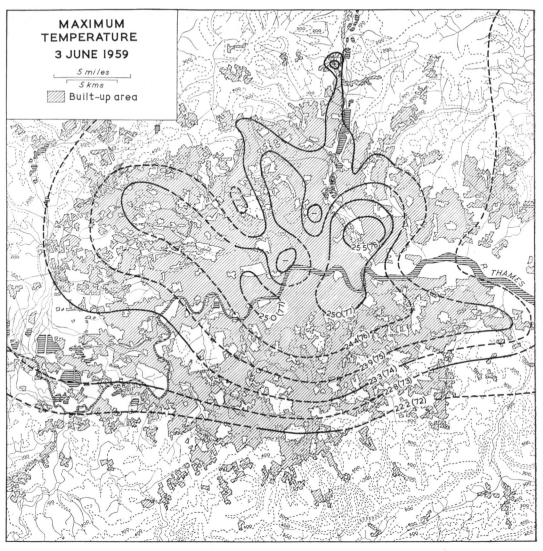

Fig 49 Distribution of maximum temperature in London, 3 June 1959. Broken
lines indicate some uncertainty of position. Isotherms are numbered in °C
with °F equivalents in brackets
(Source of data: Readings at official stations and the supplementary stations
of the London Climatological Survey)

gram traces suggest that any variation in the time of peak temperatures was small.
Temperatures were above 25·0°C (77°F) in the Lewisham, Deptford, Stepney, Poplar
and West Ham districts of east London, that is, on the leeward side of the city, and
there were high temperatures also in a small area of Kensington and Chelsea; elsewhere
they ranged between 22·2°C (72°F) and 25·0°C (77°F). This relatively intense heat-island
by normal daytime standards illustrates a distinctive complexity of conditions. There is
little doubt that the distribution of temperatures in south and west London was as
cellular as that in the northeast, and probably more so, but the station network was too

open to record this. The rather gentle temperature gradients near London's margins are typical of conditions with wind speeds of 5·4 m/sec (12·0 mi/hr) or more, and temperatures higher on the leeward than the windward side of London are probably the result of the warming of a fairly deep boundary layer as it crosses the city. On this particular day, large areas north and northeast of London had temperatures of more than 23·3°C (74°F)—areas at altitudes above those in south and southwest London where they were below 23·3°C (74°F).

The distribution of maximum temperatures on 3 June 1959, with its relatively small urban-rural temperature contrasts and a generally complex pattern of isotherms, is typical of daytime thermal conditions in London. Wind speeds and cloud amounts are also critical in the formation of heat-islands and a selection of occasions has been chosen to illustrate certain representative night-time conditions. The distribution of minimum temperatures for the night of 1–2 August 1959, for instance, shows the close relationship between amounts of cloud and the size of the urban-rural temperature contrast. During this night, northwesterly winds of about 2·6 m/sec (5·8 mi/hr) blew around the eastern margins of an anticyclone centred southwest of Ireland and there was an almost complete cover of stratus and stratocumulus cloud whose base lowered from about 1,000 ft (550 m) at midnight to little above 500 ft (152 m) at dawn on the 2nd. Fig. 51 shows the results of these conditions. In spite of only gentle breezes beneath

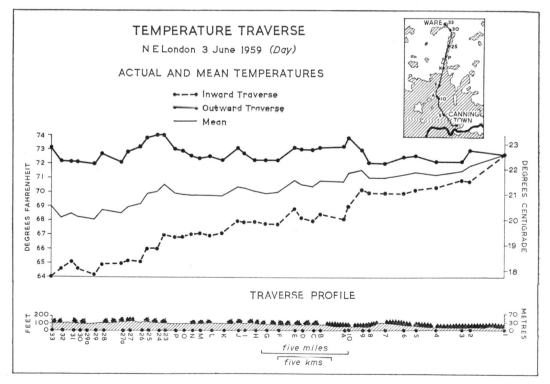

Fig 50 Lea valley temperature traverse, 3 June 1959 (day)
(Source of data: Lea Valley Climatological Survey records)

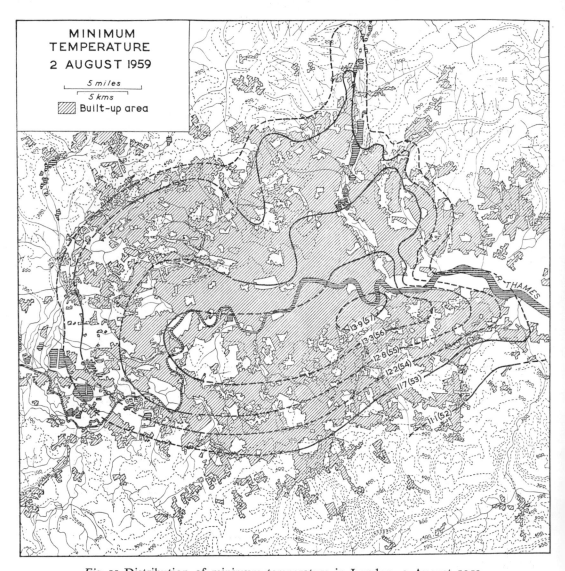

Fig 51 Distribution of minimum temperature in London, 2 August 1959.
Broken lines indicate some uncertainty of position. Isotherms are numbered
in °C with °F in brackets
(Source of data: Readings at official stations and the supplementary stations
of the London Climatological Survey)

a well-marked inversion, the cloud bank above the city intercepted much of the long-
wave radiation from the ground and thereby reduced the contrast in night-time heat
losses between rural and urban areas. The urban-rural temperature contrast was, as a
result, considerably less than under clear-sky conditions, reaching an extreme value of
only 2·8°C (5°F) in the early hours of the 2nd. The pattern of the isotherms is also
interesting, more especially the displacement of the highest temperatures to the Greenwich and Deptford districts of southeast London. Thus, apart from a sharp rise of

temperature of about 0·6°C (1°F) near the edge of the built-up area, thermal gradients were steep only on the southeast (leeward) side of the city. This type of asymmetric distribution seems to be a common feature of nights with light winds.

Fig. 52 shows temperatures recorded during a traverse on the night of 28–29 October 1959 between Ware, a small settlement (population, 1961, 10,000) outside London, and Liverpool Street in a central district of the city. A brief indication of the intensity of the urban development is given by symbols along the traverse profile on this and subsequent traverse diagrams. The mean temperature profile refers to conditions along city streets at approximately 0015 GMT on 29 October, the whole traverse being conducted between 2248 GMT on 28 October and 0145 GMT on 29 October. Skies were clear, but outside the main built-up area of London a 6·2–7·2 m/sec (13·8–16·1 mi/hr) wind blew from the northwest; the result was a smoothing of temperature contrasts by advection and the vertical transport of heat by atmospheric turbulence. The maximum temperature contrast was only 2·3°C (3·2°F). Contrasts between rural areas and small centres of settlement between stations H and 33, weakly developed at the time of the inward traverse, had disappeared by the time of the return or outward traverse. Similarly, there was no sharp boundary to the warm air above the city.

Fig. 53 shows the results of a traverse between 2144 GMT and 0058 GMT on the night of 8–9 July 1959. The mean value trace represents the temperature distribution at about 0023 GMT, the time station I was reached. There was a two-eighths cover of cirrus and a wind of 5·1–5·7 m/sec (11·5–12·7 mi/hr) backing from east to north during

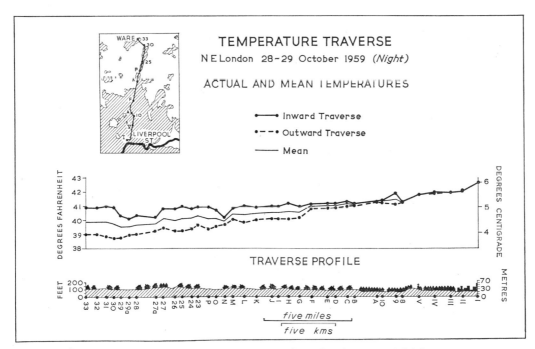

Fig 52 Lea valley temperature traverse, 28–29 October 1959 (night)
(Source of data: Lea Valley Climatological Survey records)

L

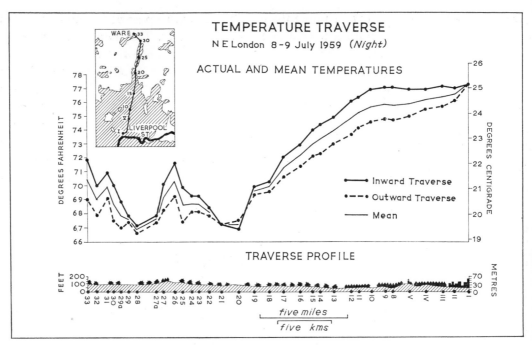

Fig 53 Lea valley temperature traverse, 8–9 July 1959 (night)
(Source of data: Lea Valley Climatological Survey records)

the time of the traverse. With this wind strength, the margins of the heat-island were gentle but the overall intensity was strong. By comparison with Fig. 56 and confirmed by many other records from both traverses and climatological stations, it would seem that wind speeds (near the margins of the city) below 5–6 m/sec (12–14 mi/hr) are necessary for the development of substantial, sharply defined night-time rural-urban temperature contrasts. Ten years (1951–1960) of daily records show that the thermal effect of the city is eliminated by wind speeds greater than about 12 m/sec (27 mi/hr): this compares with 8 m/sec (18 mi/hr) given for Bremen (Kratzer, 1937, p. 66) and 4–7 m/sec (9·0–15·6 mi/hr) for Reading (Parry, 1956a, pp. 45–7). Also of interest is the way in which generally northeasterly winds carried cool air into the northern parts of a number of settlements—such as Hoddesdon between stations 27 and 28. These winds explain in addition the gradual nature of the temperature rise towards the centre of London and the suggested displacement of peak temperatures to south of the Thames.

Modifications by wind speed of the intensity and form of London's heat-island can also be seen in a comparison of minimum temperatures over the conurbation on two spring nights. On one, 29–30 April 1959, skies were clear except for a high, thin, partial veil of cirrus, but winds were fresh; on the second night, 13–14 May 1959, cloudless skies were associated with a light air of less than 2 m/sec (4·5 mi/hr). The differences in the intensity and form of London's heat-island are striking (Figs. 54 and 55).

During the night of 29–30 April 1959 Britain lay on the southeastern side of a ridge of high pressure extending from southwest of Ireland to southern Norway. Pressure fell sharply towards a secondary depression over Belgium. Northerly winds of about 9·4 m/sec (21·0 mi/hr) blew during the night and, in association with deep and active turbulence in the boundary layer near the earth's surface, the city's warmth was diffused both laterally and vertically. The intensity of the heat-island on this night was consequently small—a matter of 2·2°C (4°F) only (Fig. 54), but the very close relationship between the pattern of isotherms and the form of the city is very striking. The correspondence is best shown in areas of the northeast where we can draw isotherms with great accuracy. Ribbon development along terraces on the western side of the Lea

MINIMUM
TEMPERATURE
30 APRIL 1959

5 miles

5 kms.

Built-up area

Fig 54 Distribution of minimum temperature in London, 30 April 1959.
Broken lines indicate some uncertainty of position. Isotherms are numbered
in °C with °F equivalents in brackets
(Source of data: Readings at official stations and supplementary stations of
the London Climatological Survey)

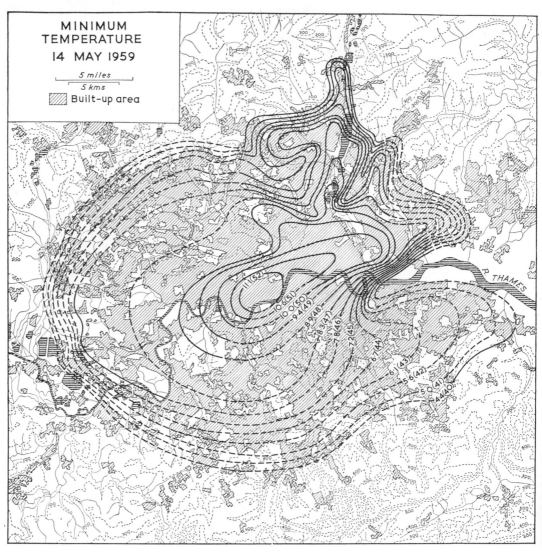

Fig 55 Distribution of minimum temperature in London, 14 May 1959.
Broken lines indicate some uncertainty of position. Isotherms are numbered
in °C with °F in brackets
(Source of data: Readings at official stations and supplementary stations of
the London Climatological Survey)

valley is mirrored in a long tongue of warm air north to Cheshunt. On the other hand, the wedge of cold air projecting inward from the northwest is related to elevation as well as to the more open development of the area between Arkley and Hampstead Heath. One must remember, of course, that in detail the isotherm patterns would be very complex in those parts of London, such as the west and southwest, where there is a more detailed intermingling of built-up areas and open spaces but it would require a much closer spacing of stations, every few hundred yards perhaps, to record these. Detailed temperature traverses (see later) shed some light on this particular feature.

The form of the heat-island early on 30 April stands in marked contrast to that revealed by the distribution of minimum temperatures on 14 May 1959 (Fig. 55). On the latter occasion, light northeasterly to northerly winds of less than 2 m/sec (4·5 mi/hr) and clear skies were associated with a deep anticyclone covering most of Great Britain and the Continent. These conditions allowed the full interplay of the several factors contributing to urban-rural temperature contrasts and an intense heat-island with steep thermal gradients paralleling the edge of the built-up area was the result. In Kensington, minimum temperatures did not fall below 11·1°C (52°F), 6·7°C (12°F) higher than in the rural districts around the city. The correspondence between the urban morphology and the degree of warming is remarkable, both on the regional and local scale, with the development of sharp temperature contrasts around and within the city. Cool air above the open, low-lying and often marshy grounds of lower Thames-side below Greenwich was separated from warm air above the closely built-up districts of West and East Ham by a thermal gradient far sharper than most major fronts, and it is hardly surprising that the Survey has indicated the existence of thermally induced local winds, similar in genesis to sea-breezes, around the margins of London. These winds would seem to move inward to the warmer central districts in a series of pulses (see p. 167), quickly losing speed through friction with the buildings. Between each series of movements thermal gradients are built up again. In this context the steepening of temperature gradients around a central 'peak' of the heat-island may mark the inner limit of such movements—although more significant than this is the near coincidence of this inner zone of warm air with the area of closest urban development (Fig. 4).

A tongue of warm air projecting north along the Lea valley is a recurrent feature of nights with pronounced heat-islands (Chandler, 1961a). The main part of the tongue lies in areas of high-density housing from Poplar, through Tottenham and Edmonton to Enfield and Waltham Abbey along the terraced western slopes of the Lea valley. Except for a ribbon of marsh, reservoirs and waterways along the valley bottom, the Lea valley is intensely settled south of Waltham Cross and Waltham Abbey. The effect of open exposure near the river has been shown by cross-valley traversing to be partly compensated on radiation nights by the moderating effect of surface water, and, except locally, urban influences more than compensate for any effects of cold-air drainage; indeed the buildings physically inhibit night-time katabatic inversions near the bottom of this wide valley. Air, cooler by about 0·6°C (1°F) on summer nights along the undeveloped axis of the valley (and by analogy, along sections of the Colne, Wandle and similar valleys elsewhere in London), owes its low temperature to the open nature, rather than the physical form, of its setting. Because of the absence of concurrent records and the scale and nature of the maps, these and similar local differences have not been shown in the accompanying illustrations. The most intense valley inversions in the Lea valley have been shown by traversing to occur in its rural northern parts and on the margins of terrace settlements where chilled air ponds against buildings. This is particularly noticeable on the eastern fringes of Waltham Abbey, where cooler air moves down the flanks of the Epping Ridge which also serves as a source area for cold air on the fringes of Chingford, Buckhurst Hill and Loughton.

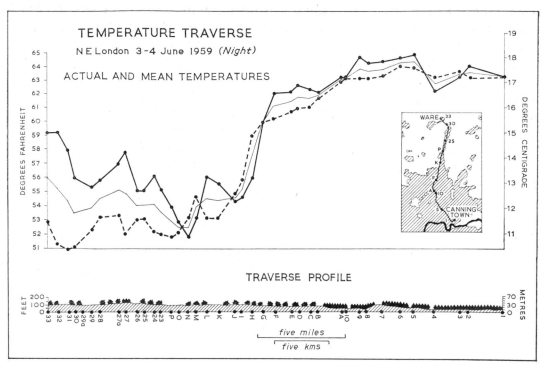

Fig 56 Lea valley temperature traverse, 3–4 June 1959 (night)
(Source of data: Lea Valley Climatological Survey records)

The steep (often cliff-like) margin of the heat-island on calm clear nights, more especially in summer and early autumn, is well illustrated in profile by Fig. 56. Daytime conditions on 3 June 1959 (Figs. 49 and 50) have already been described. By evening on the same day, the general weather situation had hardly changed except for an eastward shift of a cold front to lie, by midnight, near the western coasts of Great Britain. During the next six hours its movement was slight and had no immediate effect upon the London area. Here, calm conditions and a one-eighth cover of high cirrus allowed the processes of heat transference to differentiate urban and rural areas freely. By 2330 GMT, when Canning Town (station 1 and the midpoint of the night's traverse) was reached, the extreme temperature contrast between London and its rural envelope was 6·2°C (11·1°F). A most interesting feature is the sharp definition of the main heat-island margin near station H, the effective limit of suburban sprawl. The almost precipitous edge to the warm air, with a change of temperature of 4·4°C (8·0°F) in little more than 2 mi (3·2 km), once again seems to have been responsible for local winds centripetal across the urban margins. Evidence of such a near-surface inflow of cool air across the urban-rural fringe lies in the displacement of warm pockets of air to the southern parts of individually small settlements such as Hoddesdon, Broxbourne and Wormley between stations 33 and H. Strong thermal gradients were probably repeatedly built up on the southern side of these settlements, each time reaching sufficient intensity to initiate local reverse, that is, dominantly southerly currents, which reduced the sharp temperature differences that were their cause. This ebb-and-flow movement of air on the margins of settlements seems characteristic of intense heat-islands (Chandler, 1961b, pp. 32–8). On this particular night the more northerly positions of warm and cool pockets of air along the line of traverse by about 0100 GMT was assisted by a light southwesterly airflow of about 0·9 m/sec (2·0 mi/hr) which developed during the return traverse. This probably explains the displacement of the northern edge of the main heat-island near station H where temperatures rose in the interval (about 2 hr) between the two readings. This increase was also recorded by a thermograph near station M.

Investigations using automatic temperature and humidity recorders mounted on a Land Rover parked near station F, one and a half miles in from the steepest gradient of the heat-island margin (usually located between stations H and G in Fig. 56), and with the rough speed and direction of the near-surface airflow indicated by the timed drift of soap bubbles, have shown the existence of cool, centripetal, pulsating winds across the heat-island margins along roads running towards central London. These occurred best on summer and autumn nights when there was little or no regional wind, stable conditions and a strong heat-island. Speeds varied up to 2·3 m/sec (5·0 mi/hr): this agrees well with the theoretical ideas of Gold (1956, p. 231) and investigations in Louisville, U.S.A. (Pooler, 1963, p. 453). Any closed, cellular circulation between built-up and undeveloped areas at these times is frequently damped down or eliminated by a shallow nocturnal inversion. Daytime conditions, though they show smaller temperature differences between London and its rural surrounds, are better suited to such air movements. Many of the daytime traverses down the Lea valley, particularly during the more stable conditions of winter, suggested the existence of periodic, inblowing winds towards the warmer districts of central London but direct evidence of such light, near-surface winds is hard to establish. There is, however, one such piece of evidence in the Report by Captain Alfred Carpenter of the London Fog Inquiry 1901–2 (Carpenter, 1903). Using two-hourly observations of wind direction by a network of observers belonging to the London Fire Brigade, he showed that on at least two calm days in February and March 1902, there was a definite in-draught of air towards central London where temperatures were 2·8–3·3°C (5 or 6°F) warmer than outside. Carpenter, following a suggestion of Dr H. R. Mill, believed that the warm air over London was rising and cold air was moving in near the ground. Glider and aeroplane pilots have also testified to the existence of thermals rising from cities, including London.

The bearing of wind direction upon the form of London's heat-island has been suggested in previous examples but it is particularly well illustrated by conditions during the night of 10–11 June 1959. On this occasion, a ridge of high pressure covering most of Great Britain extended north from an anticyclone centred west of Brittany. A weak warm front over the Irish Sea had no immediate influence upon the weather of Southeast England, where skies were only partially covered by fragments of strato-cumulus and cirrus clouds. Winds of 0·9–2·7 m/sec (2·0–6·0 mi/hr) blew from the west. The result of these two sets of conditions, almost clear skies and light winds, was to create a well-developed heat-island of the order of 5·6°C (10°F), with the highest

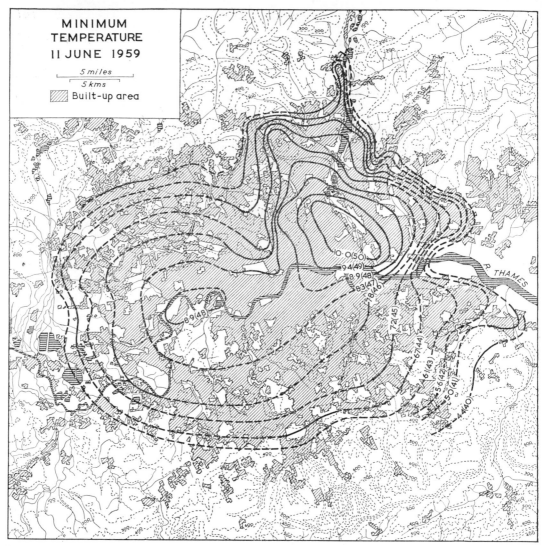

Fig 57 Distribution of minimum temperature in London, 11 June 1959.
Broken lines indicate some uncertainty of position. Isotherms are numbered
in °C with °F equivalents in brackets
(Source of data: Readings at official stations and supplementary stations of
the London Climatological Survey)

temperatures appreciably displaced towards the eastern districts of the city where
marginal temperature gradients were consequently steepest (Fig. 57). This type of
asymmetry we have already noticed to be characteristically associated with light winds.
A smaller centre of local warmth, though there may well be others unrecorded, lay in
the Richmond district of west London. The exceptional asymmetry of the heat-island
on this occasion may have been due in part to the orientation of the wind along the
line of the Thames valley but the high density urban development in the Shoreditch,
Bethnal Green, Stepney, Southwark, Bermondsey and Poplar districts of east-central

London was, and is always, important. The building and road fabric in these areas must act as a considerable reservoir of heat, stored during the day and released during the night to maintain higher temperatures than in the more openly developed parts of the conurbation, such as the southwest.

So far, a fairly broad, first order view has been taken of London's heat-island, but we have to constantly remind ourselves, as in all climatological investigations, of the important lower order and eventually micro-scale variations which they sometimes hide. Something of their nature can be seen in the results of traverses across London using autographic temperature (and humidity) recorders mounted on a Land Rover (see Introduction for details of this equipment). These have the advantage not only of detail—because of their closely spaced readings—but also of providing near-representative street air temperatures which the climatological stations, with standard exposures, cannot do. One night's records will be used to show the intricacy of very local conditions at a time when they are best developed, that is when the overall intensity of the heat-island is near its maximum.

An anticyclone covered most of western Europe during the night of 11–12 October 1961. In the London region, skies were clear and there was no measurable wind. The previous day had been sunny and maximum temperatures had ranged between 18·3 and 21·1°C (65 and 70°F). Such conditions were conducive to the development of a fairly intense heat-island. Fig. 58 shows temperatures along the traverse route during the

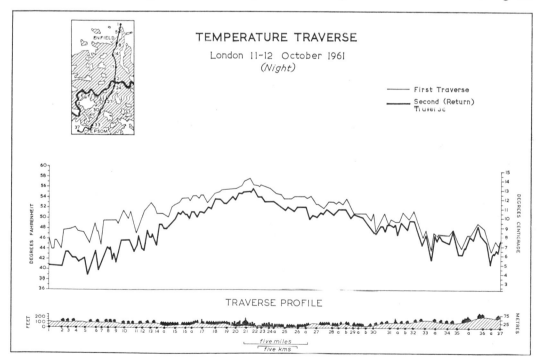

Fig 58 London temperature traverse, actual temperatures, 11–12 October
1961 (night)
(Source of data: London Climatological Survey records)

first (northeast-southwest) and second (southwest-northeast) or return traverse. The traverse began at station 1 at 2133 GMT; station 37, the turning point, was reached at 2330 GMT; and the double traverse was completed by returning to station 1 at 0125 GMT. The average of each pair of readings at points along the line of traverse is shown in Fig. 59. This represents, assuming a linearity of temperature change during the period of traverse, the temperature profile at about 2330 GMT on 11 October 1961. It will be seen that the overall heat-island intensity at this time was about 7·8°C (14·0°F), being the difference between temperatures in the Green Belt north of Cheshunt and

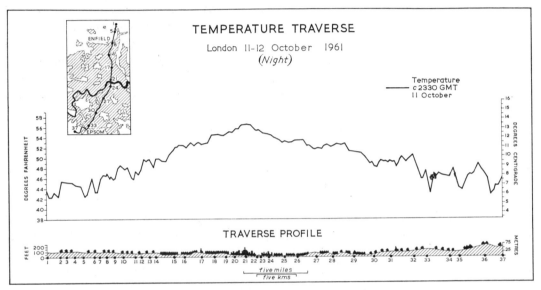

Fig 59 London temperature traverse, mean temperatures, 11–12 October 1961
(night)
(Source of data: London Climatological Survey records)

those in the City of London (station 21) at this time. This value probably increased during the early hours of the 12th but was reduced later in the night by the formation of fog around London which lowered the rate of temperature fall.

Of some interest is the cellular pattern of temperatures in suburban areas and the effect of varying urban densities and parks and commons in more central parts of London. Outer suburban areas are openly developed in comparison with the much greater building densities of inner suburban and central areas. Between stations 1 and 14 most of the settlement dates from the inter-war years: it is characterized by wide roads, two-storey semi-detached and detached houses with gardens, small groups of modern factories and also by frequent parks, playing fields and allotments. From station 14 to 19, in Tottenham, Stoke Newington, Hackney and Shoreditch, there is a much closer grouping of mainly two- and three-storey terrace houses and factories with few large gardens and open spaces. In the City of London, between stations 20 and 22, streets are narrow and the buildings are massive. South of the Thames there is a similar sequence except for rather more frequent parks (such as Kennington Park, station 25) and commons (Clapham Common, station 27) within the closely built-up inner London area. The junction between late nineteenth- and early twentieth-century urban development, and the more open inter-war and post-war expansion in southwest London lies in Merton, between stations 29 and 30 along the line of traverse. Again, in Morden, Cheam and Ewell, housing densities are low and settlement nodes are interspersed with parks (Morden Park, station 31; Nonsuch Park, station 33) and open spaces. These are, however, less evenly distributed than between stations 1 and 14.

Fig. 59, of average temperatures, reflects this urban pattern although locally, as between stations 36 and 37, relief controls are dominant. The overall increase of temperature towards the City of London is the most important general feature of the thermal pattern. On this and other calm nights, local urban morphologies are almost certainly dominant over large-scale considerations in determining the temperature anomaly. This may well be true of all occasions, the local heat-island intensity being more dependent on the geography of the immediate environment, in particular the continuity and height of the buildings and the size of the open areas between them, than on the size of the whole urban complex. This does not mean that the latter is unimportant. Air is warmed as it moves across the city, its speed is changed, and the length of the urban traverse is obviously significant in both cases.

The differentiating influences of settlement densities and pockets of open land intensified as the night of 11–12 October progressed, that is as contrasts between urban and rural heat-exchange processes were realized. Thus between stations 1 and 14, the pattern of temperatures during the return traverse, at about 0115 GMT on 12 October, more closely mirrors the urban morphology of that part of the route than during the first traverse $3\frac{1}{2}$ hr earlier. The recreation ground at Enfield (station 9), which covers about 150 acres (61 hectares) and alongside which the traverse route runs, was even at its margin about 0·8°C (1 5°F) cooler than the built-up area to the north and south; 35 acres of allotment around station 14 were cooler by 0·8°C (1·5°F) at their centre, both figures relating to the second or reverse traverse. Similarly, Nonsuch Park and the adjoining open land (totalling about 490 acres) (198 hectares) caused a drop in temperatures at its northwestern margins of about 1·4°C (2·5°F). Within central London, the influence of open land was less: Clapham Common, for instance, covering about 180 acres (73 hectares), caused a fall in temperature at its margins of less than 0·6°C (1°F). This is probably because of light winds here, even though it was calm in the outer suburbs; a common occurrence as we have already seen.

The greatest temperature gradients, viewing the heat-island as a whole, occurred where the urban morphology changed most, as between stations 14 and 15, 20 and 21, 22 and 23, and 29 and 30. There is also some indication of local thermal winds repositioning warm and cool pockets of air in the interval between the first and second legs of the traverse. In general there was a northward movement in north London during this time, but this type of development has already been discussed.

The Thames seems, in this stretch at least, to have little effect upon temperatures; but where its banks are more open and the buildings alongside less massive, it may raise air temperatures above nearby floodplain sites owing to the inherent thermal properties of water and, locally, warm water from Thames-side power stations (Lamb, 1963, p. 196). It is possible that temperatures at the Greenwich Maritime Museum climatological station are raised a little in winter and lowered in summer because of its proximity to the Thames.

The reversed honeycomb form of the urban development, with a network of streets hemmed in between tall buildings from which local relief is provided by open spaces, results, as we have seen, in a parallel, cellular thermal pattern. During the day, street-level temperatures are no doubt enhanced by the burning of fuel in vehicle engines. Gold (1954, pp. 273–4) thought this source responsible for a 1·1°C (2°F) difference in temperature on calm winter afternoons between Regent Street and Hanover Square some 400 ft (122 m) away, but one cannot neglect here the part played by site differences similar to those already noted between narrow streets and more open spaces, independent of their vehicle traffic. Whiten (1956, pp. 227–9) followed this up by suggesting a convection system comprised of ascending currents over the more congested streets and street intersections of central London, and complementary descending air over nearby squares and parks, an idea also considered possible by Gold (1956, p. 231). In order to shed a little more light on this interesting idea and to study the effect of parks and open spaces generally upon nearby temperatures and humidities, many traverses were made across Hyde Park between Paddington north of the Park and South Kensington to the south (Fig. 8). The results shown in Fig. 60 are typical of many bright, sunny days. On this particular occasion, skies were clear and easterly winds, as recorded at London Airport, increased from 2·6 m/sec (5·8 mi/hr) at 0600 GMT to 4·1 m/sec (9·2 mi/hr) at 1200 GMT and 6·7 m/sec (15·0 mi/hr) at 1800 GMT, after which they fell to 4·6 m/sec (10·4 mi/hr) by midnight. Wind speeds in the vicinity of the Park would be somewhat less. The maximum temperature contrast between the Park and its built-up surrounds was 1·3°C (2·3°F), being least around midday when the pattern of temperatures varied appreciably from hour to hour. The greatest difference recorded on any of the cross-Park traverses was 1·7°C (3·0°F) in September. It is also interesting to note that on 1 March 1963 (and other days), the contrast in temperatures between the Park and its built-up margins was slightly greater than the general difference between temperatures at Kensington Palace and Wisley. This is because of the particular site of the Kensington Palace station commented upon earlier in this chapter. On days of high wind speed and/or cloud amounts, the contrasts will be much less than shown.

Whether the lower temperatures in Hyde Park are caused by air sinking from above, as suggested by Whiten (1956) and Gold (1956), and implied by Wainwright and Wilson (1962, p. 338), or by the distance from the radiating and conducting surfaces of buildings, plus cooling by evaporation, is difficult to decide without further evidence. Readings of vapour pressure in the centre of the Park are little different from those outside on most days but this does not preclude the possibility of sinking air over the Park, for turbulent mixing would be expected to give greater uniformity to the humidity profile over cities than over open country and any reduction caused by the subsidence of dry air would be compensated by an increase resulting from evaporation and transpiration from soils and vegetation.

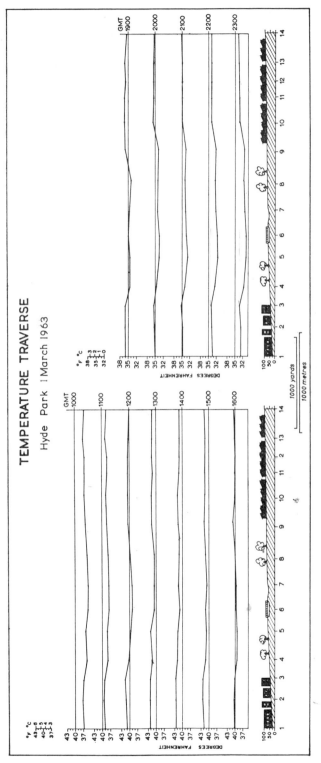

Fig 60 Hyde Park traverses, actual temperatures, 1 March 1963
(Source of data: London Climatological Survey records)

Causes, controls and depth of the heat-island

What are the contrasts in urban and rural heat exchange processes responsible for London's heat-island? The answer is not simple and, indeed, it is not at present known for certain; certainly one cannot be precise about the relative importance of the several known influences. Also, it is clear that cities differ between themselves and even between one part and another; an important contributory factor in one city or city-region may be relatively unimportant in another, and we have already seen how this affects the varying annual pattern of heat-island intensities in central and suburban London. But certain processes obviously play a critical part in the instigation and control of London's heat-island. As we have seen, by dawn, air temperatures within London are normally several degrees higher than those outside, but during the morning and early afternoon the city will not warm as quickly as the fields of the Green Belt around the city. This is in part owing to differences in heat capacity and conductivity between the fabric of the city and vegetation-covered soils (seen to be of importance in differentiating temperatures in the North Wall Screen and Stevenson Screen at Kew Observatory); partly to a haze-hood or fog above London intercepting solar radiation; and to the mixing of warmer air near the ground with cooler air above by increased mechanical turbulence over the serrated surface of the city. Thus, in spite of more evaporation cooling in the country areas, these soon warm to temperatures almost equalling and sometimes above those of the conurbation, and in the generally unstable conditions and gentle breezes of daytime, the heat stored by the buildings and road surfaces of London plus that released by combustion is relatively easily and efficiently dispersed. Daytime thermals rising high above the city are well known to pilots. By night, a number of factors will cause rural temperatures to fall more rapidly than those of the city. One of these is the heat-contribution of domestic grates, industrial boilers and vehicles. These release an enormous amount of energy into London's air and are especially significant in suburban areas where the general level of the chimneys is low, although much of the heat will be released during the day and early night. Heat produced by the burning of fuels must contribute, mainly in winter and in suburban London, but the summer peak of heat-island intensities suggest that it is not first in importance, a conclusion also reached by Sundborg (1951, pp. 90–104). Far more telling is the release of stored heat by the fabric of the city, and back radiation from the walls of tall buildings, fogs and a pollution haze in winter. There are also a number of other, contributory processes including differences in the albedo and heat conductivity of various surfaces and even Luke Howard's suggestion (Howard, 1820, p. 103) 'that the superior temperature of the bodies of men and animals is capable of elevating, in small proportion, the mean heat of a city or populous tract of country in a temperate latitude'.

But the efficiency of all these sources of heat in warming London's air is controlled by a number of meteorological elements, notably wind speed and cloud amount. The very existence of a mass of warm air in close contact with the ground (by night) also depends upon a stable lower atmosphere. Without an inversion of temperature the air will become buoyant and rise, as it does in a series of thermals by day and probably does, spasmodically, in central areas even by night, linked no doubt with marginal centripetal pulses of cooler air such as we have already seen to occur. In not too disturbed weather with clear skies a nocturnal inversion develops in the lower 400–500 ft (122–152 m): this happens on about two nights in five. These figures would suggest that the depth of air forming the heat-island is of the order of 500 ft (152 m) on nights when it is strongly developed. Near the ground during clear summer weather the temperature may well fall 16·7°C (30°F) (Table 50) from early afternoon to dawn, but at heights from about 300–1,000 ft (91–305 m) the range will be about half this (Best et al., 1952, p. 28). Hence, remembering that by day the temperature at these heights will be lower by 1·7–2·8°C (3–5°F) than at the ground, the city air could be as much as 6·7°C (12°F) warmer than outside without rising through the inversion. On rare occasions during dry weather in summer the temperature range can reach 19·4°C (35°F) over flat areas in southeast England and the nocturnal inversion of temperature will be sufficiently intense to allow a heat-island of about 10·0°C (18°F). This is likely to have been the order of temperature difference between patches of air in London and over the surrounding country in August 1911 when the minimum temperature at Old Street (Finsbury) and Wisley (Surrey) differed on two nights by 7·8°C (14°F) and on one night by 8·3°C (15°F), and in June 1959 when minima at Kensington and Bayfordbury (Hertfordshire) differed by 8·9°C (16°F).

The depth of the heat-island, as well as its intensity, are obviously governed by the level of the inversion and we surmise from this and other simple calculations that the depth is of the order of 500 ft (152 m) by night when the feature is well formed. No direct measure is at present available to confirm (or disprove) this estimate except those at the marginal site of the Crystal Palace television mast in southeast London. Records from resistance thermometers maintained by the Central Electricity Research Laboratories at seven levels of this mast rising 650 ft (198 m) above Crystal Palace Park, 357 ft (109 m) OD., show that potential temperature increases (at times of inversion) much less frequently at heights of more than 300 ft (91 m) above ground level than below.

There are several eye-witness observations of the top of the haze-hood (related to the inversion crest) above London which suggest that the heat-island is domed above the city, though frequently sharp-edged near its boundary. Some further light will eventually be shed on this by records from resistance thermometers at several levels of the Post Office Tower in central London, but the suggested order of depth of the heat-island agrees with findings in other cities such as San Francisco (Duckworth and Sandberg, 1954, pp. 205–6), where, although an area of hilly terrain, at some level between 100 and 300 ft (30 and 91 m) temperature soundings with wiresonde equipment over built-up and undeveloped areas usually coincided, indicating a possible upper limit to heating by the city. Above this point of coincidence, temperatures during half the vertical soundings were significantly cooler over the built-up area than above the open area. Some sort of convection cell circulation might explain this, so also might radiation heat losses from the top of the haze hood.

A number of authors (Callendar, 1961; Mitchell, 1953 and 1961; Lamb, 1963) have suggested that as cities grow, the mean intensity of their heat-islands is increased, but in all such studies there are several, sometimes unrealized, difficulties in comparing records over periods of years. Chief amongst these is the importance of regional climatic fluctuations such as the higher temperatures during the first four decades of this century. Several of the processes of heat-island genesis depend upon the levels of regional temperatures, cloud amounts and wind speeds, and any change in these will affect the efficiency of the processes, quite independent of city growth. On the other hand, urban growth usually involves changed local functions and form, with replacement and infilling and, as we have seen, such changes in the urban morphology are of importance in differentiating the degree of local warming. Again, there may be differences following changes in domestic and industrial heating levels, but without any direct relation to the growth of the city. The mean intensities of heat-islands are by no means a linear function

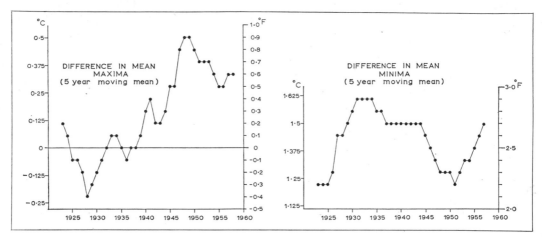

Fig 61 Smoothed differences in mean annual maximum and minimum temperatures, Kensington–Wisley, 1921–60. (5-year moving mean)
(Source of data: London, Meteorological Office *Monthly weather reports* 1921–60)

of the areas of cities or individually of their growth. The effect of quite small towns, even compact villages, is often surprisingly large. There will, of course, be a very substantial change if rural climatological station is engulfed by urban sprawl, but any subsequent expansion beyond the station will have much less effect upon its records—provided there are no changes in the character of the station environs. This is not to deny any effect of urban growth, for the importance of the length of traverse by winds over the city has already been mentioned.

London, like many other cities, seems to show a progressive intensification of its heat-island since the late nineteenth century when measured by long period means. The difference in mean annual temperatures at Camden Square and Wisley rose from 0·7°C (1·3°F) for 1901–1930 to 0·9°C (1·6°F) for 1931–60; the anomaly in minimum temperatures increased from 0·8°C (1·4°F) in the first thirty years of this century to 1·5°C (2·7°F) in the second, whilst the differences in mean maximum temperatures actually fell from 0·6°C (1·1°F) in the first period to 0·4°C (0·7°F) in the second. These changes, though based upon records which are not perfectly homogeneous, lend some support to the suggestion that increases in the mean intensity of London's heat-island during the present century might be related to increasing regional temperatures rather than the expansion of the built-up area. But over short periods there are considerable changes in average heat-island intensities. Differences in mean annual maximum and minimum temperatures at Kensington and Wisley between 1921 and 1960, using a five-year moving mean in each case, are shown in Fig. 61. Differences in mean annual maxima at the two stations were small in all years, varying between $-0.3°C$ ($-0.6°F$) in 1944 and $0.6°C$ ($1.0°F$) in 1959. The difference in mean annual minimum temperatures at Kensington and Wisley between 1921 and 1960 varied from $1.1°C$ ($1.9°F$) in 1924 to $1.8°C$ ($3.2°F$) in 1929 and 1933. The changes, far from bearing any signs of influence by London's continuous outward growth, reflect yearly alterations in those aspects of the general climate which control heat exchange processes. This is most clearly seen in the case of minimum temperatures. The cool, unsettled and generally cloudy years from 1922 to 1924 were no doubt mainly responsible for the low values of the night-time urban anomaly in those years, whilst the wet, somewhat stormy years in 1946, 1948, 1950 and 1951 probably account for the weak heat-islands at these times. The years 1933 and 1934 were warmer and calmer than the preceding years and drier than those which immediately followed. These features influence the degree to which the factors producing the heat-island are effective, and are no doubt the main determinants of annual changes in its intensity.

THE STATISTICAL RELATIONSHIP BETWEEN LONDON'S HEAT-ISLAND INTENSITY AND CERTAIN CLIMATOLOGICAL ELEMENTS

We have already seen how the temperature difference (D) between central London and its rural envelope varies with certain meteorological elements, especially wind speed, cloud amount and temperature lapse rate. Sundborg (1951, p. 86) derived an expression for the temperature anomaly in Uppsala, Sweden, using four parameters, wind speed, cloudiness, temperature and absolute humidity. But like Sundborg in Uppsala and Duckworth and Sandberg in San Francisco (1954, p. 205), little evidence could be found of a relationship between the intensity of London's heat-island and the prevailing humidity, and for the reason it was excluded in a similar statistical analysis. Conversely, it was decided to include temperature range as an expression of general stability characteristics. It would, of course, have been more satisfactory to have used some stability index based upon lapse rates, but these were not available in a suitable form, so the simpler measure was employed, although its close relationship with the two other parameters, temperature and cloudiness, made it less independent a variable.

For the two years 1959 and 1960, differences in daily maximum (D max) and minimum (D min) temperatures at Kensington and Wisley were related empirically with wind speeds (U_k) in knots, cloud amounts (N) in oktas, temperatures (T_F) in degrees

M

Fahrenheit and the temperature range (R_F) (0000–1200 or 1200–0000 GMT), also in degrees Fahrenheit, all as recorded at 1200 and 0000 GMT respectively at London Airport. The times and station were selected to express, as near as possible, general daytime and night-time conditions over London. The 1,462 sets of records, representing a helpful range of daily conditions, were transferred to punched cards and regression equations were derived on a computer. For summer (April–September) and winter (October–March) nights and days, separate partial regression equations were calculated of the form:

$$D = a_0 + a_1 N + a_2 U_k + a_3 T_F + a_4 R_F$$

where:

D is the temperature difference, Kensington–Wisley, in °F
a is the regression constant
a_1, a_2, a_3, a_4 are the regression coefficients
N is the cloudiness, in oktas, at London Airport
U_k is the wind speed, in knots, at London Airport
T_F is the temperature, in °F, at London Airport
R_F is the temperature range, in °F at London Airport

The formulae are as follows:

MINIMA (NIGHT-TIME HEAT-ISLANDS)

Summer $D_{min/s} = 2.78 - 0.22N - 0.16U_k + 0.01T_F + 0.15R_F$ (1)
Winter $D_{min/w} = 1.77 - 0.23N - 0.09U_k + 0.04T_F + 0.08R_F$ (2)

MAXIMA (DAYTIME HEAT-ISLANDS)

Summer $D_{max/s} = -3.42 + 0.06N - 0.00U_k + 0.06T_F + 0.00R_F$ (3)
Winter $D_{max/w} = 1.35 - 0.06N + 0.01U_k - 0.00T_F + 0.00R_F$ (4)

The equivalent equations in c.g.s. units are as follows:

MINIMA (NIGHT-TIME HEAT-ISLANDS)

Summer $D_{min/s} = 1.72 - 0.12N - 0.17U_m + 0.01T_C + 0.15R_C$ (5)
Winter $D_{min/w} = 1.69 - 0.13N - 0.10U_m + 0.04T_C + 0.08R_C$ (6)

MAXIMA (DAYTIME HEAT-ISLANDS)

Summer $D_{max/s} = 0.83 + 0.03N - 0.00U_m + 0.06T_C + 0.00R_C$ (7)
Winter $D_{max/w} = 0.75 - 0.03N + 0.01U_m - 0.00T_C + 0.00R_C$ (8)

where:

D is the temperature difference, Kensington–Wisley, in °C
N is the cloudiness, in oktas, at London Airport
U_m is the wind speed in metres per second at London Airport
T_C is the temperature in °C at London Airport
R_C is the temperature range in °C at London Airport

The multiple correlation coefficients (R) and the standard errors of the regression coefficient a_1, a_2, a_3 and a_4 in equations (1) to (4) are:

	R	Standard Errors			
		a_1	a_2	a_3	a_4
$D_{min/s}$	0·608	0·039	0·025	0·017	0·026
$D_{min/w}$	0·563	0·036	0·021	0·015	0·023
$D_{max/s}$	0·286	0·042	0·016	0·012	0·021
$D_{max/w}$	0·114	0·030	0·014	0·011	0·019

The multiple correlation coefficients (R) are an expression of the closeness with which the regression equations fit the data, being the correlation coefficient between the observed values of the dependent variable (D) and those predicted from the equation. Tables of significant values of R show that equations (1) and (2), and their equivalents, (5) and (6), are undoubtedly significant at much better than the 1 per cent level of R; equations (3) and (4), and their eqivalents, (7) and (8), are significant at the 5 per cent level.

We must remember that the formulae are purely empirical and do not themselves answer questions of causal relations. Also, the coefficients may not be considered as fixed numerical values, nor are they really independent; but the order of magnitude of coefficients is probably correct. One further point is that the equations were derived on the assumption that the relationships were linear, which is probably not strictly true for high and low wind speeds. Probably for this reason they do not accurately represent, and cannot be used to accurately forecast, extreme conditions.

The importance of wind speed and cloud amount in controlling the intensity of night-time heat-islands is brought out by the equations. The size of the nocturnal fall in temperature is also very important but the actual temperature is less so. Daytime conditions are far less accurately represented by the equations owing to the more variable and complex atmospheric conditions at this time. The reversed effect of cloud amount on summer days may be accidental; if it is causal, the explanation may be linked with contrasts in the rates of warming of urban and rural areas, a process already noted as responsible for temperatures outside being occasionally higher than inside London. On overcast days, a cold-island reversal of normal conditions is less likely to occur. Also noteworthy in this context are the importance of air temperature during summer days (and its lack of significance in winter) and the lack of influence of temperature range on daytime heat-islands in both summer and winter. But the low multiple correlation coefficients and regression coefficients during winter days makes equations (4) and (6) of little real value.

THERMAL CONSEQUENCES OF LONDON'S HEAT-ISLAND

The obvious consequence of higher temperatures in London is that there are more days with exceptionally high temperatures and fewer with low temperatures. This will be especially true of the centre and inner northeastern suburbs, that is, an area mainly north of the Thames from Kensington to Hackney. During the ten years 1951–60, for instance, there were on average 16·0 days per year with a maximum temperature of 25°C (77°F) or more at Wisley, 16·0 at Bromley (probably fairly typical of suburban London), 20·5 at Kensington, but only 12·3 at Hampstead (representing the higher parts of the suburbs). Similarly there were, on average, 35·1 days with maximum temperatures of 5°C (41°F) or less at Wisley, 28·5 at Bromley, 28·3 at Kensington and 41·2 at Hampstead. Turning to night-time conditions in these same 10 years, the average annual number of days with minimum temperatures of 15°C (59°F) or above was 12·1 at Wisley, 15·6 at Bromley, 24·0 at Kensington and 11·4 at Hampstead. Also, there were on average 59·7 days with minimum temperatures at or below 0°C (32°F) at Wisley, 46·1 at Bromley, 34·4 at Kensington and 50·6 at Hampstead. The influence of London's heat-island, more particularly on night-time temperatures, is very apparent. The number of days with high daytime temperatures of 25°C (77°F) or more is about the same in the low-lying suburbs as outside London, but in the centre there is a 25 per cent increase. Low daytime temperatures of 5°C (41°F) or less have roughly the same frequency in central and suburban London, and the numbers are equal to four-fifths of those outside the conurbation. These features are in close agreement with the rather weak daytime heat-islands above London. At Hampstead, during the day, the heat-island is weak or absent and is unable to compensate for the effect of altitude, so that very warm days are less frequent and cool days more frequent than at Wisley. Night-time heat-islands, generally stronger than during the day, exert a powerful influence upon temperature frequencies. Warm nights, with temperatures reaching 15°C (59°F) or more, are twice as common in central London as outside, the suburbs occupying an intermediate position; the number of night frosts is again reduced by almost half in the centre of the city. Hampstead, on the crest of a steep hill, has almost the same number of warm nights as Wisley and about 15 per cent less night frosts—a much smaller reduction than in the centre but only slightly greater than at Bromley which is nearer the urban-rural fringe.

The average date of the last screen frost at Kew is 23 days earlier than at Wisley and the date of the first frost, 49 days later (Applegate, 1960, p. 2). The substantial differences partly derive from the site of the North Wall Screen, for at Enfield, in the northeast suburbs, the date of the last screen frost is ten days earlier than at Wisley, and of the first, 36 days later. It is obvious that the heat-island, already noted as stronger in autumn than in spring, delays the first air frost more than it hastens the last. Between 1951 and 1960 the frost-free period was longer than outside by more than 2 months in central London, and 1½ months in suburban London.

Ground frosts, defined as a grass minimum temperature of −0·9°C (30·4°F) or less, have a similar frequency distribution pattern to air temperatures. There is, for instance, a marked reduction in occurrence as one nears the centre of London. For the period 1951–60 the yearly averages of ground frost frequency were 101 days at Wisley, 89 at Kew, 73 at Kensington and 89 at Hampstead.

Air and ground frost frequencies are also modified by local topographies and soils, being far more numerous in hollows and over light, sandy soils, although because of the hindrance to air movement by built-over slopes and because so much of the ground in London is covered or disturbed, these features are less important here than in open country. Nevertheless, we should expect some notable differences between valley and hill-top sites, more especially in the more deeply dissected parts of the northern and southern suburbs (Fig. 1). During dry weather there will also be differences between sites on the sandy soils of river terraces, such as those of the Thames, Lea and Wandle, or the gravel-capped hills of north and southeast London, and the London Clay soils of most other districts. But when the water table is high, differences will be small. Indeed, clay soils tend to retain their water, and, for this reason, low temperatures do not penetrate so deeply.

Earth temperatures at 1 ft and 4 ft are available for a number of stations within Greater London (London, Meteorological Office, 1960) and comparisons show the importance or even dominance of local soil conditions, although it is still true that over the year as a whole, 1 ft soil temperatures are generally higher in the centre than in the suburbs or outside London and such differences are greatest in summer. In winter the picture becomes rather more complicated owing to higher water tables, snow and frozen ground; and a number of the stations, such as Southgate on clay and Greenwich Observatory on gravels, have winter 1 ft soil temperatures which are higher than in the centre.

Although empirical in approach and not capable of precise interpretation (Jackson, 1963, pp, 290–1), it is usual to regard the 'active growing season' for vegetation in a temperate climate as the period of the year during which the mean temperature exceeds 5·6°C (42°F). (Some workers have used 6°C (43°F) as their base temperature.) Accepting this as at least a rough indication of a relevant parameter, we find that for the period 1931–60 there is an average annual 'active growing season' of 259 days at Wisley, 105 ft (32 m); 264 at Bromley, 213 ft (64·9 m); 269 at Croydon, 220 ft (66·8 m); 279 at Regent's Park, 129 ft (39·3 m); 281 at Camden Square, 110 ft (33.8 m); and 275 at Kensington, 81 ft (24·7 m), but only 260 at Wealdstone, 175 ft (51·2 m) and 261 at Hampstead, 450 ft (137·2 m). There is obviously a rapid reduction of the 'active growing season' with height, as in England as a whole (Manley, 1945), but this is complicated by differences in the urban setting of the stations. Even so, we may fairly compare the Regent's Park record with Hampstead, 2·5 mi (4 km) to the northwest (Fig. 5). From these it emerges that the period diminishes with altitude by 10 days for every 180 ft (55 m). This is an even more rapid fall-off than in England generally (Manley, 1945, p. 411) owing, no doubt, to the exaggerated lapse rate in urban areas above 200–300 ft (61–91 m), especially in autumn when night-time heat-islands are often very strong and about 400 ft (122 m) deep. In this context it is interesting to note that whilst the mean temperature at Regent's Park reaches 5·6°C (42°F) three days earlier, on average, than at Hampstead, it remains above this base temperature for 15 days longer.

Although the 'active growing season' is a useful rough tool in applied climatology, far better is an expression of accumulated temperature which is defined as the integrated excess or deficiency of temperature relative to a fixed base temperature, calculated over an extended period of time. Thus accumulated temperature above a base temperature of 5·6°C (42°F) has been widely used in agriculture, but in calculating the heating requirements of buildings, engineers are interested in accumulated temperature *below* certain base temperatures. In England a base temperature of 15·6°C (60·0°F) has been been adopted for a number of studies of heating problems (Knight and Cornell, 1959), as it has been shown that for buildings maintained at an indoor temperature of 18·3°C (65°F) there is quite a close relationship between fuel consumption and the accumulated temperature below 15·6°C (60°F) over corresponding periods of time. The unit of accumulated temperature is the day-degree, but averages of accumulated temperature

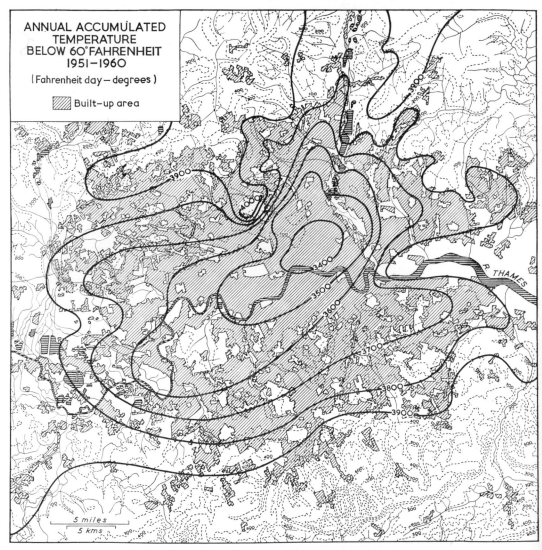

ANNUAL ACCUMULATED
TEMPERATURE
BELOW 60°FAHRENHEIT
1951–1960
(Fahrenheit day–degrees)

▨ Built-up area

Fig 62 Distribution of annual accumulated temperature below 60°F in London, 1951–60
(Source of data: Readings at official stations and supplementary stations of the London Climatological Survey—see Fig. 5)

TABLE 62

Accumulated temperature below 60°F, London, 1951–60

	Height		Jan	Feb	Mar	Apr	May	June
	ft	m		Fahrenheit day-degrees				
Westminster	27	8·2	614	560	470	324	152	60
Camden Square	110	33·5	620	566	500	318	152	60
Kensington Palace	81	24·7	626	563	479	327	161	54
Regent's Park	129	39·3	620	578	482	336	164	66
Kew Observatory	18	5·5	620	578	491	351	173	66
Hampton	39	11·9	638	590	485	297	173	66
Greenwich*	24	7·3	623	569	491	339	179	72
London Airport	82	25·0	641	590	494	351	188	75
Bromley	213	64·9	644	593	503	363	197	81
Dartford	17	5·2	638	596	497	363	209	90
Croydon	220	67·1	656	599	512	375	203	81
Southgate	221	67·4	674	605	515	354	203	84
Wisley	105	32·0	659	584	503	366	203	99
Addington	474	144·5	680	626	533	393	212	96
Hampstead	450	137·2	677	623	563	384	212	99

	July	Aug	Sept	Oct	Nov	Dec	Yr
		Fahrenheit day-degrees					
Westminster	28	28	66	211	414	508	3435
Camden Square	31	28	66	205	414	508	3468
Kensington Palace	31	34	69	229	420	520	3513
Regent's Park	31	34	81	213	417	517	3539
Kew Observatory	31	34	84	235	423	514	3600
Hampton	34	40	84	229	441	529	3606
Greenwich*	31	40	90	245	429	523	3631
London Airport	34	40	87	247	441	550	3738
Bromley	37	43	96	253	447	541	3798
Dartford	37	43	99	253	441	541	3807
Croydon	34	43	96	259	432	544	3834
Southgate	34	43	96	256	450	553	3867
Wisley	46	52	126	274	471	559	3942
Addington	43	46	108	247	474	565	4023
Hampstead	52	52	108	265	468	568	4071

* 1951–2, Greenwich Observatory, 149 ft (45·4 m)

Source of data: London, Meteorological Office *Monthly weather reports* 1951–60

may be derived in a number of ways (Shellard, 1959a, pp. 1–3). For present purposes, the method described in Meteorological Office Form 330 (designed for use with a 5·6°C (42°F) base) has been employed to derive accumulated temperature below 15·6°C (60°F) by using suitably adjusted individual monthly values of mean daily maximum and minimum temperatures. Maps were first prepared for 1959–62 using records from stations in the London Climatological Survey as well as permanent synoptic and climatological stations. This short-period analysis was then used as a guide for a longer-period study from 1951–60 based upon 15 stations. Fig. 62 shows the pattern of distribution of accumulated temperature below 60°F, and Table 62 gives the mean monthly values.

Two main factors differentiate accumulated temperature in the London area: altitude and urban exposure. Totals of more than 4,000 day-degrees occur in the elevated rural areas of south Hertfordshire, north of London, and on the North Downs to the south of the city. Similar values also occur on Hampstead Heath and, no doubt, comparable areas such as Harrow Hill. The lowest values occur in the inner suburbs of Islington, Finsbury and Shoreditch in northeast London. The urban influence accounts for a reduction of about 400 day-degrees or about 10 per cent of values at comparable heights outside London. The consequences of elevation are more complex since they cannot be separated from associated changes in the urban morphology. Even so, the fall-off in day-degrees totals from Upper Holloway, Tufnell Park and Kentish Town to Hampstead Heath is quite outstanding, and about twice normal (Dufton, 1934, p. 83; Shellard, 1959a, p. 10). Between Regent's Park and Hampstead (both stations with a fairly open exposure), there is a decrease of 532 day-degrees in 321 ft (98 m), an average of about 1·7 day-degrees per foot. This is considerably more than the 1·0 day-degrees per foot in Southern England (Dufton, 1934, p. 83; Shellard, 1959a, p. 10) and underlines the position of Hampstead Heath and comparable areas above the majority of London's heat-islands.

The map of accumulated temperature (Fig. 62) may be taken as a summary of London's heat-island as it affects regional temperatures. London clearly stands distinct from its regional setting as a climatic as well as a topographic feature, and although London's climatic distinction is composed of a number of interrelated and closely knit changes wrought by the city upon its atmospheric environment, there is little doubt that temperature modifications constitute a leading element in the pattern of spatial change. The general, though varied, increase in air temperature within and immediately above the conurbation is one of the main facets of London's climatic scene and in its turn is responsible for a sequence of other modifications. One of these modifications affects the levels of absolute and relative humidity.

7 Evaporation and humidity

*We know that aqueous vapours exhale from both the sea and land,
are suspended for a time over the earth, are in time condensed, and
fall in the form of dew, rain, or snow; it may not therefore be difficult
to account for the very small quantity of rain that falls in the metropolis in two ways; the aqueous exhalations cannot be abundant from
a surface so altered from its pristine state, so covered with buildings,
human beings, and constantly burning fires, the quantity of vapour
supplied, therefore, may be taken as little or none; again, if watery
vapours should find their way towards, and hang over, the town,
heated air rising from half a million fires, instead of promoting the
the condensation of vapour, must assist very materially in rarifying
the surrounding atmosphere, and dispersing the supernatant clouds.*

John Hogg, 1837

AN ESSENTIAL COG in the atmospheric machine is the cycle of moisture between the earth and atmosphere. In this and the succeeding three chapters, some aspects of this cycle will be discussed in relation to conditions in London.

Remembering the importance of evaporation and transpiration in atmospheric processes, it is at first surprising how limited is our regional knowledge of the quantities of moisture involved, but even a brief study of the difficulties inherent in measuring this highly complex process would quickly supply ample reasons. Penman (1950, p. 372) went so far as to say that 'the direct measurement of evaporation from natural surfaces is almost impossible' and Crowe (1957, pp. 56–75), amongst others, has discussed the difficulties of measuring and estimating evapotranspiration. Certainly the design and siting of evaporation gauges are as problematical as interpreting their results. The British network of evaporation-tank gauges is still very open (London, Meteorological Office, 1963b, I, pp. 93–7, and III, pp. 10–14) but it is fortunate that the record of evaporation at Camden Square, London, is the longest in Great Britain. The record at Kew Observatory began in 1949 and this is the only other evaporation-recording station within the London region, but the great difficulties involved in comparisons of evaporation from tank readings, more especially in local investigations as here, cannot be overemphasized.

EVAPORATION

Evaporation (tank) records at Camden Square were begun in 1885, with a very poor exposure by normal standards though typical of much of inner suburban London. For the 71 years from 1885–1955 the annual evaporation averaged 16·08 in. (408·43 mm) but with a marked monthly variation as shown in Table 63.

Of the annual total of evaporation, more than 14 in. (355·6 mm), or 87 per cent, occurred during the six summer months, April–September. The comparison with precipitation is striking and of great importance for, during this same period, the average summer precipitation was 12·12 in. (307·85 mm), only slightly less than winter's 12·72 in. (323·09 mm). Stanhill (1960, p. 243) has estimated a soil moisture deficit at Camden Square rising from zero (a balance between evaporation and precipitation) in April to a maximum of 3·6 in. (91·44 mm) in August and falling to zero again in late November.

For the reasons already mentioned, no extensive comparisons will be made between stations. Table 64 does, however, list the average evaporation amounts at Camden Square and Kew Observatory for their common period of records.

There is obviously more evaporation (from a water surface) at Kew than at Camden Square, especially in summer. Remembering wind and temperature contrasts between

TABLE 63

Average monthly evaporation, Camden Square, 1885–1955

	Jan	Feb	Mar	Apr	May	June	
in.	0·09	0·24	0·73	1·54	2·50	3·07	
mm	2·29	6·10	18·54	39·12	63·50	77·98	

	July	Aug	Sept	Oct	Nov	Dec	Yr
in.	3·10	2·40	1·43	0·65	0·24	0·09	16·08
mm	78·74	60·96	36·32	16·51	6·10	2·29	408·43

Source: Stanhill, G. 1960 The variance of evaporation, rainfall, soil moisture deficit and run-off. *British rainfall 1957*, III, pp. 240–5 (H.M.S.O.)

the two stations it would seem that the higher near-surface wind speeds at Kew more than compensate for the slightly lower maximum temperatures.

Evaporation from a plant cover amply supplied with water would be very roughly three-quarters of that from a nearby evaporation pan. One would, of course, expect much less evaporation from the mortar and macadam-sealed surfaces of London where the water is fed quickly underground through drains, than from the soils, vegetation and water surfaces of the surrounding country. Water bodies within London, on the other hand, will, during calm weather, give somewhat higher humidities in their immediate vicinity. This will happen near the Thames, the reservoirs of the Lea valley, the flooded gravel pits of the Colne valley, Staines and elsewhere, and close to even such relatively minor water bodies as the Grand Union Canal and the New River.

HUMIDITY

Based upon the readings of dry- and wet-bulb thermometers housed in the North Wall Screen, values of humidity at Kew Observatory must be influenced by its particular

TABLE 64

Average monthly evaporation, Camden Square and Kew, 1949–55

		Jan	Feb	Mar	Apr	May	June
Camden Square							
	in.	0·19	0·22	0·77	1·90	2·73	3·51
	mm	4·83	5·59	19·56	48·26	69·34	89·15
Kew							
	in.	0·39	0·50	1·17	2·36	3·27	3·92
	mm	9·91	12·70	29·72	59·94	83·06	99·57

		July	Aug	Sept	Oct	Nov	Dec	Yr
Camden Square								
	in.	3·82	3·08	1·79	0·76	0·25	0·14	19·16
	mm	97·03	78·23	45·47	19·30	6·35	3·56	486·66
Kew								
	in.	4·41	3·52	2·28	1·11	0·50	0·36	23·79
	mm	112·01	89·41	57·91	28·19	12·70	9·14	604·27

Difference

		Jan	Feb	Mar	Apr	May	June
Kew–Camden Square							
	in.	0·20	0·28	0·40	0·46	0·54	0·41
	mm	5·08	7·11	10·16	11·68	13·72	10·41

		July	Aug	Sept	Oct	Nov	Dec	Yr
Kew–Camden Square								
	in.	0·59	0·44	0·49	0·35	0·25	0·22	4·63
	mm	14·99	11·18	12·45	8·89	6·35	5·59	117·60

Source of data: London, Meteorological Office *British rainfall* 1949–55

site. The errors are, however, likely to be small and the Observatory record can be taken as typical of the more open, vegetation-covered parts of suburban London.

Diurnal changes

Fig. 63 shows the average hourly values, at exact hours GMT, of vapour pressure at Kew for the 20 years 1937–56. There was a remarkably small diurnal range of values between the afternoon and early evening with a minimum around sunrise, but this is to be expected at a place not far from the sea. The fall around sunrise is caused by a faster rate of dispersal than supply of vapour at a time of low temperatures and a stable lower atmosphere, and by the extraction of moisture from the air by the deposition of dew. After sunrise the dew evaporates and water vapour is mixed into the lowest layers

causing a rise in vapour pressure. As the morning progresses and the temperature rises.
a balance is eventually reached between evapotranspiration and mixing by convection.
Convection dies down towards sunset but evaporation from the warm ground remains
high so that maximum humidities are often reached at this time. Later in the night,
temperatures fall rapidly, wind speeds are reduced and dew formation abstracts moisture

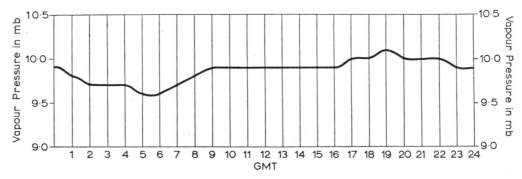

Fig 63 Average diurnal variation of vapour pressure at Kew, 1937–56
(Source of data: *Observatories' year book* 1937–56)

from a lower, stable layer. The time of maximum humidity varies from early afternoon
in January to the late evening in July when there is also a secondary morning maximum.
In January the saturated ground and weak convection gives a single maximum in the
diurnal cycle of vapour pressure.

Monthly changes in the average diurnal range are given in Table 65.

TABLE 65

Average diurnal range of vapour pressure, by months, Kew, 1886–1915

Jan	Feb	Mar	Apr	May	June	July	Aug	Sept	Oct	Nov	Dec	Yr
						mb						
0·5	0·5	0·8	0·7	0·9	1·2	1·1	1·2	1·2	0·9	0·7	0·6	0·7

Source of data: London, Meteorological Office 1959 *Averages of humidity for the British Isles.*
M.O. 421 (H.M.S.O.)

The diurnal range of relative humidity is much greater. Fig. 64 shows the average
hour-to-hour variation of relative humidity throughout the year and the basic pattern
is almost a mirror image of that of temperature and vapour pressure. Values are at
a minimum, less than 56 per cent, between 1400 and 1500 GMT in April when humidities
are little above their winter levels but temperatures have already begun their steep spring
rise. The shift of minimum relative humidities from July—they occurred then, on average, during the 30 years 1886–1915 (London, Meteorological Office, 1959, pp. 22–3)—
to April for the period 1937–56, is linked partly with the tendency to warmer Aprils in
more recent years (Manley, 1952, p. 243). Mid-afternoon values remain little above

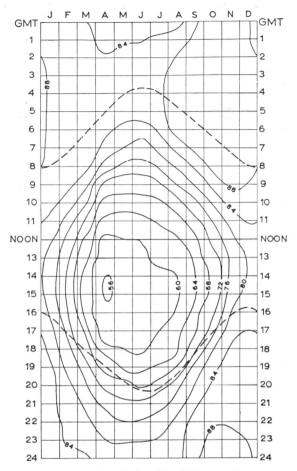

Fig 64 Average hourly relative humidities at Kew, 1937–56.
Broken lines indicate the times of sunrise and sunset
(Source of data: *Observatories' year book* 1937–56)

the April levels during the succeeding two months. The highest average hourly values of relative humidity, 90·7 per cent, occur in the early morning between 0300 and 0700 GMT from September to November, not around dawn in February as we should expect if there were a perfect inverse relationship between relative humidity and temperature. The reason for this disparity is the non-parallelism of the autumn trends of temperature and absolute humidity, with the formation of early morning fogs in autumn. The average diurnal range is smallest in December when it is 8·9 per cent: the largest mean diurnal range occurs in May when it reaches 30·5 per cent.

Expressed in a rather different and perhaps more useful way than in Fig. 64, Table 66 gives the ratio between hourly values of relative humidity (at exact hours GMT) and the mean value for that month. In conjunction with Fig. 66 or Appendix 4 it can be used to calculate approximate mean hourly values of relative humidity for each hour of the year.

TABLE 66

Ratio of the average relative humidity at exact hours GMT to the average monthly values, Kew, 1937–56

hr	Jan	Feb	Mar	Apr	May	June
1	1·03	1·05	1·10	1·14	1·17	1·17
2	1·03	1·06	1·12	1·18	1·19	1·19
3	1·04	1·06	1·12	1·19	1·20	1·20
4	1·04	1·06	1·12	1·20	1·22	1·22
5	1·03	1·06	1·13	1·20	1·22	1·20
6	1·03	1·06	1·12	1·20	1·14	1·15
7	1·03	1·07	1·12	1·14	1·12	1·10
8	1·03	1·06	1·10	1·08	1·05	1·04
9	1·02	1·04	1·04	1·00	0·98	0·97
10	1·01	1·01	0·99	0·93	0·92	0·92
11	0·98	0·97	0·93	0·87	0·87	0·87
12	0·95	0·93	0·87	0·83	0·84	0·85
13	0·93	0·90	0·83	0·80	0·81	0·82
14	0·92	0·88	0·81	0·78	0·79	0·81
15	0·92	0·87	0·80	0·78	0·79	0·80
16	0·94	0·88	0·81	0·79	0·79	0·80
17	0·96	0·92	0·84	0·81	0·80	0·81
18	0·98	0·95	0·89	0·85	0·83	0·83
19	1·00	0·98	0·95	0·92	0·89	0·87
20	1·00	1·00	0·99	0·98	0·97	0·95
21	1·01	1·01	1·02	1·02	1·02	1·00
22	1·02	1·02	1·05	1·06	1·07	1·07
23	1·02	1·03	1·07	1·10	1·11	1·12
24	1·02	1·04	1·09	1·12	1·14	1·14

hr	July	Aug	Sept	Oct	Nov	Dec
1	1·16	1·15	1·12	1·03	1·04	1·02
2	1·18	1·16	1·13	1·08	1·04	1·02
3	1·20	1·18	1·13	1·08	1·04	1·02
4	1·20	1·18	1·14	1·09	1·04	1·02
5	1·20	1·19	1·14	1·09	1·05	1·02
6	1·16	1·18	1·14	1·09	1·05	1·02
7	1·11	1·14	1·12	1·09	1·06	1·02
8	1·06	1·08	1·08	1·08	1·05	1·02
9	0·98	1·00	1·02	1·04	1·03	1·02
10	0·93	0·94	0·94	0·98	1·00	1·00
11	0·88	0·88	0·89	0·93	0·96	0·98
12	0·85	0·84	0·84	0·89	0·93	0·95
13	0·83	0·81	0·81	0·85	0·90	0·93
14	0·81	0·79	0·80	0·83	0·90	0·93
15	0·81	0·79	0·80	0·83	0·90	0·93
16	0·81	0·79	0·83	0·86	0·93	0·95
17	0·82	0·81	0·85	0·91	0·96	0·97
18	0·84	0·84	0·90	0·96	0·98	0·99
19	0·88	0·91	0·97	1·00	1·00	1·00
20	0·95	0·98	1·01	1·02	1·00	1·00
21	1·02	1·04	1·04	1·04	1·02	1·00
22	1·06	1·08	1·07	1·06	1·02	1·01
23	1·10	1·10	1·08	1·06	1·03	1·02
24	1·14	1·08	1·10	1·07	1·04	1·02

Source of data: London, Meteorological Office *Observatories' year book* 1937–56

Seasonal changes

Changes in mean monthly vapour pressure are simple in broad outline as Table 67 shows.

TABLE 67

Average and extreme mean monthly vapour pressures, Kew, 1937–51

Jan	Feb	Mar	Apr	May	June	July	Aug	Sept	Oct	Nov	Dec
						mb					
Average (0000–2400 GMT)											
7·1	7·0	7·4	8·5	10·1	12·5	14·3	14·4	13·4	10·7	9·1	7·1
Highest											
8·4	9·0	8·8	9·5	11·8	14·1	15·9	15·9	15·6	12·2	10·5	8·6
Lowest											
5·0	4·6	6·4	7·2	8·4	11·2	13·2	12·8	11·4	9·6	8·0	5·9
Maximum											
11·6	11·2	11·7	12·8	15·9	18·3	20·0	19·3	19·4	16·2	13·9	12·2
Highest											
13·6	13·3	13·5	14·4	20·1	22·1	23·9	21·1	21·7	19·2	16·5	13·6
Lowest											
8·7	8·3	9·5	11·0	13·2	16·4	17·1	16·7	17·2	14·3	11·1	9·7
Minimum											
4·0	4·1	3·9	4·7	5·3	7·4	9·0	8·9	7·9	6·1	5·3	4·2
Highest											
5·6	5·9	5·3	6·1	6·9	8·9	11·1	10·4	9·9	9·0	6·8	5·2
Lowest											
2·1	2·0	2·4	2·8	3·9	3·3	6·8	7·2	6·0	4·3	3·9	2·8

Source: London, Meteorological Office 1951 *Climate of Kew Observatory, 1871–1950*, Appendix, p. 2 (Typescript)

Average vapour pressures during July and August are double those of December, January and February, and the range of mean minimum (early morning) values between summer and winter is even greater, but the range of mean maximum (afternoon) values is slightly less. It is interesting to note that the three winter months from December to February have very similar average vapour pressures, but the smallest mean maximum humidity falls quite clearly in February and the trough of mean minima comes as late as March. Contrasts here are related to those months giving the lowest average maximum and minimum temperatures and wind speeds, commented upon in previous chapters.

July quite definitely has the highest mean maximum humidity and its mean minimum value is also above that for August, although only marginally; the average vapour pressure is slightly higher in August, a consequence of its tendency to a longer wave length, though equal amplitude, curve of daytime humidity.

Table 68 treats relative humidities in a similar manner.

TABLE 68

Average and extreme mean monthly relative humidities, Kew, 1937–56

Jan	Feb	Mar	Apr	May	June	July	Aug	Sept	Oct	Nov	Dec
						per cent					
Average (0000–2400 GMT)											
85·0	80·8	77·2	72·5	71·7	71·6	73·1	76·2	79·7	83·1	85·7	85·9
Highest											
88·8	87·5	82·9	77·4	79·4	84·1	83·4	83·6	85·4	87·5	89·7	90·1
Lowest											
78·1	74·5	69·9	64·9	62·3	64·5	63·5	66·2	72·4	79·1	80·5	79·1
Maximum											
88·4	87·2	87·8	86·8	87·2	87·3	87·8	90·1	91·0	90·6	90·8	89·6
Highest											
92·2	93·0	93·9	91·4	91·2	91·3	92·2	94·0	93·3	94·5	94·3	92·9
Lowest											
83·0	80·2	82·5	78·3	83·5	83·2	82·3	86·8	87·3	87·3	87·4	86·4
Minimum											
77·7	70·6	62·1	55·4	56·0	56·6	58·6	59·3	63·3	69·2	76·8	80·1
Highest											
81·9	80·0	72·7	60·2	62·9	64·6	64·5	68·0	72·8	72·8	83·7	85·9
Lowest											
69·8	63·1	53·2	50·0	46·1	47·9	52·2	45·5	55·3	62·4	71·3	75·4

Source of data: London, Meteorological Office *Observatories' year book* 1937–56

As one would expect, the annual range of relative humidity is much less than that of vapour pressure for apart from air-mass considerations, the cycle of air temperature is similar to that of vapour pressure. But high temperatures give somewhat smaller average relative humidities in summer than in winter. Maximum relative humidities in the early hours of the morning vary very little from month to month, but the range of minimum (afternoon) relative humidities is quite large. This reflects, in part, differences in the spread of mean monthly minimum and maximum temperatures respectively. December has the greatest average and mean minimum relative humidities but the highest average maximum humidities fall in November. The lowest average maximum and minimum relative humidites fall in April for the period 1937–56 (June and July for the period 1921–35), but the smallest average relative humidities occur in May and June. The differences are not large: they are related to contrasts in the forms of the respective diurnal cycles, for the average relative humidity is computed from hourly values.

As in previous chapters, the monthly picture is seen in a more realistic light by frequency analyses of daily means of hourly readings, and these are given in Tables 69 and 70. Each list is based upon about 11,000 values.

TABLE 69

Percentage frequency of average daily vapour pressures, Kew, 1927–56

mb	Jan	Feb	Mar	Apr per cent	May	June
(0000–2400 GMT)						
0·0– 2·0						
2·1– 4·0	3·04	6·69	1·20	0·11		
4·1– 6·0	23·75	29·03	21·98	7·92	1·61	
6·1– 8·0	39·48	36·80	36·89	36·41	13·16	0·44
8·1–10·0	23·75	19·24	29·16	34·32	27·71	11·55
10·1–12·0	9·22	7·88	10·12	16·39	34·99	30·47
12·1–14·0	0·76	0·37	0·65	3·52	16·59	30·69
14·1–16·0				0·11	4·28	19·58
16·1–18·0					0·96	5·06
18·1–20·0					0·21	0·88
20·1–22·0						0·33
22·1–24·0						

mb	July	Aug	Sept	Oct per cent	Nov	Dec
0·0– 2·0						
2·1– 4·0						1·28
4·1– 6·0				1·07	4·95	17·66
6·1– 8·0			0·66	11·45	27·61	37·45
8·1–10·0	0·96	0·76	9·46	23·97	36·41	26·00
10·1–12·0	12·63	8·77	19·03	33·17	21·12	15·30
12·1–14·0	30·17	31·57	32·78	20·12	7·81	1·82
14·1–16·0	32·64	32·42	22·44	8·56	0·99	
16·1–18·0	15·84	19·47	11·44	1·18		
18·1–20·0	5·24	5·46	3·19			
20·1–22·0	0·86	0·65	0·11			
22·1–24·0	0·11	0·43				

Source of data: London, Meteorological Office *Observatories' year book* 1927–56

These tables convey something of the variety of conditions in any one month, more particularly of vapour pressure during summer: there are much smaller differences between months in the scatter of relative humidity. One very notable feature is the limited range of high values of relative humidity in October and November; these are associated with humid southwesterly airstreams giving moderately high vapour pressures at a time of rapidly falling temperatures, especially night-time temperatures, in late autumn. The modal relative humidity falls, in all months, into one of only two 10 per cent ranges. From September to February the mode is 80·1–90·0 per cent and from March to August it is 70·1–80·0 per cent. In each month, between one-third and one-half of the actual average daily values fall within one or other of these ranges.

Day-to-day variations of vapour pressure and relative humidity are shown in Figs. 65 and 66. In both cases there is a simple, smooth, first-order change between the months, and mean daily values oscillate very closely around the long-period trend values. The few notable departures from this trend have a very low level of significance.

TABLE 70

Percentage frequency of average daily relative humidities, Kew, 1927–56

(0000–2400 GMT)

per cent	Jan	Feb	Mar	Apr	May	June
			per cent			
0·0– 40·0						
40·1– 50·0			0·32	1·00	0·54	0·66
50·1– 60·0	0·11	2·02	3·44	7·26	10·06	8·91
60·1– 70·0	4·15	10·36	17·74	31·24	30·60	35·09
70·1– 80·0	20·45	30·83	38·17	38·06	37·88	35·75
80·1– 90·0	47·07	39·29	33·87	18·70	19·15	16·72
90·1–100·0	28·22	17·50	6·45	2·64	1·28	1·54

per cent	July	Aug	Sept	Oct	Nov	Dec
			per cent			
0·0– 40·0						
40·1– 50·0	0·11					
50·1– 60·0	6·09	2·46	0·44			0·43
60·1– 70·0	30·17	19·80	9·68	4·49	2·42	4·17
70·1– 80·0	42·48	48·58	37·95	28·25	19·80	16·59
80·1– 90·0	18·83	25·79	43·78	49·01	45·87	43·23
90·1–100·0	2·25	2·68	7·15	17·76	30·91	35·07

Source of data: London, Meteorological Office *Observatories' year book* 1927–56

The scatter of extreme vapour pressures during the 30 years analysed follows the annual curve of mean values with a fairly constant band width, so that the highest recorded winter values of vapour pressure are well above the lowest recorded summer values. This overlap does not apply to relative humidities where, as one would expect, there is a broader, more erratic scatter.

Dry and humid heat

Lawrence (1956) has compiled frequency distributions of the hourly observations of dry-bulb and wet-bulb temperatures at Croydon Airport during the 10 years 1946–55, and Dight (1934) has made an analysis of warm spells in London from 1900–33 with special reference to the prevailing humidity. Both of these studies were concerned with a very interesting aspect of climate, namely combinations of temperature and humidity;

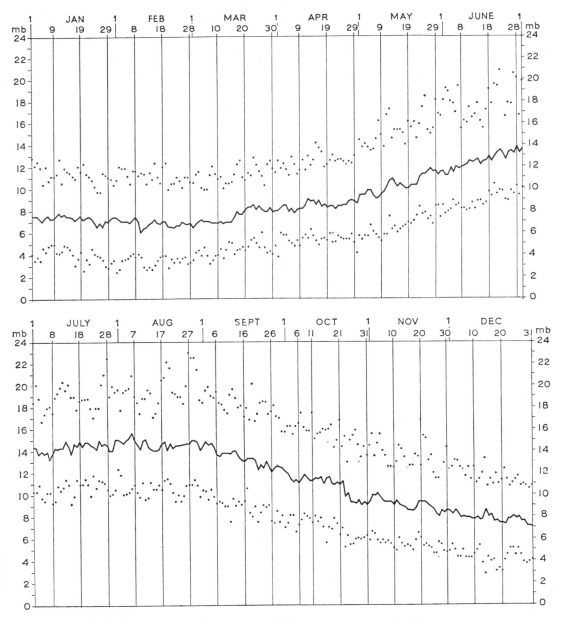

Fig 65 Average and extreme mean daily vapour pressures at Kew, 1927–56.
Extremes are shown by dots
(Source of data: *Observatories' year book* 1927–56)

these are most extreme when high and low temperatures are combined with either very
high or very low humidities.

The relative humidity in London on days with temperatures above 29·4°C (85°F)
usually ranges from 35–45 per cent at the warmest part of the day, but from 10–12
July 1921, when temperatures rose to these levels, the relative humidity was never greater

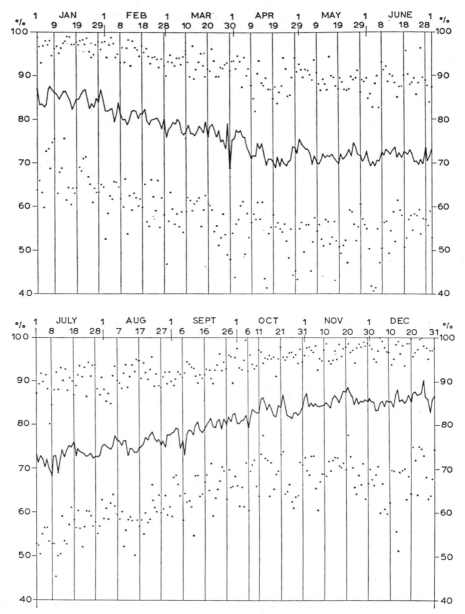

Fig 66 Average and extreme mean daily relative humidities at Kew, 1927–56.
Extremes are shown by dots
(Source of data: *Observatories' year book* 1927–56)

than 33 per cent and was for the most part below 30 per cent. Hawke (1944, p. 274) cites a day, 15 April 1942, when the relative humidity at 1515 GMT at Kew fell to the extraordinarily low level of 10 per cent, and three others when it was 15 per cent or less. These were quite pleasant days of dry heat; much more harrowing were the hot, humid days of July 1900, August 1930 and August 1932 (Dight, 1934, p. 113). Individual days

TABLE 71

Average and extreme mean monthly wet-bulb temperatures, Kew, 1937–51

(0000–2400 GMT)

	Jan	Feb	Mar	Apr	May	June	July	Aug	Sept	Oct	Nov	Dec
Mean (0000–2400 GMT)												
Average (°F)	38	38	41	45	49	55	58	58	55	49	44	39
(°C)	3·3	3·3	5·0	7·2	9·4	12·8	14·4	14·4	12·8	9·4	6·7	3·9
Highest (°F)	42	44	45	48	53	58	60	60	59	52	48	43
(°C)	5·6	6·7	7·2	8·9	11·7	14·4	15·6	15·6	15·0	11·1	8·9	6·1
Lowest (°F)	30	29	37	41	45	53	56	56	52	46	41	34
(°C)	−1·1	−1·7	2·8	5·0	7·2	11·7	13·3	13·3	11·1	7·8	5·0	1·1
Maximum												
Average (°F)	41	42	45	49	54	59	62	62	59	53	47	43
(°C)	5·0	5·6	7·2	9·4	12·2	15·0	16·7	16·7	15·0	11·7	8·3	6·1
Highest (°F)	46	48	51	52	57	62	64	65	63	56	52	46
(°C)	7·8	8·9	10·6	11·1	13·9	16·7	17·8	18·3	17·2	13·3	11·1	7·8
Lowest (°F)	34	31	41	45	50	56	60	59	56	50	44	37
(°C)	1·1	−0·5	5·0	7·2	10·0	13·3	15·6	15·0	13·3	10·0	6·7	2·8
Minimum												
Average (°F)	34	34	36	40	44	50	54	54	50	44	40	35
(°C)	1·1	1·1	2·2	4·4	6·7	10·0	12·2	12·2	10·0	6·7	4·4	1·7
Highest (°F)	38	40	39	43	47	53	57	56	55	47	44	39
(°C)	3·3	4·4	3·9	6·1	8·3	11·7	13·9	13·3	12·8	8·3	6·7	3·9
Lowest (°F)	26	26	34	37	40	39	52	51	47	42	37	31
(°C)	−3·3	−3·3	1·1	2·8	4·4	3·9	11·1	10·6	8·3	5·6	2·8	−0·5

Source: London, Meteorological Office 1951 *Climate of Kew Observatory, 1871–1950*, Appendix, p. 1 (Typescript)

in any month can, of course, be found to range through the whole spectrum of the temperature-humidity relationship.

The wet-bulb temperature has frequently been used as an index of human comfort, being related both to temperature and humidity, although the same wet-bulb temperature can be associated with an infinite number of combinations of these two elements. Table 71 lists the average and extreme mean monthly wet-bulb temperatures at Kew for the period 1937–51.

HUMIDITIES IN GREATER LONDON

Because the majority of the climatological stations in Greater London report wet- and dry-bulb temperatures at the 0900 GMT observation only, and because of the frequent difficulties imposed by the methods of measurement when the spatial range of humidities is small (as it will be at this hour), it is difficult to construct a detailed picture of this element within and about the city. But this does not mean that we are without any knowledge of local differences in humidity, for the broad lineaments at least are available.

By day there is usually a humidity lapse near the ground which is several times stronger in summer than in winter. By night there is frequently an inversion of humidity near the surface which is broken down after sunrise. These features are explained by processes leading to dew formation at night followed by evaporation in a turbulent daytime regime. Humidities in the higher parts of London will obviously differ from those in low-lying areas. During winter nights, differences in vapour pressure will be small, in spring and autumn there will be a tendency to slightly higher night-time humidities at heights of 300–350 ft (91–107 m) in comparison with lower levels, but in summer, values will be less. During the day in all months, vapour pressures at these higher altitudes will be less than at lower levels (Best et al., 1952, pp. 30–9).

Some indication of the order of humidity differences between central London and its rural surrounds is provided by Table 72 which uses 0900 GMT readings. It is often assumed that the 0900 GMT value is very close to the daily mean but Applegate and Smith (1960) have demonstrated that this is not strictly so, although the reading quite obviously lies somewhere between the highest and lowest values on most days.

TABLE 72

Differences in mean vapour pressure and relative humidity at 0900 GMT,
West Malling–Kensington Palace, 1946–56

Jan	Feb	Mar	Apr	May	June	July	Aug	Sept	Oct	Nov	Dec	Yr
Vapour pressure (mb)												
0·0	0·0	0·3	0·4	0·5	—0·2	0·2	0·4	0·2	0·2	0·1	0·0	0·2
Relative humidity (per cent)												
4	4	6	6	7	3	4	6	4	3	5	5	5

Source of data: London, Meteorological Office *Monthly weather reports* 1946–56

The air around Kensington Palace is a little drier than at West Malling (Kent) at 0900 GMT, though the differences of mean vapour pressure are small and become almost insignificant when one remembers that they are due in part to wider regional gradients generally decreasing from the coast inland in southeast England. The limited control of the city upon average regional vapour pressures is to be expected for, except when the air is calm, the water vapour content of London's air will be derived from outside and will remain unaltered over the city, except perhaps by diffusion through deepened

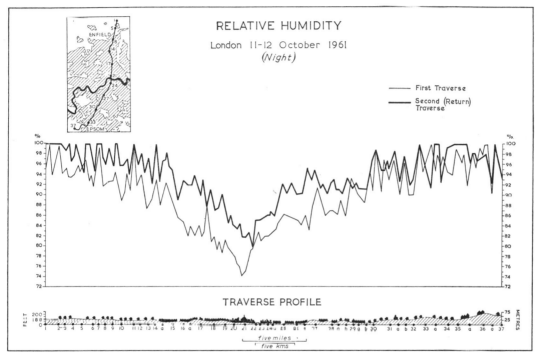

Fig 67 London relative humidity traverse, actual humidities, 11–12 October
1961 (night)
(Source of data: London Climatological Survey records)

turbulence, and loss through condensation and precipitation over the city. Where there are evaporating surfaces, the higher temperatures in London will also encourage higher vapour pressures. Contrasts of relative humidity between central London and outside are more marked than differences in absolute humidity but they are due primarily to comparisons of temperature, and once again are only slightly more than is to be expected from the position of the conurbation in the climatic context of southeast England. Analysis showed almost no difference at 1500 GMT between the readings at Kensington Palace and West Malling.

It would seem that London has very little effect within its region upon the long period means of vapour pressure. On individual days and nights, on the other hand, there may well be substantial differences, but these are far from simple to analyse. A comparison of daily 0900 GMT readings of vapour pressure and relative humidity at Wisley (Surrey) with those at other stations in London reveals a very erratic relationship within a wide range of positive and negative differences. Some of these undoubtedly result from errors in reading, or in the functioning of the wet-bulb. Few meaningful deductions can be made from this material but some interesting results have been obtained from humidity traverses across London.

Fig. 67 shows relative humidities for the same night as a previously described temperature traverse (Fig. 58) but, as might be expected, relative humidity changes along

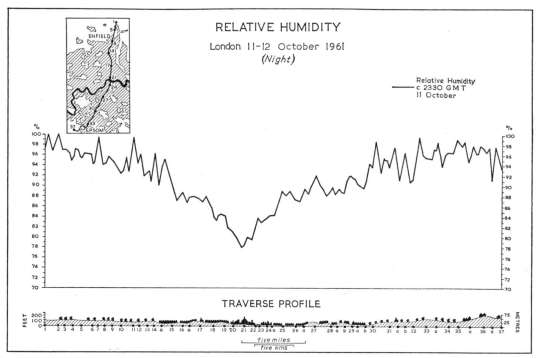

Fig 68 London relative humidity traverse, mean humidities, 11–12 October
1961 (night)
(Source of data: London Climatological Survey records)

the traverse route were more complex. While pockets of fog lay in parts of the suburbs, central districts had relative humidities as low as 74 per cent during the first, north-east–southwest, crossing of London. In the low-density settlement areas with a great deal of open land, between stations 1 and 14, and 30 and 37, average humidities ranged between 90 and 100 per cent; in the intensely developed residential areas between 15 and 19, and between 25 and 29, relative humidities varied between 82 and 90 per cent; in the City of London they were less than 82 per cent. These differences were almost entirely the consequence of higher temperatures for, except for a few suburban stations, vapour pressures in London were *higher* than outside.

Although a great deal of the surface of London is impervious and there is a rapid removal of precipitation through sewers, the cellular morphology of its buildings may, on suitably calm, clear nights, enmesh pockets of warm air which, free from excessive mixing, will better maintain their high daytime humidities as well as temperatures. Because of the higher temperatures, more especially surface temperatures, there will be less dew formation and abstraction of moisture from the air of central London. Thus at about 2330 GMT on 11 October 1961 (Fig. 68) the vapour pressure between stations 1 and 7, an essentially rural area with only small settlements, ranged from 9·0 to 10·5 mb; between stations 8 and 14, characterized by low-density suburban development and numerous small open spaces along the line of traverse, vapour pressures were very

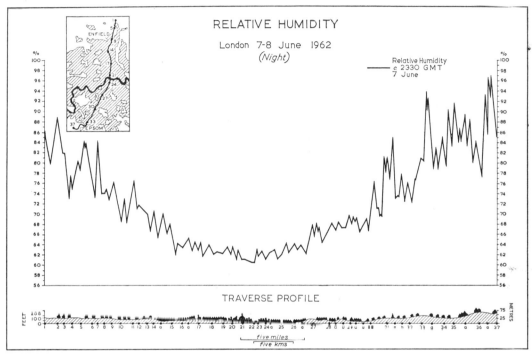

Fig 69 London relative humidity traverse, mean humidities, 7–8 June 1962
(night)
(Source of data: London Climatological Survey records)

variable. On the margins of settlement nodes, humidities were sometimes less than in the rural areas beyond London (at station 5 the humidity was 8·7 mb), but where temperatures were high and the urban development was open, they ranged from 10·6 to 10·8 mb. In the intensely developed central area between stations 15 and 29, with its canyon-like streets and tall buildings grouped around atmospheric wells, humidities ranged between 10·9 and 12·3 mb. In Merton, Morden, Cheam and Ewell, that is between stations 30 and 35, humidities were about 11·0 mb, and in the rural area west of Epsom (i.e. stations 36 and 37), about 9·7 mb. Vapour pressures in central London were thus about 3·3 mb higher than in the surrounding Green Belt.

Fig. 69, for another clear night with winds never more than 5·8 m/sec (2·6 mi/hr) (at London Airport), shows the distribution of relative humidity when the heat-island had an intensity of 7·8°C (14°F) at its centre. Again, relative humidities at about 2330

GMT were more than 27 per cent lower in central London and vapour pressures about 1·4 mb higher. The smaller difference in vapour pressures compared with the previous example was probably due in part to lighter dew formation in marginal areas.

Lower vapour pressures in central London than outside are likely to occur when light winds are associated with cloudy skies. The former will allow local site conditions to assert themselves and the latter will ensure a weak heat-island, and limit dew formation and the lowering of extra-metropolitan humidities. Humidities on fifty such 0900 GMT occasions during the two years 1959–60 were analysed but the mean difference was again small—of the order of 0·3 mb lower at Kensington Palace than Wisley (Surrey).

It would seem, then, that higher and lower vapour pressures in London occur with almost equal frequency, and that there is only a weak overall tendency to drier air in the built-up area. Differences in relative humidity are also small, except when heat-islands are strong.

8 Visibility

But Juan saw not this: each wreath of smoke
Appeared to him but as the magic vapour
Of some alchymic furnace, from whence broke
The wealth of worlds (a wealth of tax and paper):
The gloomy clouds, which o'er it [London] as a yoke
Are bowed, and put the sun out like a taper,
Were nothing but the natural atmosphere,
Extremely wholesome, though but rarely clear.

George Gordon Byron

WIND, pollution, temperature distributions (both lateral and vertical) and humidity are the four main parameters governing variations in time and space of visibility. In London the levels of visibility are notoriously low in winter and the city is widely associated with fogs which form an almost internationally recognized type, the 'pea-souper' (Lawrence, 1953, pp. 367–9). Droplet formation around, and mixture with, pollution particles produces a dirty, yellow mixture described by Charles Dickens as a 'London particular' but known colloquially today as a smog. True advection fogs are not common over most of London and poor visibilities are the consequence of mainly radiation fogs and smoke. The so-called high fogs, occasioned by a concentration of smoky fog at no great height and giving an eerie yellowish light in the streets, are also notable occurrences, one such instance in 1931 being described in the following terms (Johnson, 1957, p. 69):

> There has just come on, at five minutes past 12, a fog as nearly approaching the utter darkness as can be imagined. All business was suspended in the streets, not an orange-woman could sell an orange except by feel. And what is remarkable is, that there was no thickness in the air; you might see as far as Paternoster Row as at any time when it is not quite dark. The fog lay between us and the sun; and the sun shone on it with a lurid light like a conflagration.

Daytime darkness has been studied recently by Helliwell and Blackwell (1955) and Gildersleeves (1962).

At the lower end of the visibility scale, it is the nature and frequency of London's fogs rather than their intensity which are most characteristic, for really intense fogs, that is visibilities less than 220 yd (200 m), are more common in, say, the rural parts of East Anglia than in central London (Shellard, 1959b). The connection between smoke and droplet fogs is, of course, indirect as well as direct, for meteorological conditions favouring fog are precisely those inhibiting the rapid removal of smoke. Smoke alone may occasionally reduce the visibility below 1,100 yd (1 km), which is the upper limiting value for fog, although droplet fogs frequently form in urban areas, with their abundant small condensation nuclei, when relative humidities lie between 90 and 100 per cent. Thus out of 210 fogs at Kew from 1 October 1923 to 31 March 1927, 90 occurred with humidities of 95 per cent, 43 with 90 per cent and 11 with 80 per cent (Pick, 1929, p. 306). Occasions have also been reported of visibilities of about 200 yd (183 m) at Northolt in west London with a relative humidity of 60–70 per cent (Sugden, 1952, p. 175) and no wind: such instances were almost certainly 'dry' fogs. The pollution content of London's droplet fogs will vary of course, and they are called smogs when the amount of impurity is high and visibilities are low as a result of the large number of small, polluted droplets. There is a tendency for urban fogs to form earlier and disperse later than cleaner rural fogs because of the numerous active nuclei; London smogs are both dense and persistent.

The occurrence and severity of London fogs, as elsewhere, is closely controlled by the general synoptic situation. There is a tendency for the maximum frequency to occur with calms or light northeast winds, and less markedly, southeast winds in winter, often blowing around an extended Continental high. Fog is rare with wind speeds of 5 m/sec (12 mi/hr) or more, but the connection with surface winds is indirect as well as direct for surface inversions will be rare when wind speeds are high.

VISIBILITY AT KEW AND LONDON AIRPORT

Kew Observatory, sited on the floodplain of the River Thames within a major open space of suburban London, is likely to suffer more fogs in general and more dense fogs in particular than the more intensely built-up parts of London's suburbs, but its records are long and reliable and hence for most purposes they are the most useful. There are, indeed, very few London stations which make visibility measures and only London Airport, apart from the unpublished readings at Northolt Airport and the now terminated observations at Croydon Airport, makes hourly observations throughout the day and night. For this reason, diurnal changes in fog frequency will be illustrated by data from London Airport.

Figs. 70 and 71 show mean hourly frequencies of fog (visibilities less than 1,100 yd (1,000 m)) and thick fog (visibilities less than 220 yd (200 m)) for each month of the year. The outstanding points of the variations are:

1 The very high frequency of fog and thick fog on October mornings followed by a rapid clearance by convection about 4 hr after sunrise.
2 The tendency for November fogs to persist throughout the day. This is a time of moist maritime air masses, fairly long nights and intense pollution from domestic fires.
3 The occurrence in winter of two maxima in the diurnal cycle of fog, one about an hour after sunrise and the other about midnight. The main minimum occurs at about 1500 GMT, with a secondary minimum at about 0500 GMT. There is also evidence that on Sunday mornings the poorest visibilities occur an hour or more

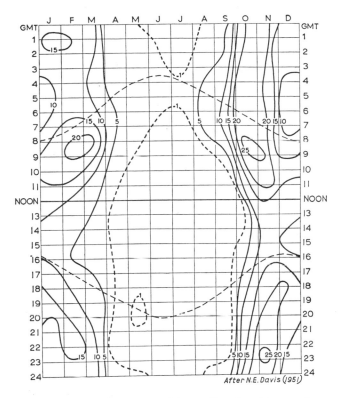

Fig 70 Percentage frequency of fog at London Airport, August
1946–July 1950. The two unnumbered broken lines indicate the
times of sunrise and sunset
(Source: Davis, N. E. 1951 Fog at London Airport. *Met. Mag.*,
London, 80, p. 12)

later than on weekdays, probably owing to the delayed lighting of domestic fires on
Sundays (Evans, 1957, p. 336). Gentle turbulence bringing down smoke from beneath
a low inversion frequently contributes to the early-morning decrease in visibility.

4   The low frequency of early-morning fogs in December and January when dry, cold,
easterly air masses are common, but the high frequency of fogs two to three hours
after sunset in these months and in February. These are times of frequent night-
time inversions and intense evening pollution.

5   The large number of fogs about 2 hr after sunrise in February and March, probably
the result of the influx of moist air masses while the ground is still cold and there
is night-time cooling during frequent calms. Gentle overturning of the air may also
help to deepen the fog, temporarily, after sunrise.

6   The increasing tendency from December to March for an afternoon clearance of the
fog (Davis, 1951, p. 12).

Though not apparent in Figs. 70 and 71, Evans (1957, p. 336) noted (for a longer period),
a well-developed tendency to a marked improvement of visibilities between 2100 and

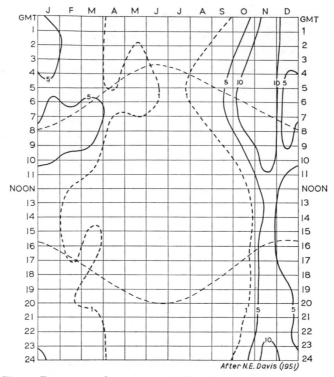

Fig 71 Percentage frequency of thick fog at London Airport,
August 1946–July 1950. Two unnumbered lines indicate the times
of sunrise and sunset
(Source: Davis, N. E. 1951 Fog at London Airport. *Met. Mag.*,
London, 80, p. 13)

2200 GMT, probably owing to a contemporaneous fall in local concentrations of suspended smoke (Fig. 24), but on many other occasions this was offset by radiation fog at this time.

Table 73 shows how great are the month-to-month changes in the average frequency of various visibility ranges at Kew. The highest visibilities occur during summer afternoons, and over the year as a whole, good visibilities or better, i.e. visibilities of 7 mi (10 km) or more, are about 30 per cent more frequent in the afternoon than at either the morning or late evening observations. At 2100 GMT, visibilities tend to be more concentrated in the intermediate ranges than at 0900 GMT.

VISIBILITY IN GREATER LONDON

As one would expect in an area of such differentiated climates as we have already found in Greater London, local visibilities cover a very wide range of values, even when averaged over long periods. Fig. 72, after a diagram by Marshall (1952, p. 51), shows the number of days with fog i.e. a visibility less than 1,100 yd (1,000 m), at the early morning, noon and evening observations at Kingsway, Kew and Croydon from 1941–4, an un-

TABLE 73

Average number of days with various visibility ranges, by months, Kew, 1945–61

0900 GMT

Code	Jan	Feb	Mar	Apr	May	June	July	Aug	Sept	Oct	Nov	Dec
						Average number of days						
0	0·6	0·3	0·3	0·0	0·0	0·0	0·0	0·0	0·0	0·5	0·9	0·7
1	1·0	0·7	0·8	0·0	0·0	0·0	0·0	0·0	0·4	1·5	1·2	1·2
2	1·2	1·2	0·8	0·1	0·0	0·0	0·0	0·0	0·1	1·7	1·5	1·4
3	2·1	1·7	2·3	0·7	0·1	0·1	0·0	0·3	0·5	1·7	2·2	2·6
4	4·6	3·8	4·1	1·6	1·3	0·4	0·1	0·5	1·8	3·3	2·8	3·1
5	8·2	7·2	6·2	4·0	2·5	1·3	1·2	1·9	3·9	4·4	6·4	6·2
6	9·2	9·6	10·6	9·9	10·5	9·2	8·4	10·0	8·5	9·7	9·4	10·0
7	2·9	3·0	3·9	8·3	8·2	7·4	8·7	7·4	7·5	4·5	3·7	3·8
8	1·0	0·8	1·8	4·7	7·3	9·1	9·9	8·7	6·7	2·9	1·4	1·9
9	0·2	0·1	0·2	0·7	1·1	2·5	2·7	2·2	0·6	0·8	0·5	0·1

1500 GMT

Code	Jan	Feb	Mar	Apr	May	June	July	Aug	Sept	Oct	Nov	Dec
						Average number of days						
0	0·2	0·0	0·0	0·0	0·0	0·0	0·0	0·0	0·0	0·0	0·9	0·3
1	0·2	0·0	0·1	0·0	0·0	0·0	0·0	0·0	0·0	0·1	1·2	0·9
2	0·9	0·2	0·3	0·0	0·1	0·0	0·0	0·0	0·0	0·1	1·5	1·2
3	1·4	1·1	1·0	0·2	0·0	0·0	0·0	0·0	0·1	0·4	2·2	2·2
4	4·2	2·7	1·4	0·3	0·6	0·1	0·1	0·0	0·4	1·4	2·8	3·6
5	8·4	5·5	5·2	1·5	0·8	0·5	0·4	0·4	1·2	3·6	6·4	7·1
6	11·8	12·1	12·8	10·9	7·9	6·1	4·3	5·4	6·0	11·9	9·4	11·9
7	2·9	4·2	5·3	7·8	7·4	6·2	7·6	6·5	7·9	6·3	3·7	2·4
8	0·9	1·9	4·2	7·8	11·3	13·8	14·1	15·1	12·6	5·9	1·4	1·2
9	0·1	0·7	0·7	1·5	2·9	3·3	4·5	3·6	1·8	1·3	0·5	0·2

2100 GMT

Code	Jan	Feb	Mar	Apr	May	June	July	Aug	Sept	Oct	Nov	Dec
						Average number of days						
0	0·6	0·1	0·1	0·0	0·0	0·0	0·0	0·0	0·0	0·7	0·8	0·9
1	1·0	0·4	0·4	0·0	0·0	0·0	0·0	0·1	0·1	1·1	1·5	1·8
2	0·7	0·5	0·5	0·0	0·0	0·0	0·0	0·1	0·0	1·1	0·5	1·1
3	1·5	1·8	1·1	0·2	0·2	0·1	0·0	0·0	0·2	1·5	1·3	1·2
4	3·8	3·5	4·3	0·9	0·8	0·4	0·2	0·2	1·1	4·2	3·8	3·8
5	7·1	6·7	8·5	4·2	3·0	1·5	1·6	1·1	2·1	5·5	5·3	4·9
6	11·7	11·2	12·2	13·7	11·8	9·4	8·7	7·0	10·1	9·4	9·8	10·8
7	3·7	3·2	3·0	7·6	9·4	9·9	9·4	9·6	9·1	5·9	5·1	4·7
8	0·9	1·0	0·9	3·2	5·4	7·8	10·3	12·0	7·0	1·5	1·8	1·6
9	0·0	0·0	0·0	0·2	0·4	0·9	0·8	0·9	0·3	0·1	0·1	0·2

Annual Averages

GMT	0	1	2	3	4	5	6	7	8	9
					Average number of days					
0900	3·4	6·8	8·1	14·5	27·5	53·8	114·3	69·2	56·1	11·6
1500	0·7	1·7	3·2	7·8	17·7	42·0	113·7	67·4	90·2	20·9
2100	3·2	6·4	4·4	9·3	27·3	51·8	124·8	80·8	53·4	3·9

Table 73—*contd.*

Visibility ranges:

Code
No.

0	0– 44 yd	0– 40 m	Dense fog
1	45– 210 yd	41– 190 m	Thick fog
2	220– 430 yd	200– 390 m	Fog
3	440–1,090 yd	400– 990 m	Moderate fog
4	1,100–2,190 yd	1,000–1,990 m	Mist or haze
5	2,200–4,390 yd	2,000–3,990 m	Poor visibility
6	3– 6 mi	5– 9 km	Moderate visibility
7	7–12 mi	10–19 km	Good visibility
8	13–24 mi	20–39 km	Very good visibility
9	25 mi and over	40 km and over	Excellent visibility

Source of data: London, Meteorological Office *Monthly weather reports* 1945–61

avoidably short period. Early-morning observations were changed from 0700 GMT to 0600 GMT and midday observations from 1300 GMT to 1200 GMT on 1 August 1944. At all three stations there is a similar variation of fog frequency, with a pronounced winter maximum. The smaller number of fogs at 0700 GMT in February compared with both January and March is noteworthy; as is the failure, outside central London, of November to justify its reputation as a particularly foggy month. In an investigation by Evans (1957) of 10 years of observations at London Airport, November was slightly more foggy than October, December and January, but differences were small.

Contrasts between inner London and its suburbs were greatest in February and

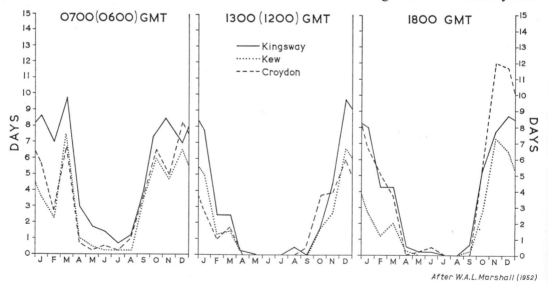

After W.A.L. Marshall (1952)

Fig 72 Average number of days per month with fog at Kingsway, Kew and Croydon, 1941–44
(Source: Marshall, W. A. L. 1952 *A century of London weather*, London, p. 51)

November. Midday fogs were common everywhere from November to January but they were noticeably more frequent in inner London. Croydon's higher susceptibility to October fogs probably arose because of the number of occasions when central fogs were prevented from forming or were evaporated by the warmth of these areas, although the fog sometimes lifts to an inversion not much above roof level. The evening pattern is particularly interesting, especially the higher frequency of fogs at Croydon than at either Kingsway or Kew during November and December. Normally, evening fogs form first in the cool, humid air above the fields around London and then girdle a relatively clear built-up area. Later in the night, temperatures fall and the margins of the fog-free central core contract, until by dawn the whole London region may be masked in fog, though not necessarily of uniform density. In the early morning, however, increasing temperatures and turbulence frequently cause a rapid dispersal of the rural fog, while city temperatures increase more slowly and the winds in city streets are generally lighter with the result that its fogs are more persistent. Town fogs usually absorb more radiation than the cleaner rural fogs and for this reason the ground beneath is cooler and there is less overturning in the fog layer. This is one reason why urban fogs last longer, but small quantities of sulphuric acid may also delay the evaporation of its droplets (Dobson, 1948, p. 143). Thus the pattern of fog in and around London during the early morning is commonly seen to be reversed by night, for during the morning a fog, roughly coincident with the city but probably densest in the suburbs, replaces a swirling annular distribution around the built-up area. Later in the day the fog will frequently clear, even from city streets.

This sequence of change explains certain features of Fig. 73 which compares fog frequencies at Kingsway and Croydon. At 1800 GMT, differences are small in all months except November and December when the higher air temperatures of the centre delay the fogs which have already formed in the suburban fringe areas. Early morning fogs are normally more common at Kingsway than Croydon for the reasons mentioned, but this is not true in December. There may be some anomaly in the small number of years sampled but one would expect a certain reduction in December because the sun has not yet risen at this hour and the effects of increasing wind speeds, turbulence and temperatures, differentiating rural and suburban areas, are not fully operative.

For a wider range of visibilities than those defining fog, Smith (1961, pp. 355–9) has studied the extent of afternoon haze, when water fogs are least likely. The effect of Greater London is very apparent in his maps, the average number of days per year (1923–51) with afternoon visibilities less than 4,400 yd (4 km) ranging from more than 100 in central London to less than 50 outside the conurbation. The average number of days per year with afternoon visibilities of 6 mi (9 km) or less varies from more than 250 in central London to between 150 and 200 outside.

At the opposite end of the visibility scale, Fig. 74 shows the difference between the three London stations in their average monthly frequencies of good visibility of more than 6 mi (9 km). Good visibility is rare in central London (Kingsway) between October and March inclusive and at the 0700 GMT observation there is an appreciable improvement of visibility outward from central London where pollutants are trapped close to

o

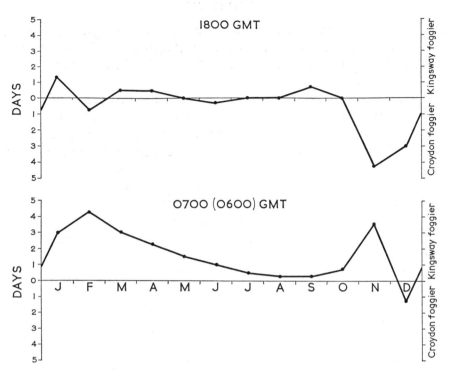

Fig 73 Differences in average monthly fog frequency, Kingsway–Croydon,
1941–4
(Source of data: Marshall, W. A. L. 1952 *A century of London weather*,
London)

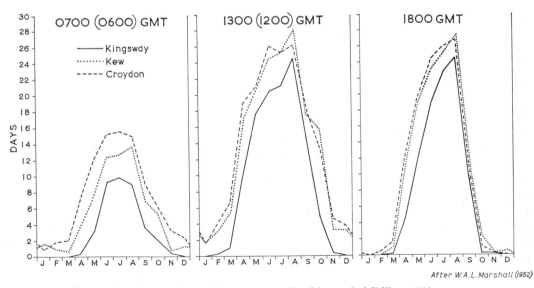

After W.A.L.Marshall (1952)

Fig 74 Average number of days per month with good visibility at Kingsway,
Kew and Croydon, 1941–4
(Source: Marshall, W. A. L. 1952 *A century of London weather*, London, p. 53)

the surface, little disturbed by deep, vertical mixing. In August the visibility at midday in the centre of London is almost as good as in the outer suburbs (Croydon). Autumn evening mists are mainly responsible for a sharp fall in the frequency of days with good visibility at 1800 GMT.

The infrequency of measures makes it impossible to construct maps of the distribution of fog (or any other visibility measure) except when special networks have been established or notable events have occasioned particular posthumous investigations (Brooks, 1918; Carpenter, 1903; Stewart, 1953). Because of the difficulties and uncer-

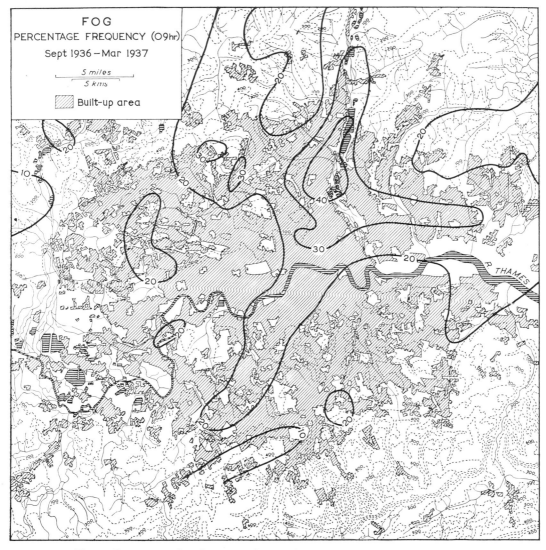

FOG
PERCENTAGE FREQUENCY (09hr)
Sept 1936 – Mar 1937

5 miles
5 kms

Built-up area

Fig 75 Percentage fog frequency in London, 0900 GMT, September 1936–
March 1937
(Source of data: Durst, C. S. 1940 Winter fog and mist investigation in the
British Isles. London, *Meteorological Office Memoir*, No. 372)

tainties of measurement, participants in the London Climatological Survey were not asked to record visibility and the only recent, long period investigation was Durst's enquiry for the winter of 1936–7 (Durst, 1940, pp. 27–8). This showed (Fig. 75) that London's foggiest regions were the low-lying parts of the Lea valley, lower Thames-side, and the higher parts of the northern suburbs of Barnet, Mill Hill and Elstree; but smaller areas where fogs readily form, are dense, or last a long time, can be found all over London. Thus a ribbon of fog can be seen on many autumn and winter nights to follow the winding course of the New River through northeast London, the rivers Brent and Colne in northwest London and the Wandle in south London. The floodplain of the Thames, especially in its undeveloped parts, is also particularly liable to fogs, whilst more elevated areas such as Hampstead and Wimbledon often rise above the shallower fogs, although the former may sometimes be enveloped in low cloud or advection fog. Fogs also have a tendency to thicken near the margins of parks and this may be related to local atmospheric circulations, already discussed, between open spaces and nearby built-up areas. In any particular suburb of London, the drift of smoke will also impair visibilities wherever the surface wind has crossed the city (Corby, 1951, Figs. 2–6). The broad distribution of visibilities can be judged from Table 74.

TABLE 74

Estimated fog frequencies, London, 1947–56

(based on 0300, 0900, 1500 and 2100 GMT observations)

	< 44 yd < 40 m	< 220 yd < 200 m	< 440 yd < 400 m	< 1,100 yd < 1,000 m
		hours per annum		
Kingsway	19	126	230	940
Kew	79	213	365	633
London Airport	46	209	304	562
Southeast England*	20	177	261	494

* mean of Abingdon, Boscombe Down, Cranfield, Mildenhall, South Farnborough, West Malling, West Raynham

Source of data: Shellard, H. C. 1959b The frequency of fog in the London area compared with that in rural areas of East Anglia and south-east England. *Met. Mag.*, London, 88, pp. 321–3

The right-hand column of Table 74 shows that fog is far more frequent in central London, represented by Kingsway, than in the inner suburbs, represented by Kew, and more frequent here than in the outer suburbs represented by London Airport. London as a whole has appreciably more fogs than the surrounding country. For visibilities below 440 yd (400 m) the position is rather different, since in this range frequencies in central districts are markedly below those in the suburbs and are even below those in rural districts outside London. Visibilities below 44 yd (40 m), that is dense fogs, occur most commonly in the suburbs, central London having values almost equalling those of country areas. To understand these differences we should recall that fog frequency and intensity vary with a number of elements including wind speed, pollution, temperature and humidity. Outward from central London, near-surface wind speeds and humidities generally increase and temperatures decrease. It would seem, therefore, that the high frequency of visibilities below 1,100 yd (1,000 m) results mainly from pollution and light winds, but that many urban fogs are prevented from becoming as dense as in rural areas by the higher night-time temperatures within London. On those few occasions each year when meteorological conditions are suitable for the build-up of smog over several days, the intense pollution of the centre gives visibilities as low as some of the thickest, though cleaner, fogs outside.

One such occasion was the smog of early December 1952 (pollution aspects were considered on p. 104). An anticyclone had spread from the northwest and become stationary over the Thames valley which was filled with a pool of cold, stagnant air to a depth of 200–500 ft (61–153 m); at this level there was a strong, impenetrable inversion. Within this cold, almost motionless air a fog was formed to which the outpourings of London's innumerable chimneys were added. The effect of the pollution alone on visibilities was possibly small, for in spite of the 'thickness' of the smog at least 98 per cent of the suspended matter was made up of water droplets (Douglas and Stewart, 1953, p. 70). But the indirect effect of the pollution upon visibilities was very substantial, for the smoke particles provided abundant nuclei so that the fog droplets were smaller and more stable than outside London. This produced a denser fog, quick to form and slow to disperse, and it is not surprising that visibilities were below 20 yd (18 m) for long periods and sometimes below 10 yd (9 m). Conditions indoors were almost as bad and on 8 December in the Festival Hall the fully lit balcony was invisible from the stage (Stewart, 1953, p. 2). Unfortunately, the fog of December 1952 was not unique and similar intensities seem to recur, though not perhaps in quite so disastrous or persistent a form, at intervals of only a few years (Bonacina, 1950). From 1947 to 1956 there were five occasions when thick fog, i.e. a visibility less than 220 yd (200 m), lasted 24 hr or more at Kingsway, giving a total of 159 hr. In the same ten years there were ten such occasions (373 hr) at London Airport and 3 (107 hr) at Croydon. The longest periods of thick fog were 51 hr at Kingsway, 69 hr at London Airport and 44 hr at Croydon (Kelly, 1963, p. 182). Persistent (24 hr or more) dense fog, i.e. visibilities of 44 yd (40 m) or less, occurred twice at Kingsway and Croydon, and once at London Airport during the same decade. Differences between the three stations are in line with previous findings in this chapter but with an amelioration of conditions at Croydon because of its height (220 ft (67 m)).

London is indeed a foggy place, especially the low-lying suburbs which suffer some of the densest, most persistent visitations. They have provided the climatological setting for many novels and a series of special investigations, and Londoners who have experienced them will agree with Dr Ewart (1902, p. 27) who described them as 'the climax of evil and of suffering'. There is, on the other hand, some evidence of a recent improvement in conditions, probably an encouraging consequence of a less polluted atmosphere.

9 Cloud amount

*The few who lift their eyes to London sunsets find in them
Turneresque beauties which are purely ideal and exceedingly
gorgeous.*

Wm. Ewart, M.D., 1902

POLLUTION, fogs and chasm-like streets combine to rob Londoners of the extensive
sky panoramas enjoyed by those living in the surrounding country. There is, indeed,
some evidence of increased cloud cover over the city, but urban-rural contrasts in
cloudiness are less easily documented than most other elements. This is because of the
inadequacy of records of comparable accuracy (cloud amounts are estimated), free from
orographic and other non-urban influences. Since 1949, estimates of cloud cover have
been made in oktas (eighths) of sky; before this the units were tenths. Table 75 gives
some indication of the diurnal cycle of cloud amounts at Kew for a period when
published records are available and the times of observations remained constant.

TABLE 75

Average cloud amount, 0700–2100 GMT, Kew, 1926–37

GMT					
0700	0900	1300	1500	1800	2100
			tenths		
7·1	7·3	7·5	7·5	6·7	5·9

Source of data: London, Meteorological Office, *Observatories' year book* 1926–37

There are no observations of cloud amounts at Kew during the middle of the night but
the indications are that average amounts fall from about three-quarter cover in the mid-
afternoon to little above half-sky cover in the hours before dawn when thermals and turbulence are weak. There will, of course, be changes of cloud type as well as amount,
with a tendency to stratiform clouds by night and cumuliform types by day, though the
differences are of degree only and many of the fluctuations are non-periodic, depending
upon irregular changes in the physical properties of the atmosphere.

Annual changes in average cloud amounts are given in Table 76 which is based
upon six daily observations between 0700 and 2100 GMT.

TABLE 76

Average monthly daytime cloud amount, Kew, 1926–37

Jan	Feb	Mar	Apr	May	June	July	Aug	Sept	Oct	Nov	Dec	Yr
						tenths						
7·2	7·2	6·8	7·3	6·8	6·8	6·8	6·5	6·4	6·8	7·4	7·4	7·0

Source of data: London, Meteorological Office, *Observatories' year book* 1926–37

Daytime London skies are clearest in autumn when anticyclones are common, and cloud-iest in the disturbed, Westerly weather of winter, although differences are relatively small. The only notable exception in the years analysed was April, with a mean cloud cover in excess of both the preceding and following months. This is partly the result of the frequent northeasterly and easterly cold airstreams with high humidities in this month, particularly before about 1930. Averages of 0900, 1500 and 2100 GMT observations during a more recent decade show the reverse condition (Table 77).

TABLE 77

Average monthly daytime cloud amount, Kew, 1951–60

Jan	Feb	Mar	Apr	May	June	July	Aug	Sept	Oct	Nov	Dec	Yr
					oktas							
6·0	5·9	5·6	5·2	5·5	5·6	5·6	5·4	5·3	5·3	6·0	6·1	5·6

Source of data: London, Meteorological Office, *Monthly weather reports* 1951–60

Daytime skies in April were clearer than in any other month between 1951–60 and in six of the 10 years, April was sunnier than usual. Apart from this spring break, the most obvious transition was from clearer skies in autumn to more overcast skies in winter, with a rapid change from October to November.

Table 78 shows the average number of observations per month, at 1500 GMT, of the stated cloud amounts.

TABLE 78

Average monthly frequency of stated cloud amounts, 1500 GMT, Kew, 1951–60

Oktas	Jan	Feb	Mar	Apr	May	June	July	Aug	Sept	Oct	Nov	Dec
					Average number of days							
0	0·8	0·5	1·5	1·6	0·7	0·3	0·4	0·1	0·6	1·4	0·3	0·7
1–2	2·2	1·8	1·2	2·5	2·1	2·0	2·0	1·7	2·0	2·1	2·3	2·0
3–5	4·7	3·7	6·6	5·5	6·1	6·6	5·6	6·8	7·4	6·2	4·9	4·9
6–7	9·3	11·2	12·1	13·4	15·5	14·8	16·9	15·5	14·2	12·0	11·6	10·4
8	12·8	10·9	9·3	7·0	6·6	6·3	6·1	6·9	5·8	9·2	10·4	11·3
9*	1·2	0·2	0·3	0·0	0·0	0·0	0·0	0·0	0·0	0·1	0·5	1·7

* sky obscured or cloud amount impossible to estimate owing to darkness

Source of data: London, Meteorological Office *Monthly weather reports* 1951–60

In all months except January the modal afternoon cloud cover is 6–7 oktas; in January, completely overcast skies occur on almost half the days, in September on about one afternoon in five. Clear skies, on the other hand, are rare in all months and particularly in August. Their highest frequency is in spring and autumn when anticyclones are common but convection is relatively weak.

Brunt (1918, p. 3) found that westerly winds at Kew in winter were generally less cloudy than those from the east, and showed a much stronger tendency to night-time clearance. In April he found the beginning of a marked summer tendency to a night-time clearance but this was delayed longer after sunset than in winter because of the stronger daytime heating (and stronger heat-islands?). Brunt (1918, pp. 5–6) also co-pared cloud amounts at Kew Observatory and Greenwich (in east London) but with in-conclusive results.

An analysis of mean daily values of cloud cover for each day of the year was made by Ellis (1896) using the Greenwich Observatory values for the 50 years 1841–90. Day-to-day variations of this mean were, as one would expect, very irregular and incapable of logical explanation other than pure chance. There was little correspondence with more recent singularities in the pattern of weather.

CLOUD AMOUNTS IN GREATER LONDON

For the reasons mentioned, it is impossible to compose a detailed picture of variations of cloudiness over Greater London. Published records are at present available for only London Airport and Kew, less than 6 mi (9·7 km) apart in west London (Fig. 5), but even over this short distance there are measurable differences in daytime cloud amounts (0900–2100 GMT). From 1948–60 the average annual excess in the estimated cloud cover at Kew above that at London Airport was 0·1 oktas at 0900, 0·2 oktas at 1500 and 0·1 oktas at 2100 GMT. Contrasts were greatest in summer and least in winter. During these 13 years Kew had 6·2 per cent less clear days and 5·9 more overcast days than London Airport at the 1500 GMT observation. This suggests a tendency, especially in summer, for cloud to develop over London, and the most important cause is likely to be mechanical and thermal turbulence over the city. Observation suggests that con-vection may also be triggered off by high ground in the London area such as the ridge between Hampstead and Alexandra Palace. Certainly these areas, as we shall now see, receive appreciably more precipitation than the low-lying valley tracts of the Thames and its tributaries.

10 Precipitation

. . . and over the tree-tops I saw the London towers and spires
appear and disappear as the weather cleared or thickened.

Hans Christian Andersen, 1857

IT SEEMS, at first sight, plausible to postulate that because of increased pollution, and the consequent increase in condensation nuclei, as well as more active thermal and mechanical turbulence above London, there will be not only increased cloud amount but also more precipitation over the urban area. The idea has been tested in a number of cities (two of the most recent résumés of findings are those by Landsberg (1956) and Veryard (1958)) with varying results, although many of the studies seem to show slightly increased precipitation over the built-up areas. But all such studies, indeed all comparisons of precipitation at different sites, suffer from the fickleness of the element, the relatively poor sampling inherent in normal rain-gauge measurements and the large number of parameters involved in differentiating one station from another.

Before embarking on an investigation of rainfall in and about Greater London the position at Kew will be considered to establish the basic patterns of change.

PRECIPITATION AT KEW

Diurnal changes

For obvious reasons, we would not expect to find a diurnal cycle of rainfall as definitive as those of other elements such as temperature but, averaged over a sufficiently long period and for all days of the year, there are some significant and understandable changes during the course of the day. Hourly totals of annual precipitation (Fig. 76) are fairly uniform from late evening to early morning, declining a little before noon and then rising steeply to their peak in the late afternoon. There is a sharp reduction after 1900 GMT to the diurnal minimum at 2100 GMT. The afternoon and early evening peak in totals is the most significant feature of this daily cycle and follows strong convection at this time of the day. The morning reduction may be explained partly by temperature increases with the consequent break-down of inversions and the dispersal of stratiform clouds.

On a monthly basis an extremely complex picture of diurnal change emerges, the details of which appear to have no meaning beyond pure chance. Fig. 77 shows that there are two peaks in the mean diurnal cycle of annual rainfall duration. One occurs one to two hours before dawn, and the other one to two hours after sunset. Minima occur in the hour before midday and between 2100 and 2200 GMT. By combining the statistics used in Figs. 76 and 77 we obtain a measure of rainfall intensity (Fig. 78). This

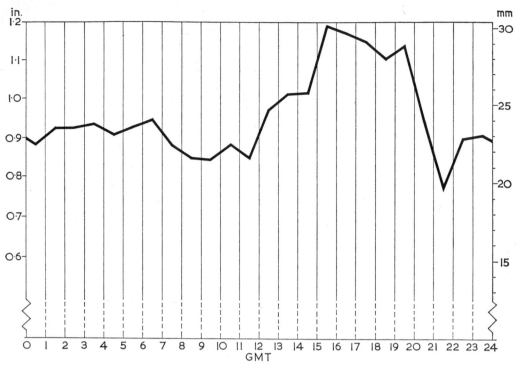

Fig 76 Average diurnal variation of rainfall amount at Kew, 1927–56
(Source of data: *Observatories' year book* 1927–56)

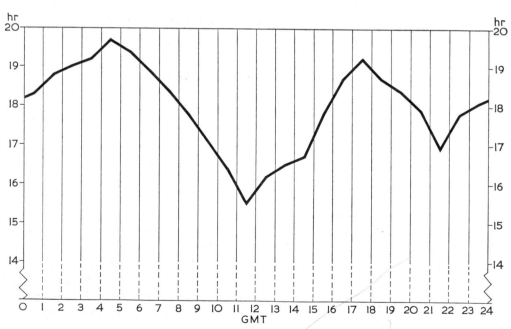

Fig 77 Average diurnal variation of rainfall duration at Kew, 1927–56
(Source of data: *Observatories' year book* 1927–56)

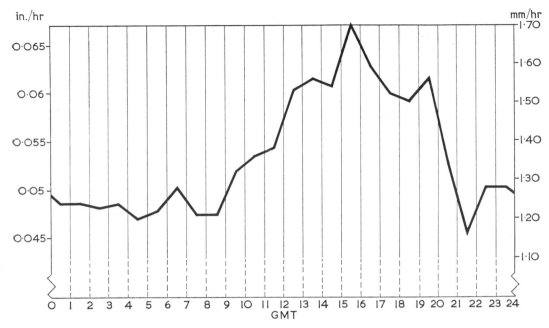

Fig 78 Average diurnal variation of rainfall intensity at Kew, 1927–56
(Source of data: *Observatories' year book* 1927–56)

makes it clear that although rain falls most frequently and/or continuously during the early morning and late afternoon, and with almost equal average durations at these times, the intensity of the early-morning rain is low whilst that in the afternoon is almost 50 per cent higher. Obviously, late-night and early-morning rain is prolonged but light compared with afternoon rain which has a tendency to fall in heavy showers— a contrast of type which is to be expected.

Monthly features of these hourly parameters are highly complex and many of the intricacies depend upon a few exceptional occurrences; for this reason they are not illustrated here.

Seasonal changes

Table 79 gives the monthly and annual averages of precipitation for the period 1916–50 at Kew. If the average annual precipitation of 23·95 in. (610·87 mm) were evenly distributed throughout the year then 8·49 per cent would fall in each 31-day month, 8·22 per cent in each 30-day month and 7·67 (or 7·92) per cent in February. We see, then, that the wettest months, July and November, have appreciably more than an 'even share' and that the driest month, March, has very much less. Using this same form of comparison, January, July, August, October and November are wetter than average and the months from February to June are drier than average, with September and December receiving very nearly their mean proportional total. The most notable feature of the annual distribution is the fairly dry period from late winter to early summer, which may seem surprising to anyone familiar with the often waterlogged soils in the first part of this period. The explanation lies, of course, in the build up of ground water in autumn and winter at a time when evaporation is low.

TABLE 79

Monthly and annual averages of precipitation, Kew, 1916–50

	Jan	Feb	Mar	Apr	May	June
in.	2·14	1·55	1·46	1·81	1·81	1·72
mm	54·86	40·64	37·85	45·97	45·97	43·69
per cent	8·9	6·4	6·1	7·6	7·6	7·2

	July	Aug	Sept	Oct	Nov	Dec	Yr
in.	2·44	2·24	1·98	2·25	2·49	2·06	23·95
mm	61·98	56·90	50·29	57·15	63·25	52·32	610·87
per cent	10·2	9·3	8·3	9·4	10·4	8·6	100·0

Source: London, Meteorological Office 1958 *Averages of rainfall for Great Britain and Northern Ireland, 1916–50.* M.O. 635 (H.M.S.O.)

Table 80 gives the mean monthly and annual values of precipitation duration. The period of years is not the same as for total precipitation (Table 79), but this should make only small differences.

TABLE 80

Monthly and annual averages of precipitation duration, Kew, 1927–56

	Jan	Feb	Mar	Apr	May	June
hr	51·5	38·1	35·0	34·6	32·9	26·9
per cent	11·9	8·8	8·1	8·0	7·6	6·2

	July	Aug	Sept	Oct	Nov	Dec	Yr
hr	26·0	27·6	28·7	35·1	50·6	44·6	431·6
per cent	6·0	6·4	6·7	8·1	11·7	10·5	100·0

Source of data: London, Meteorological Office *Observatories' year book* 1927–56

The large number of hours of precipitation in November is the only break in a smooth progression from high values in winter to low values in summer. In July the duration averages about 50 min per day but in January it is almost double this. On average, the number of hours with precipitation totals about 5 per cent of the year. For the same period as the duration analysis, Table 81 gives values of mean monthly precipitation intensity.

There is fairly simple progression from a minimum of precipitation intensity in February when some will fall as snow, to a maximum in August, when thunderstorms will be frequent. Sharp changes in intensity between June and July, and August and September are obviously connected with changes in the amount and depth of convective activity.

TABLE 81

Monthly and annual averages of precipitation intensity, Kew, 1927–56

	Jan	Feb	Mar	Apr	May	June
in./hr	0·042	0·041	0·041	0·045	0·054	0·067
mm/hr	1·06	1·03	1·04	1·13	1·38	1·69

	July	Aug	Sept	Oct	Nov	Dec
in./hr	0·084	0·086	0·065	0·060	0·052	0·044
mm/hr	2·13	2·19	1·65	1·52	1·32	1·11

Source of data: London, Meteorological Office *Observatories' year book* 1927–56

These in turn are related not only to the annual cycle of solar radiation and temperature but also to changes in air-mass types, especially the high frequency of Polar maritime air during summer.

In computing the average precipitation amount and duration, totals have in each case been divided by the number of days in each month. It is of some interest, however, to determine the average precipitation amount and duration per rain-day. But first, Table 82 lists the average number of rain-days (with 0·01 in. (0·2 mm) or more) per month.

TABLE 82

Monthly and annual averages of rain-days, Kew, 1927–56

Jan	Feb	Mar	Apr	May	June	July	Aug	Sept	Oct	Nov	Dec	Yr
15·9	12·0	11·1	12·1	11·6	11·2	11·6	11·3	12·4	12·9	14·8	14·4	151·3

Source of data: London, Meteorological Office *Observatories' year book* 1927–56

Rain-days account for about 41 per cent of the year and their frequency varies from about one day in two from November to January to approximately two days in five in June.

Using these data we can calculate the average precipitation per rain-day. The results are given in Table 83.

TABLE 83

Monthly and annual averages of precipitation per rain-day, Kew, 1927–56

	Jan	Feb	Mar	Apr	May	June	July	Aug	Sept	Oct	Nov	Dec
in.	0·14	0·13	0·13	0·13	0·15	0·16	0·19	0·21	0·15	0·16	0·18	0·14
mm	3·43	3·29	3·27	3·23	3·91	4·06	4·80	5·33	3·84	4·14	4·50	3·46

Year

in.	0·15
mm	3·94

Source of data: London, Meteorological Office *Observatories' year book* 1927–56

In this analysis July and August have by far the highest falls of precipitation on rain-days, in other words, if on a particular day it rains at all, more rain is likely to fall in

July or August than in February, March or April. But the pattern of duration is rather different, as Table 84 shows.

TABLE 84

Monthly and annual averages of precipitation duration per rain-day, Kew, 1927–56

	Jan	Feb	Mar	Apr	May	June	July	Aug	Sept	Oct	Nov	Dec	Yr
hr	3·2	3·2	3·2	2·9	2·8	2·4	2·2	2·4	2·3	2·7	3·4	3·1	2·9

Source of data: London, Meteorological Office *Observatories' year book* 1927–56

It will be observed that when rain does fall, it lasts up to 50 per cent longer in winter than in summer and longest of all in November, a month noted for its extended periods of light rains.

In order to correct any impression of uniformity in monthly averages, Tables 85 and 86 have been prepared. These show the percentage frequency of various monthly precipitation amounts and durations during the 30 years 1927–56.

TABLE 85

Percentage frequency of various monthly totals of precipitation, Kew, 1927–56

mm	in.	Jan	Feb	Mar	Apr	May	June
				per cent			
0·1– 20·0	0·01–0·79	3·3	23·3	33·3	16·6	13·3	10·0
20·1– 40·0	0·80–1·58	36·6	40·0	26·6	33·3	26·6	30·0
40·1– 60·0	1·59–2·36	23·3	20·0	20·0	40·0	33·3	40·0
60·1– 80·0	2·37–3·16	16·6	3·3	10·0	6·6	13·3	6·6
80·1–100·0	3·17–3·94	13·3	6·6	6·6	3·3	10·0	10·0
100·1–120·0	3·95–4·72	3·3	3·3	3·3		3·3	3·3
120·1–140·0	4·73–5·51	3·3	3·3				
140·1–160·0	5·52–6·30						
160·1–180·0	6·31–7·09						
Average	mm	54·6	39·4	36·3	39·1	45·5	45·4
	in.	2·2	1·6	1·4	1·5	1·8	1·8

mm	in.	July	Aug	Sept	Oct	Nov	Dec
				per cent			
0·1– 20·0	0·01–0·79	6·6	16·6	13·3	13·3	6·6	13·3
20·1– 40·0	0·80–1·58	23·3	13·3	20·0	23·3	23·3	26·6
40·1– 60·0	1·59–2·36	30·0	23·3	40·0	30·0	20·0	36·6
60·1– 80·0	2·37–3·16	23·3	20·0	20·0	16·6	13·3	6·6
80·1–100·0	3·17–3·94	10·0	16·6	3·3	6·6	13·3	10·0
100·1–120·0	3·95–4·72	3·3	3·3	3·3		13·3	6·6
120·1–140·0	4·73–5·51	3·3	3·3		10·0	6·6	
140·1–160·0	5·52–6·30		3·3				
160·1–180·0	6·31–7·09					3·3	
Average	mm	55·6	60·3	47·5	53·3	66·7	49·9
	in.	2·2	2·4	1·9	2·1	2·6	2·0

Source of data: London, Meteorological Office *Observatories' year book* 1927–56

There is clearly an appreciable scatter of monthly totals of precipitation and many months when the accumulated precipitation differs noticeably from the average. This is also true of monthly totals of precipitation duration (Table 86).

TABLE 86

Percentage frequency of monthly totals of precipitation duration, Kew, 1927–56

hr	Jan	Feb	Mar	Apr	May	June
				per cent		
0·1– 20·0	3·3	20·0	33·3	16·6	16·6	26·6
20·1– 40·0	40·0	36·6	26·6	56·6	56·6	56·6
40·1– 60·0	20·0	30·0	26·6	23·3	23·3	16·6
60·1– 80·0	26·6	6·6	10·0		3·3	
80·1–100·0	10·0	3·3		3·3		
100·1–120·0		3·3	3·3			
Average (hr)	51·5	38·1	35·0	34·6	32·9	26·9

hr	July	Aug	Sept	Oct	Nov	Dec
				per cent		
0·1– 20·0	26·6	26·6	26·6	23·3	13·3	13·3
20·1– 40·0	60·0	50·0	53·3	36·6	23·3	33·3
40·1– 60·0	13·3	20·0	20·0	33·3	26·6	33·3
60·1– 80·0		3·3		3·3	20·0	6·6
80·1–100·0				3·3	16·6	13·3
100·1–120·0						
Average (hr)	26·0	27·6	28·7	35·1	50·6	44·6

Source of data: London, Meteorological Office *Observatories' year book* 1927–56

As one would expect, the greatest variations from the average occur in winter when the character of the general circulation can vary enormously one year from the next.

Extending the period of analysis will generally widen the range of eventualities. The following Tables, 87, 88, show this and will define the limits of occurrence which can be reasonably expected.

TABLE 87

Monthly and annual averages and extremes of precipitation, Kew, 1866–1950

	Jan	Feb	Mar	Apr	May	June	
Average							
in.	2·00	1·51	1·53	1·67	1·74	1·97	
mm	50·80	38·35	38·86	42·42	44·20	50·04	

	July	Aug	Sept	Oct	Nov	Dec	Yr
in.	2·33	2·24	2·03	2·47	2·28	2·18	23·95
mm	59·18	56·90	51·56	62·74	57·91	55·37	608·33

Table 87—*cont.*

	Jan	Feb	Mar	Apr	May	June
Highest monthly total						
in.	5·02	4·11*	4·66	3·90	4·11	7·21
mm	127·51	104·39	118·36	99·06	104·39	183·13

	July	Aug	Sept	Oct	Nov	Dec	Yr
in.	5·11†	6·51	5·71	5·95	6·76	6·37	38·18
mm	129·79	165·35	145·03	151·13	171·70	161·80	969·77

Lowest monthly total

	Jan	Feb	Mar	Apr	May	June
in.	0·44	0·09	0·02	0·05	0·17	0·04
mm	11·18	2·29	0·51	1·27	4·32	1·02

	July	Aug	Sept	Oct	Nov	Dec	Yr
in.	0·15	0·09	0·16‡	0·15	0·29	0·24	12·20
mm	3·81	2·29	4·06	3·81	7·37	6·10	309·88

* 4·99 in. (126·6 mm) in 1951
† 5·92 in. (150·37 mm) in 1956
‡ 0·10 in. (2·54 mm) in 1959

Sources: London, Meteorological Office 1951 *Climate of Kew Observatory, 1871–1950.* (Typescript); London, Meteorological Office 1963d Rainfall over the areas of the Thames and Lee Conservancies, London, and the Brent, the Wandle and the Ravensbourne valleys, 1916–50. *Hydro. Mem.* No. 22 (Typescript)

TABLE 88

Monthly and annual averages and extremes of rain-days, Kew, 1871–1950

Jan	Feb	Mar	Apr	May	June	July	Aug	Sept	Oct	Nov	Dec	Yr
						number of days						
Average												
17	14	14	13	13	12	13	13	13	17	16	17	171
Highest monthly total												
28	24	28	25	22	23	26	26	26	30	25	26	255
Lowest monthly total												
6	2	1	2	3	1	5	3	2	4	5	5	104

Source: London, Meteorological Office 1951 *Climate of Kew Observatory, 1871–1950* (Typescript)

The figures in Tables 87 and 88 speak for themselves: their lesson of climatic variability in London needs no emphasis.

Of considerable importance in precipitation studies is the incidence of heavy falls of rain in short periods (of two hours or less). Most of these occur in summer, particularly on days with thunderstorms. The standard classification of rainfall intensities in short periods follows the terms and definitions proposed in *British rainfall 1935.* This divided the precipitation-time complex into four areas labelled: 'very rare' falls (intensities), 'remarkable' falls, 'noteworthy' falls, and falls too numerous for discussion. Records representing a frequency of less than once in 160 years are classed as 'very rare', less than once in 40 years as 'remarkable' and less than one in ten years as 'noteworthy'. The annual issues of *British rainfall* give details of some of the more exceptional rainfall intensities, and those from 1860–1960 in the London area are listed in *Hydrological Memoranda* No. 22 (London, Meteorological Office, 1963d). A general impression of the frequency of heavy falls of precipitation is given by Table 89. The first grade in each column represents (or in one case, very nearly so) a 'noteworthy' occurrence.

TABLE 89

Mean number of days per annum on which specified amounts of rain fell in specified times, Kew, 1937–56

0·4 in. (10·16 mm)			0·6 in. (15·24 mm)		
within	5 min	0·10	within	15 min	0·20
	15 min	0·55		30 min	0·35
	30 min	1·20		60 min	0·55
	60 min	1·80		120 min	0·80

0·8 in. (20·32 mm)			1·0 in. (25·4 mm)		
within	30 min	0·15	within	60 min	0·20
	60 min	0·30		120 min	0·30
	120 min	0·35			

Source: London, Meteorological Office 1960 *British rainfall 1957* (H.M.S.O.)

Thus at Kew there will be falls equivalent to 0·4 in. (10·16 mm) in one hour on about two days in each year; 0·6 in. (15·244 mm) in one hour, once in two years; 0·8 in. (20·32 mm) in one hour, once in three years; and 1·0 in. (25·4 mm) in one hour, in one year in five.

Some of the most intense falls of rain are very short-lived and although they often do a great deal of local damage, heavy rain over long periods usually leads to more widespread flooding. Table 90 lists the maximum daily precipitation at Kew during the past 91 years.

TABLE 90

Maximum daily precipitation, Kew, 1870–1960

	Jan	Feb	Mar	Apr	May	June
in.	1·60	1·13	1·12	1·38	1·31	2·36
mm	40·64	28·70	28·45	35·05	33·27	59·94

	July	Aug	Sept	Oct	Nov	Dec
in.	2·29	2·14	1·83	1·41	1·39	1·46
mm	58·17	54·36	46·48	35·81	35·31	37·08

Sources: London, Meteorological Office 1951 *Climate of Kew Observatory, 1871–1950.* (Typescript); London, Meteorological Office 1963d Rainfall over the areas of the Thames and Lee Conservancies, London, and the Brent, the Wandle and the Ravensbourne valleys, 1916–50. *Hydro. Mem.* No. 22 (Typescript)

P

As before, the highest daily totals come during the summer months when they almost equal, or even exceed, the average monthly figure.

For the period 1927–56 Table 91 lists the frequencies of various daily precipitation totals by months. Like others for this period, it is based upon nearly 11,000 records.

TABLE 91

Monthly percentage frequencies of various daily precipitation totals, Kew, 1927–56

in.	<0·01	0·01 to 0·03	0·04 to 0·20	0·21 to 0·40	0·41 to 0·59	0·60 to 0·79	0·80 to 0·99	>0·99
mm	0·0 to 0·1	0·2 to 0·9	1·0 to 5·0	5·1 to 10·0	10·1 to 15·0	15·1 to 20·0	20·1 to 25·0	>25·0
				per cent				
Jan	48·80	17·32	22·57	7·74	2·04	0·96	0·11	0·43
Feb	57·00	14·54	18·55	7·02	2·26	0·48	0·12	
Mar	64·29	12·26	16·01	4·41	2·26	0·54	0·11	0·11
Apr	59·55	13·12	18·76	5·99	1·89	0·44	0·22	
May	62·56	9·79	16·87	6·45	2·90	1·08	0·22	0·11
June	62·55	11·01	16·65	5·56	2·78	0·78	0·33	0·22
July	62·67	11·50	15·05	6·02	2·26	1·08	0·54	0·86
Aug	63·53	8·50	15·90	6·02	3·01	1·51	0·65	0·86
Sept	58·77	13·68	17·43	4·99	3·56	1·22	0·22	0·11
Oct	58·48	13·88	15·90	6·87	3·01	0·54	0·75	0·64
Nov	50·66	15·44	19·21	8·11	3·89	1·33	0·67	0·67
Dec	53·54	16·35	19·34	7·53	2·26	0·43	0·32	0·26

Source of data: London, Meteorological Office *Observatories' year book* 1927–56

This is a simpler analysis than that by Dewar (1934) who classified rainfall amounts at Kew into four grades and studied their frequency in six-hourly as well as 10-day periods. But rainfall's characteristic variability tends to place severe limitations upon such very short period analyses, as Bonacina pointed out in the discussion following Dewar's paper (Bonacina, 1934, p. 312), and this makes one hesitate before using too refined tools in the analysis of rainfall. The main features of Table 91, such as the incidence of rain-days and high rainfall totals, have already been commented upon. The other details are related to changes in the character of the atmospheric circulation as it affects London; these will be considered in the following sections in the light of day-to-day changes.

Day-to-day changes

Day-to-day changes in the averages of precipitation (0000–2400 GMT) at Kew, 1871–1950, are shown in Fig. 79. They form a very complicated sequence with high frequency changes having an amplitude of about 0·3–0·4 in. (7·6–10·2 mm). Many of these do not appear to be attributable to anything beyond pure chance but certain of the more pronounced differences, or changes of trend, are obviously related to fluctuations in the sequence of air masses.

The period of generally high precipitation from 29 January to 3 February coincides with a notable period of Cyclonic weather which ends as suddenly as it frequently

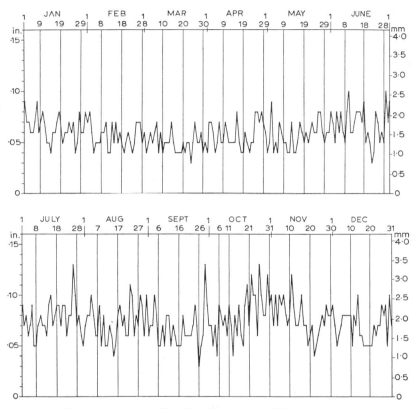

Fig 79 Average daily rainfall amount at Kew, 1871–1950
(Source of data: London, Meteorological Office 1951 *Climate of Kew Observatory*, 1871–1950. Typescript)

begins. The period of much lighter average rainfall from 10–26 March, on the other hand, occurs at a time when surface temperatures are still low and anticyclones are particularly common at Kew. Very different conditions arise in the second half of May, also a time of high Anticyclonic frequency. Daytime warming is, at this time, sufficient to generate strong lapses of temperatures and high, towering cumulus and cumulo-nimbus clouds, particularly near the margins of anticyclones which often give heavy showers so that the whole trend of the average daily rainfall graph rises to a higher level (Fig. 79). The notably dry period around 22 June occurs at a time when the Azores high frequently extends (usually in the form of a ridge) to cover southeast England, and strong subsidence inhibits cloud development giving clear skies and low rainfall.

Equally notable is the sudden increase of precipitation in late July. This coincides with a well-marked period of Cyclonic weather with shallow, slow-moving depressions giving many heavy showers and longer periods of rain. Another period of light rain, from 11–16 August, appears to be associated with Anticyclonic weather which is terminated by a return to a dominantly Westerly type circulation. Precipitation amounts fall again in the middle of September with an increase in the frequency of anticyclones affecting Kew, but this period is broken by a short but intense period of Cyclonic weather which is probably responsible for the very notable equal-highest average precipitation of 0·13 in. (3·81 mm) on 29 September. The second half of October and the first half of November frequently form one of the stormiest periods of the year and certainly amongst the rainiest (Fig. 79). A peak in Anticyclonic weather and a minimum in Westerly and Cyclonic weather in the third week in November is reflected in a fall in average precipitation, but a return to stormy, Westerly weather in the first half of December sees an increase in daily amounts. Soon after mid-December, an extension of a Continental winter high frequently dominates the weather, and skies are clearer and rainfall less, but soon after Christmas Day, stormy, cloudy weather with frequent rain is usual in most years.

No attempt has been made to plot or discuss daily extremes of rainfall because of their erratic and somewhat fortuitous nature. A study of heavy rains lasting from 1–48 hr at Kew Observatory has, however, been made by Bilham and Hay (1934).

Lowndes (1962) has made a study of spells of rainy days at Kew for the period 1935–59. For the purposes of his study he defined a wet spell as a period of five days with (i) at least 15 mm (0·59 in.) of precipitation, and no day with less than 1 mm (0·04 in.); or (ii) at least 20 mm (0·79 in.) with one such day having less than 1 mm (0·04 in.); or (iii) at least 25 mm (0·98 in.) with two such days. The average monthly frequency of these spells is given in Table 92.

TABLE 92

Average number of wet spells, Kew, 1935–59

Jan	Feb	Mar	Apr	May	June	July	Aug	Sept	Oct	Nov	Dec
1·1	0·6	0·6	0·4	0·8	0·6	0·6	0·9	0·5	1·0	1·3	0·7

Source: Lowndes, C. A. S. 1962 Wet spells at London. *Met. Mag.* London, 91, pp. 98–104

The number of spells in one year ranged from four in 1955 to fourteen in 1958; the average number was nine, of which five occurred in the winter half of the year and four in the summer half. Though relatively infrequent in occurrence, they accounted for 45 per cent of the precipitation at Kew (Lowndes, 1962, p. 104). Of the total precipitation during these spells, 63 per cent was associated with depressions or waves and 32 per cent with fronts. Depressions from the south and southwest and fronts from the south provided the highest average precipitation. Nearly all the wet spells during summer were associated with thunderstorms in southern England but in winter, only one-third to a half were so associated.

Fig. 80 shows the annual progression of average daily values of the duration of

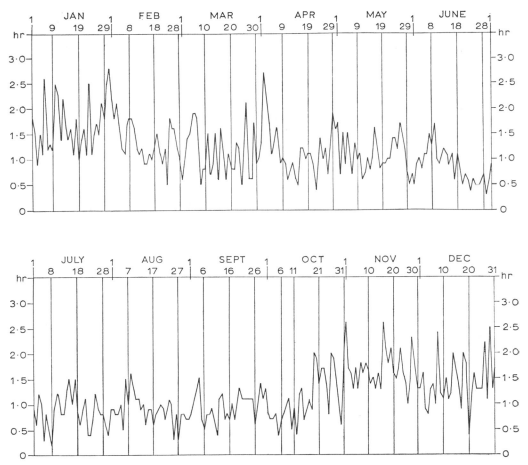

Fig 80 Average daily rainfall duration at Kew, 1927–56
(Source of data: *Observatories' year book* 1927–56)

precipitation at Kew, 1927–56, a measure of obvious importance. The period is unavoidably different from, and shorter than, that used for Fig. 79 and chance occurrences are likely to be even more influential. Nevertheless, in a number of periods, characteristics seem to be maintained over several days departing notably from the general trend. The broad features of the month-to-month changes have already received comment and need not be repeated here: our present concern is with changes over shorter periods of a few days, such as the week of high average precipitation durations at the end of January and the beginning of February which we have previously seen to be associated with considerable precipitation during a period of Cyclonic weather. Even so, the significance of the peak value of 1·8 hr at this time is small, for in only 16 of the 30 years analysed was the daily duration above the period trend value of approximately 1·5 hr.

After 31 January there are only three days until 19 October when the daily duration reaches 2 hr per day. Late February and early March are usually stormy, with depressions centred over the North Sea, and there are at this time two blocks of four days, each with high average numbers of hours with precipitation, but broken by low values around 1 April (Fig. 80). Early April is again noted as a period which is frequently cyclonic in character, and the second highest average daily precipitation duration of the whole year occurs on 2 April. On this date, values were above the period mean of 1·2 hr in 19 of the 30 years analysed.

After 7 April, values oscillate about 1 hr per day until about 10 June when the period average falls to 0·8 hr and remains at this level until a sharp increase, on about 19 October, to its winter level of about 1·6 hr per day. These features are closely associated with marked changes in the ratio of Westerly and Cyclonic weather on the one hand and Anticyclonic and Southerly weather on the other (Fig. 13). We have already noted how the number of anticyclones affecting the weather in southeast England falls dramatically after 10 October when, it is noted, daily precipitation durations commence their rise to high winter levels. The very low average on 30 October occurs during a period of fine weather known as St Martin's Summer. In 24 of the 30 years analysed, the rainfall was below the period average (1·4 hr) on this day. Another day with a notably small average number of hours with precipitation is 20 December, a day in which the weather in many years is dominated by the first major advance of the winter Continental high. During the years analysed, precipitation was below the period average of 1·5 hr on 26 of the 30 occasions; indeed, there was no rain at all on 23 occasions. This day has one of the highest frequencies of no measurable rainfall, but is soon followed by days with very high averages (Fig. 80).

Changes in the average daily intensity or rate of fall of precipitation are shown in Fig. 81. In this context it is useful to remember that precipitation is classified as slight, moderate or heavy according to the following criteria: slight rain is equivalent to falls of not more than 0·02 in. (0·5 mm) per hour; moderate rain to falls of 0·02–0·16 in. (0·5–4·0 mm) per hour; and heavy rain to falls of more than 0·16 in. (4·0 mm) per hour. Day-to-day variations are very erratic, particularly in summer, but many are the result of outstanding occurrences on just one of the thirty occasions analysed for each day. For this reason, one cannot read too deeply into the details of change. But the almost uniform general intensity from late December to the end of the first week in May is noticeable, after which there is a rise to a peak of smoothed intensity values in the last week in August. Finally, there is a gradual reduction of intensities which levels off in the last week of December.

In many circumstances, whether or not it will rain on a particular day is more important than the amount or even its duration, and for this reason Figs. 82 and 83 have been drawn. Fig. 82 shows the percentage frequency of occasions of no measurable rainfall (including all forms of precipitation), i.e. less than 0·005 in. (0·127 mm), at Kew 1871–1950. In general, chances of a fine day are generally less than even in winter and somewhat better than even in summer. Many of the minor, short period, changes are not significant but certain of the more persistent singularities fit in with previous findings about the annual pattern of weather. This was commented upon by Belasco (1948) in a similar investigation. The higher frequency of dry days from 24–27 January, for instance, coincides with a notable period of calm, clear weather associated with an expansion of

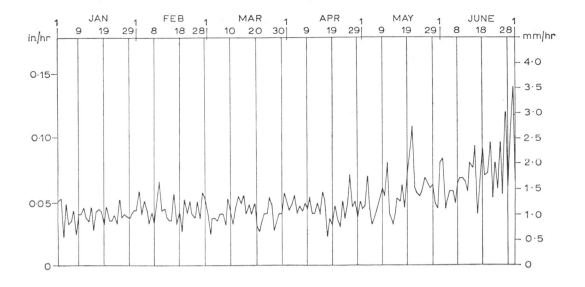

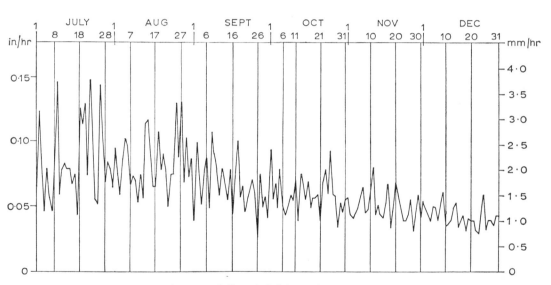

Fig 81 Average daily rainfall intensity at Kew, 1927–56
(Source of data: *Observatories' year book* 1927–56)

the winter Continental high, but this spell is broken by a well-defined increase in the incidence of Cyclonic weather and a sharp fall in the occurrence of fine days from 30 January to 2 February. This interlude is in most years succeeded by a return of Anti-cyclonic weather and frequent fine days until 26 February, when stormy conditions return with more frequent rain until about 1 March. One outstanding feature of Fig. 82 is the period from 18–25 April when dry days are particularly common. This comes

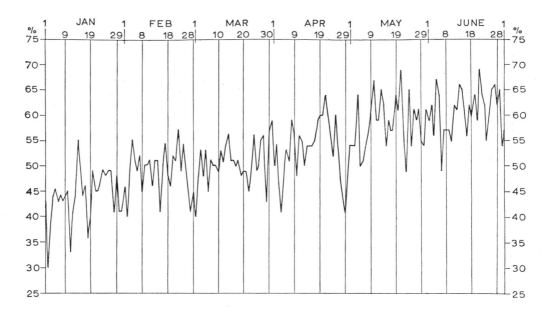

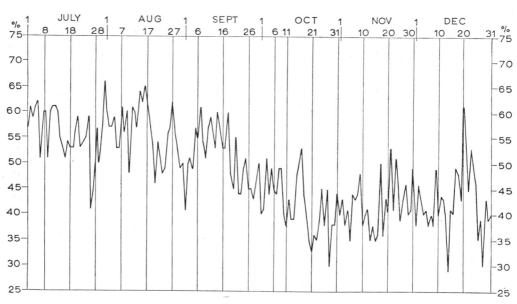

Fig 82 Daily percentage frequency of no measurable rainfall at Kew,
1871–1950
(Source of data: London, Meteorological Office 1951 *Climate of Kew
Observatory*, 1871–1950. Typescript)

at the end of a stormy period and accompanies a decrease in the occurrence of cyclones. In the second half of May, an increase in the frequency of Anticyclonic and Southerly weather and fine days is accompanied by many days without rain. The annual peak frequency of Anticyclonic weather falls on 21 May (Fig. 13), which is also the day on which the equal highest frequency of days of no measurable rainfall occurs. Dry days frequently accompany the pulsating expansion of the Azores high during June and two-thirds of the days in this month register a percentage frequency of days of no measurable rainfall of 60 per cent or more. This ratio falls to about 30 per cent in July and August and rainy days are particularly common on 26 and 27 July in a period when shallow lows centred over the British Isles are quite common. After a recovery to brighter days in mid-August, there are frequent rainy days from 20th to 24th. August ends and September begins with a series of rainy days, but during the second and third weeks of this month there are many fine, clear, Anticyclonic days; after 18 September they become much rarer and the majority of days have an above-average chance of rain. This trend continues into October and on half of the days there is only a two in five chance, or less, of there being no rain. October is one of the stormiest and wettest months of the year, especially its second half. This is also true of the first two weeks in November but in the middle of the month dry days are fairly common, in many years associated with a peak in the frequency of anticyclones. Days in the first half of December are amongst the most consistently rainy of the whole year and on 14 December the frequency of days with no measurable rainfall reaches its annual minimum of 29 per cent. Six days later, on 20 December, there is one of the highest frequencies, 61 per cent, at a time when the Continental high repeatedly dominates the weather. But after Christmas, days with rain are very common in a recurrence of stormy, Westerly conditions.

Belasco (1948) studied the frequency of rainless spells at Kew, defined as periods of one or more consecutive days with less than 0·1 mm (0·04 in.) of precipitation, and Table 93 has been taken from this analysis.

TABLE 93

Monthly and annual frequencies of rainless spells, Kew, 1878–1947

	Jan	Feb	Mar	Apr	May	June	July	Aug	Sept	Oct	Nov	Dec	Yr
						frequency in 70 years							
Duration of spell more than													
6 days	22	27	34	40	54	53	41	43	33	21	18	19	405
14 days	1	2	5	7	7	10	11	7	3	3	0	0	56
20 days	0	1	1	3	1	3	3	1	1	1	0	0	15

Source: Belasco, J. E. 1948 Rainless days of London. *Quart. J. R. Met. Soc.*, London, 74, p. 345

Short-lived rainless spells of only one or two days are most frequent in October and least frequent in July, those of more than six days being at a maximum in May and a minimum in November. The frequency of spells exceeding 14 days reaches its maximum in

July and, in the 70 years analysed, failed to appear in November and December. This, and the frequency of really long spells of rainless days of more than 20 days, shows that dry weather is much less persistent in autumn and winter than in summer and late spring, as one would expect.

The synoptic situation associated with dry spells, though briefly considered by Belasco, received more detailed treatment from Lowndes (1960) who found that the most striking feature was the high proportion (62 per cent) of dry spells, of three days or more, associated with high pressure to the southwest of the British Isles. In July and August this figure rose to about 80 per cent. A further 10 per cent were associated with high pressure to the west of Ireland. Davis (1963) has also shown a highly significant absence of rain at London Airport when at the 100 mb level, a marked ridge to the west of the British Isles gives winds at these heights between 290 and 020 degrees true.

As with temperature, neither McIntosh (1955, p. 369) nor Brazell (1963) found any evidence of compensation, either immediately following a wet or dry spell or after a time lag; if anything, quite the reverse was true.

The opposite side of this particular climatic coin is illustrated in Fig. 83. A total of 0·1 in. (2·54 mm) or more of rain represents the type of fall likely to bring all the multifarious consequences of a wet day. The frequency of such falls is therefore of some interest, but it is not intended to follow the changes day by day throughout the year since these are largely a consequence or development of what has already been said earlier.

Snow, hail and thunder

To this point, 'precipitation' and 'rainfall' have been taken to include all forms of precipitation. It is impossible to isolate the contribution of each of the several precipitation types but the occurrence of hail and snow is usually recorded and can be analysed.

The average number of days (0000–2400 GMT) per month on which snow or sleet has been observed to fall at Kew, 1871–1950, is given in Table 94.

TABLE 94

Average and extreme number of days with snow or sleet, Kew, 1871–1950

Jan	Feb	Mar	Apr	May	June	July	Aug	Sept	Oct	Nov	Dec
Average monthly total											
3	3	3	1	1					0+	1	2
Highest monthly total											
15*	18†	11	9	2					2	8	12

* 21 in January 1963
† 20 in February 1963

Source: London, Meteorological Office 1951 *Climate of Kew Observatory, 1871–1950* (Typescript)

For this particular period (although records are less reliable before 1900) the annual average was 14 days, but for the 30 years from 1926–55 it was 15·6 days (Manley, 1958,

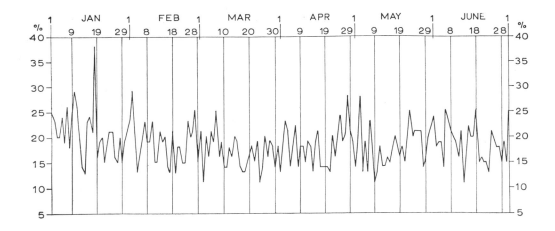

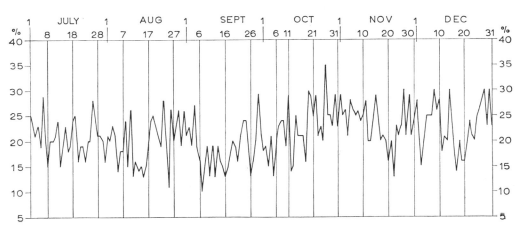

Fig 83 Daily percentage frequency of 0·1 in. (2·54 mm) or more of rainfall at
Kew, 1871–1950
(Source of data: London, Meteorological Office 1951 *Climate of Kew Ob-
servatory*, 1871–1950. Typescript)

p. 70). January, February and March supply about two-thirds of the total although
snow has fallen as early as October and as late as 27 May. The greatest frequency of
days with snow falling occurs about 10 January (Manley, 1963b, and 1957a, p. 43).

Kew's standards in the observation of snow falling, since about 1900, are classed
as 'first class' (Manley, 1958, p. 70) but this is not true of many stations. Much depends
upon the availability or alertness of the observer and, for this reason, the number of
'days of snow lying', i.e. occasions when half or more of the ground representative of
the station is covered with snow at 0900 GMT, is more frequently used. This is a particularly useful index in comparative studies. For Kew, the monthly and annual averages and extremes of this measure are shown in Table 95.

TABLE 95

Average and extreme number of days with snow lying, Kew, 1912–50

	Jan	Feb	Mar	Apr	May	June	July	Aug	Sept	Oct	Nov	Dec	Yr
Average monthly total													
	2	2	1	0+							0+	1	6
Highest monthly total													
	14*	26	4	1							2	9	44

*27 in January 1963

Source: London, Meteorological Office 1951 *Climate of Kew Observatory, 1871–1950* (Typescript)

Perhaps the most striking feature of Tables 94 and 95 is the disparity between averages and extremes; this is the feature which should be more widely realized and to some extent planned for.

For Croydon, details of the depths of undrifted snow at 0900 GMT for the ten winters from November 1946 to April 1956 also exist (Haywood, 1959). Only occasions when more than half the ground representative of the station was covered with snow were taken into consideration. The figures must be used with caution because of the short period covered by the analysis and the special features of site and situation at Croydon (201 ft (61·3 m)); nevertheless, the results are of some interest (Table 96).

TABLE 96

Percentage frequency of various undrifted snow depths at 0900 GMT,
Croydon, 1946–56

cm	0 to 2	3 to 5	6 to 10	11 to 15	16 to 20	21 to 30	over 30
in.	0 to 0·8	1·2 to 2·0	2·4 to 3·9	4·3 to 5·9	6·3 to 7·9	8·3 to 11·8	over 11·8
	43	42	8	3	3	1	

Source: Haywood, P. 1959 Frequencies of snow depth within given ranges at selected stations in England, Wales and Northern Ireland. London, Meteorological Office, *Clim. Mem.*, No. 24 (Typescript)

There are, it will be seen, very few days when undrifted snow is more than 2 in. (5 cm) deep although occasionally, as during the winter of 1954–55, it reaches as much as 8·3–11·8 in. (21–30 cm).

So far as the occurrence of hail at Kew is concerned, here as elsewhere a day with hail includes all days (0000–2400 GMT) on which hail is observed, whether true hail, soft hail or small hail. For this reason there are records of days with hail in all months, although true hail is mainly a summer phenomena and falls from thunderclouds. Table 97 gives the general picture.

TABLE 97

Average and extreme number of days with hail, Kew, 1871–1950

Jan	Feb	Mar	Apr	May	June	July	Aug	Sept	Oct	Nov	Dec
Average monthly total											
1	1	1	1	1	0+	0+	0+	0+	0+	0+	0+
Highest monthly total											
3	3	6	5	6	4	3	3	2	3	2	2

Source: London, Meteorological Office 1951 *Climate of Kew Observatory, 1871–1950* (Typescript)

Hail, in any form, is comparatively rare in London. True hail is even rarer and most frequent in May, a time we have already noted as prone to the development of deep cumulonimbus clouds and heavy showers, especially in the second half of the month.

The latest theory of the electrification of thunderclouds is closely linked to the growth of hail pellets, which may or may not reach the ground. These processes, as has already been mentioned, are mainly a summer phenomenon and thunder is most frequently heard at this time (Table 98).

TABLE 98

Average and extreme number of days with thunder heard, Kew, 1871–1950

Jan	Feb	Mar	Apr	May	June	July	Aug	Sept	Oct	Nov	Dec
Average monthly total											
0+	0+	1	1	3	3	3	3	1	1	0+	0+
Highest monthly total											
1	1	3	5	8	7	12	9	6	4	2	2

Source: London, Meteorological Office 1951 *Climate of Kew Observatory, 1871–1950* (Typescript)

From May to August (inclusive) thunder has been heard at Kew, on average, on one day in ten. This differs very little from the ratio of one day in eleven which Bishop (1957, p. 109) gives for the shorter period 1910–35. From November to February (inclusive) during these 36 years, thunder was heard, on average, on only one day in 178. A notable feature of the summer incidence of thunder at Kew is the almost identical frequency of occurrence during each of the four summer months May–August and the sharp change in frequency between these and the months of April and September. This pattern is of course related to changes in the form of the lapse rate (Best et al., 1952, pp. 8–30) which also controls the diurnal variation in the frequency of thunder. The chief hours of thunderstorm activity are from 1200 to 1800 GMT, more than half the occasions falling within these six hours (Bishop, 1947, p. 111). It must be mentioned, however, that the system of observing thunder at Kew must allow a number of more distant or short-lived night thunderstorms to pass unrecorded.

PRECIPITATION WITHIN GREATER LONDON

Bearing in mind the difficulties inherent in comparisons of precipitation at different sites, but making certain assumptions of sampling efficiency, Fig. 84 has been drawn to show variations in average precipitation, 1916–50, over Greater London. It differs in detail, though not in broad outline, from the first map of this type, published by Glasspoole (1934, p. 271) for the period 1881–1915.

It is quite obvious that there are two dominant controls upon the distribution: a general fall in rainfall totals from west to east, and increased amounts in the higher parts of the area, particularly the North Downs, the higher parts of north London and south Hertfordshire, and the Epping ridge. Less than 24 in. (609·6 mm) falls near the Thames in a strip whose width is constricted from Richmond to Westminster between upstanding areas with higher falls, such as Hampstead to the north and the commons of Richmond, Wimbledon and Clapham to the south. The area of low rainfall widens out in the extensive lowland around Walton-on-Thames in the west and in the Thames-side areas of the estuary to the east. There are also tongues of low precipitation extending from this axial strip northward along the Lea and southward along the Wandle valleys. The lowest precipitation of all occurs in a small area of the Erith marshes south of Dagenham. The highest rainfall, over 34 in. (863·6 mm), falls on the crest of the North Downs north of Limpsfield and Oxted, southeast of London, and many of the suburban fringe areas of the conurbation in south and southeast London receive an annual average of more than 27 in. (685·8 mm). There are also heavy falls over Hampstead and over the south Hertfordshire plateau area of north London. More than 28 in. (711·2 mm) falls in Barnet. The higher parts of the Epping ridge and a small upstanding area north of Hornchurch, in the northeast, have over 26 in. (660·4 mm). Regional trends and orographic influences are mainly responsible for the overall range of precipitation of 9–10 in. (482·6–508·0 mm) over Greater London; this represents a very large percentage of the mean value. Whether or not the city changes the amount or type of precipitation is less certain. The basic difficulty here is to isolate any such influence from the much stronger controls of synoptic climatology and topography.

Three main factors may be the cause of urban-induced changes in precipitation. These are additional condensation nuclei of a particular type; turbulence resulting from increased surface roughness; and thermal convection resulting from higher temperatures. Additional nuclei are not only seasonal in their numbers but are also thought to play a more important role in the field of frontal precipitation which is most common in winter in Britain. Supposedly as the result of these several influences, a number of cities have been noted to have more rain-days, more thunderstorms and more total precipitation than the country around them. Urban-rural differences in the number of days with light rain and thunderstorms average from 11–18 per cent in European and

Fig 84 Average annual rainfall in London, 1916–50
(Source of data: London, *Hydro. Mem.* Nos. 20,
21 and 22)

North American studies, and with precipitation from 5–10 per cent higher in the built-up areas (Changnon, 1961, p. 38). An investigation by Veryard (1958), however, failed to find any significant differences in total precipitation that might reasonably be caused by large English conurbations, and a brief study by the author of differences in the percentage changes of precipitation in successive decades since 1881 for groups of stations west of London, within the conurbation, and east of the city (and all at comparable heights), was inconclusive. If anything the balance was towards lower percentage increases within London than outside, but there was a large, overlapping diversity of increase in all three areas.

Heavy thunderstorms, roughly coincident with the built-up area of London, have occurred on many occasions and similar instances have been commented upon in Reading (Parry, 1956b, p. 48) and certain Midland towns (Barnes, 1960, p. 23), but here again it is impossible to be sure about their relationship with the towns, particularly, in the absence of very detailed surface and upper air observations. Certainly in London, many thunderstorms can be observed to form or intensify near the Hampstead–Highgate ridge north of the Thames, but the reasons for this are likely to be orographic rather than topographic. On the other hand, observation suggests a tendency for thunderstorms to develop or intensify in inner north London and this might be related to the characteristic asymmetry of its heat-island with the highest temperatures in the northeast. A satisfactory answer to these and other questions about London's role in modifying local precipitation can be gained only by very detailed analyses of conditions in the light of the known meteorological processes and the periods required for their operation. This would necessitate an extension of the present area of study to cover much more than Greater London and its immediate rural surrounds. Such an investigation is being undertaken at University College London, and the solution to many of these problems must await the results.

The city is unlikely materially to differentiate the frequency of snowfall in the London region, for much of the snow falls on windy days when the heat-island will be poorly developed; even on winter days of relative calm, the heat-island is unlikely to be warm or deep enough to do more than convert a little of the snow into sleet. But in the absence of orographic controls, fallen snow will melt more quickly in central parks than in suburban gardens where it will often disappear several days before that covering the farmlands around London. For the period 1921–50, the average number of days on which snow covered more than half the ground representative of the station at the 0900 GMT observation varied from 5·4 per year at Kensington Palace, 81 ft (24·7 m); 6·1 at Greenwich, 149 ft (45·4 m); 6·2 at Kew, 18 ft (5·5 m); 7·0 at Croydon, 201 ft (61·3 m) on the margins of London, to 7·6 at Wisley, 105 ft (32·0 m) in Surrey. At Hampstead and other elevated parts of Greater London, totals were much higher. For the 16 years from 1927–42, for instance, the average annual number of days with snow lying at Kensington Palace was 5·2, at Wisley, 5·8, and at Hampstead, 12·8, or double the total outside London.

There are still gaps in our knowledge of the precise manner and degree to which London's climate is related to its urban morphology and some of the largest lie in the field of precipitation. There are very substantial differences in rainfall between the various parts of the metropolis, but there is no doubt that these are mainly, if not entirely, the result of regional and orographic controls.

11 Climatic regions of London

The idea of the immense area which is covered by this gigantic town [London] may be approximately realized from the fact that many learned physicians discuss the climatic differences of various parts of the town exactly as if they were comparing the climates of Italy and Germany.

Max Schlesinger, 1853

WILLIAM EWART, writing in 1902 (Ewart, 1902, p. 3), said of London:

Everything is artificial, from the 'made ground' upon which it is built, to its water courses some of which are turned away from their natural beds, and to the composition of its air, so much altered by its smoke-laden fogs and mists, that the meteorology of London is one *sui generis*.

He then went on to discuss the influence of local climatic conditions (mainly of soil moisture and fog frequency) upon health. Some of his findings seem odd in the context of present-day London, but their interest lies in an ability to recognize different climates within the comparatively limited compass of the city. Since the turn of the twentieth century our climatological knowledge has grown in both volume and understanding, with the result that we can now base our regions upon a broader and surer range of elements.

All attempts to define climatic regions are handicapped by at least two major difficulties: first, changes in any single element are gradual, though zones of sharper gradient may exist; secondly, the zones of transition for the several elements are rarely, if ever, coincident. Fig. 85, which attempts to define four major climatic regions within London, must be viewed in the light of these limitations and also (perhaps more important in a city than almost anywhere else) it must be remembered that each region is an assemblage of micro-climates which may, locally and on occasions, bring them closer to a different climatic region. Nevertheless, it may be useful to draw together the previous separate accounts of climatic elements in London by defining and briefly describing broad climatic regions within the city, remembering of course that the most obvious climatic divide coincides with the boundary of the city itself. London as a whole stands in marked contrast to its rural setting and the built-up area is the primary climatic region. Within it are regions of lesser unity and distinctiveness.

I CENTRAL LONDON

In central London, from the West End administrative and shopping districts eastward to the City of London, the climate is characterized by strongly developed urban features

Q

which include the following: lighter winds, though fewer calms, than outside; intense concentrations of pollution, though less so in recent years; drastically reduced sunshine hours in winter; temperatures above those of most other parts of London, particularly by night in summer and autumn; lower relative humidities than elsewhere, except near parks and other open spaces and near the Thames; poor visibilities and a susceptibility to retentive early-morning fogs; slightly fewer clear days and more overcast days than outside London; and less rainfall than on higher ground to the north and south.

II INNER SUBURBAN LONDON

The connection between the form of London and the climate of its parts has been noted in several chapters and there are frequently well-marked breaks of climatic gradient where the building patterns change suddenly. There is thus a great deal of climatic unity in this inner suburban area (Fig. 85) where mainly high density, old residential, industrial and in the east, dockside areas, nearly all developed before 1914, form a broken ring around the central areas. But the climate of this part of London is distinguished mainly by degree from that of the centre (I) and the outer suburbs (IV). Pollution levels are still high and in the lower Lea valley sub-region (IIa), they are amongst the highest in London; sunshine amounts in winter are well below those outside London; temperatures are higher, especially in the northeast (IIa); relative humidities tend to be reduced below those of the Green Belt except near open, low-lying spaces such as the floodplain of the river Lea; fogs are common and frequently very intense in this region, again more especially in the northeast sub-region IIa where rainfall is also very light in the rain-shadow of the South Hertfordshire plateau and the Hampstead–Highgate ridge.

III NORTH LONDON HEIGHTS

This is an area of very varied relief and urban morphology, and to a certain extent it is this diversity which is the basis of its climatic unity. There are many smaller areas within Greater London with similar conditions such as Epping ridge in the northeast and Croydon, Sydenham and Black Heath in the southeast, but these are rather smaller and it is impossible to differentiate them on the map (Fig. 85) or specifically in the text. The northern area has been separately distinguished because of its size and continuity.

The climate of the higher parts, often capped by open spaces, is very different from that of the broad expanse of low-lying suburbs, for these elevated areas are frequently raised above the shallow layer of a town-modified atmosphere. Winds are stronger here than elsewhere in London (or in the low-lying parts outside); pollution is relatively light;

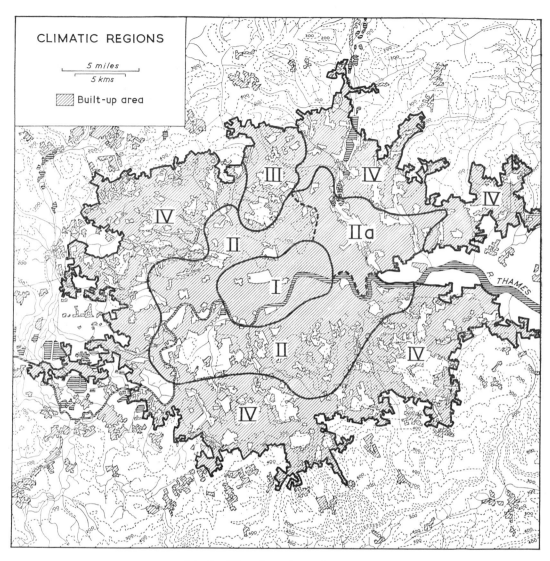

Fig 85 Climatic regions of London

sunshine amounts, even in winter, differ little from outside; daytime temperatures are below those at lower levels outside London but the nights are usually slightly warmer, particularly in summer and autumn; absolute humidities on spring and autumn nights are somewhat higher than elsewhere, but they are lower in summer and little different in winter; relative humidites tend to be in excess of those in the surrounding heavily built-up areas; visibilities are variably related to conditions in other parts of London but, on average, fogs will be less frequent here than in the centre and thick fogs will be more common, though still less frequent than in lower-lying suburban areas; precipitation is higher than over most of Greater London and snow lies longer.

IV OUTER SUBURBS

This outer ring of mainly post-1918 development is characterized by two-storey, semi-detached and detached houses with gardens along fairly wide roads, by groups of single-storey factories and by frequent open spaces. The lace-like pattern of development along the urban-rural fringe is best developed in southwest and west London. The more fragmented, intricate nature of the urban development in this area generates a more complex climatic response with nodes of well-developed urban features interspersed between inliers of a rural, extra-metropolitan character.

Winds are more turbulent but mean velocities are only slightly below those beyond the city; pollution levels are quite low; sunshine amounts are reduced, but by only small amounts; temperatures, especially on summer nights, are still appreciably higher than those outside, though less so than in either regions I or II, and in the larger open spaces they fall to values comparable with those of the Green Belt; absolute humidities are almost the same as outside but relative humidities are lower in the built-up areas; visibilities are generally better than in the centre or inner suburbs but there are more frequent dense fogs here than in either central London or rural southeast England; precipitation, except in suburbs on the slopes of the South Downs or other elevated areas, is light.

In all the above cases, the individual chapters should be consulted for details.

12 Consequences of an urban climate

An increased death rate, lowered health, and depressed vitality are serious losses in themselves, but to them must be added the enormous financial cost of each day of fog, and the cost of repairing the destructive effects of smoke on valuable property throughout the year.

Smoke, which spoils everything else, beautifies London by disguising its ugliness.

The health advantages of inner London for residential purposes are its relative evenness and mildness. London enjoys less exposure, greater warmth, and less humidity than the outlying country, and these advantages might be missed by some delicate persons in giving up their residence in London for a suburban one.

Wm. Ewart, M.D., 1902

THE INFLUENCES OF CLIMATE upon man and his activities are legion. Some aspects of this relationship in the British Isles have been considered by Brooks in his book *Climate in everyday life*; all that this present chapter aims to do is to consider, briefly, some of the medical, social and economic consequences of London's urban climate.

Although scattered references exist in many early books to the ill-effects of London's smoke and fog upon people and property, there is little doubt that the pioneer of climatic reform was John Evelyn, the seventeenth-century apostle of clean air. Three centuries later, his appeals are being realized. Another notable study was the Report of the Committee of the Royal Medical and Chirurgical Society of London published in a book called *The climates and baths of Great Britain*. In this there is a statement by Ewart on the counties of London and Middlesex in which suburbs are compared, with particular reference to the incidence of pollution, fogs and high humidities and their bearing upon chest complaints. But the picture of climatic control is not entirely adverse; there are advantages as well as disadvantages to be gained from the changes wrought by London on its atmosphere.

Atmospheric pollution

A number of estimates have been made of the cost to the country of atmospheric pollution as it affects health, loss of work, cost of cleaning, damage to crops and buildings, etc. (Great Britain, Committee on Air Pollution, 1955, p. 11; Scorer, 1957); a somewhat conservative estimate puts this at about £5 per head of population per year. Remembering the general severity of its pollution, the yearly total for London must be of the order of £50,000,000. This is a terrible price to pay although many of the consequences, such as ill health, cannot be expressed in monetary terms. The replacement of stonework on the Palace of Westminster and the cleaning of St Paul's Cathedral are examples of the most obvious effects of pollution upon the deterioration of buildings; window-cleaning is far more frequently needed than in the country, which is one reason why sections of the Lea valley glasshouse industry are moving out of London. The almost hopeless task of keeping the home clean during winter was thought by Ewart (1902, p. 28) to be partly responsible for the drunkenness of women!

The most serious indictment of atmospheric pollution is its effect upon health and

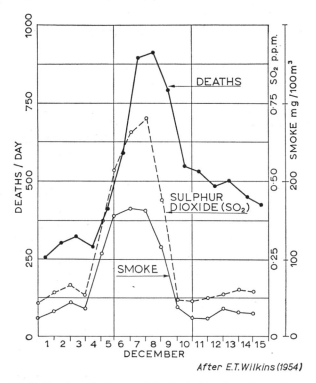

After E.T.Wilkins (1954)

Fig 86 Daily air pollution and deaths in London, December 1952
(Source: Wilkins, E. T. 1954 'Air pollution aspects of the London
fog of December 1952' *Quart. J. R. Met. Soc.*, London, 80, p. 270)

well-being, and although the two had been connected for a very long time, little was done to improve the the situation, nor was the public conscience very deeply disturbed, until the disastrous smog of December 1952. The health consequences of this notable occurrence were considered by a special Ministry of Health report (Ministry of Health, 1954) and since then there has been accelerated research into the physiological effects of smog and pollution generally (e.g.) Boyd, 1960; Daly, 1959; Stocks, 1959). Fig. 86 needs little explanation, its lesson is too obvious; although the details of the relationship between smoke, sulphur dioxide and other urban pollutants on the one hand and ill health and death on the other are still not completely established. More particularly, views differ as to whether smoke, SO_2, SO_3 or some other impurity is the most toxic ingredient of pollution. The subject of specific etiology was summed up by the report of a Government Committee in the following words:

> While the available evidence does not allow of a clear indictment of any one constituent of the fog, the conclusion is inescapable that the excessive mortality and increased incidence of respiratory illness during and immediately after the fog of December 1952 were the result of irritation of the respiratory tract by the contaminants of fog. The irritants mainly responsible were probably those derived from the combustion of coal and its products and their lethal effects were almost wholly exercised in persons already suffering from chronic respiratory or cardiovascular disorders. (Heimann, 1961, pp. 174–5)

It is of course the combination of high humidities and pollution, the two essential ingredients of smog, which is so injurious to the lungs and causes so much bronchitis, although low temperatures are also thought to aggravate the condition, for the irritant effects of sulphur dioxide, especially bronchiolar spasm, are intensified by cold air. One thing is certain: people with bronchitis and other chest complaints suffer far more in London and other cities than in rural areas, and during times of intense smog, their conditions are worsened and many of them die (Howe, 1963). During the smog of December 1952, about 4,000 deaths were attributable to the prevailing atmospheric conditions; in the smog of December 1962, the number was 340. There are too many uncertainties to justify any conclusion that credit for the reduction in mortality since the 1952 disaster can be attributed to a reduction in smoke in the air; indeed there is a growing opinion that sulphur dioxide may be as important, if not more important, a cause of ill-health. Certainly this was the chemical component of the December 1952 smog which was proposed as the cause of morbidity and mortality amongst animals at the Smithfield Show in London at this time.

Though a great deal of work needs to be done, we know that there are small amounts of proved carcinogens in the air and some, for instance, 3:4–benzpyrene, occur in much larger quantities in urban than in rural areas. On the other hand, pollution acts as a partial screen to ultra-violet light which is accepted as capable of inducing skin cancer.

Pollution is also harmful to certain plants. Smoke clogs the stomata, and sulphur above a certain concentration attacks the cells of the mesophyll which are first inactivated and then killed. When extensive areas are affected, the tissues dry and collapse; but injury by sulphur dioxide is normally local. While injured areas of leaves never recover, uninjured areas quickly and fully regain their functions and new leaves develop normally. Research has also shown that soil loses its stock of accessory plant foods very rapidly under the action of polluted rain (Meetham, 1956, p. 217).

Many materials are affected by pollution. Iron rusts more quickly in urban areas and zinc is badly corroded. Wool, cotton and leather are attacked by absorbed sulphur dioxide when it oxidizes to sulphuric acid and this has been found of some consequence in the deterioration of leather book-bindings in libraries.

Buildings disfigured by smoke particles and other pollutants are a part of the London scene. Surfaces of stone containing carbonates will tend to suffer the most, for these are converted by polluted rainwater in soluble sulphates and chlorides and quickly flake.

Sunshine

Though it would be difficult to isolate its influence, it seems reasonable that the severe reduction in winter sunshine hours in central London will have undesirable psychological as well as physical effects. It was believed at one time that the associated loss of ultra-violet radiation in cities (amounting to from 25–50 per cent in winter) was important in the high incidence of ailments such as rickets, but in the present days of improved diets, this particular effect is not thought to be of great consequence. The loss of sunlight does mean that on many days in winter, artificial indoor lighting is needed an hour or more earlier than outside London.

Temperature

The extra warmth of the city has several repercussions. Reference has already been made to the extended frost-free period and 'active growing season' (Chapter 6). Another consequence of the generally higher temperatures is a decrease in fuel requirements for the heating of buildings. Professor Manley has argued the case for a datum of 14°C (57°F) mean temperature below which some form of artificial heating becomes necessary (Manley, 1957b, p. 20) but for present purposes the customary 15·6°C (60°F) will be used. This is 2·7°C (5°F) below what in this country can be regarded as the desirable comfort temperature of 18·3°C (65°F), the difference being accounted for by solar radiation through windows and by the incidental heat gains from lighting, cooking and persons within the buildings. The mean annual day-degree total below 15·6°C (60°F) measures a large percentage of the heating requirements of buildings, particularly where the incident wind speeds are low, as in the more densely settled parts of cities. Strictly it can be applied only where the indoor temperature is maintained at 18·3°C (65°F), but such fluctuations as do occur do not materially rob the measure of its value in such investigations. In order to calculate the precise heating requirements of a building, it is necessary to allow for the strength of the wind because the rate of air change through the building, and thereby the heat lost through ventilation, is proportional to the wind speed. This, as we have seen, is very variable in urban areas and the use of standard measures can give no more than an approximation to actual conditions. Another important complication is that the heat balance of any building greatly depends upon its size and design. If every allowance were made for architectural style, the problem would become impossibly complex, so that we must assume a uniform type of house. The errors in this assumption are all to obvious but can hardly be avoided.

Because of the unknown variables, no attempt will be made to use the rather more laborious techniques employed by Parry in Reading and Bath (Parry, 1957) or the more specialized findings of Knight and Cornell (1959). Rather, the simple formula derived by Lacy (1951) has been used to calculate the fuel requirements of a particular type of house maintained at a uniform indoor temperature of 65°F at different points in the London area. The results are as follows.

	Average fuel requirements per day, *October–April inclusive* kilowatt-hours
Kingsway	50·3
Kew	52·8
London Airport	54·3
Outside London	59·8

To obtain these results, wind speeds were taken from the Kingsway, Kew, London Airport, Abingdon, Shoeburyness and South Farnborough records; temperatures from the Kensington, Kew (where mean temperatures in the North Wall Screen are roughly equal to those in the nearby suburbs—see Table 59), Croydon, Rothamsted, St Albans, Wisley and Tunbridge Wells records; and sunshine from readings at Bunhill Row, Kew, Croydon, Rothamsted, Wisley and Tunbridge Wells. Because of the very considerable assumptions in the use of the equation, the unavoidable mixture of data sources, the errors in using Kew's North Wall Screen temperatures, plus the impossibility of knowing wind speeds and temperatures close to the buildings, the results cannot be interpreted too closely; they give only a broad indication of the differences to be expected. These, it will be seen, amount to a saving of roughly 20 per cent in fuel costs in central London and about 10 per cent in the low-lying suburbs. There is probably little or no saving in the more elevated suburbs where temperatures are lower and wind speeds higher.

Another interesting consequence of London's heat-island became apparent when London Transport made an investigation of rail temperatures on exposed sections of the Underground network, with a view to improved forecasting of icing risks on the conductor rails. Temperatures in different parts of the network ranged over 5·6–6·7°C (10–12°F) on more than one occasion during the winter of 1950–1, the suburban sites at Kingsbury and Queensbury almost invariably giving lower minimum readings than the in-town, sheltered, Baron's Court site (London Transport Executive, 1959, p. 2). Understandably, the warmest Underground sections were found to lie in heavily built-up areas, and it was proposed to dispense with de-icing precautions on the District Line.

Humidity

There is only scanty evidence of the influence of humidity changes across London upon its economic and social life. Indeed, we have already seen how small the average differences are. Ewart (1902, p. 19) described how 'the town as a whole has undergone for years, and particularly during the past few years, a strong desiccating process owing to the protection of large areas of its surface by roofs and roads and the leading of surface water underground'. He added that 'the influence of this drying process, added to the smallness of the rainfall special to the Thames valley, has been conducive to the health and comfort of its inhabitants'. Little is known of the relationships between humidity and health although high humidities are known to aggravate many chest complaints. There is also some evidence that rapid changes in humidity are harmful and may encourage colds. But no real connection has been convincingly proved and, in any case, differences in humidity between centrally heated buildings and the open air are frequently larger than those suffered by commuters in their daily journeys.

Fog

The part played by fogs in disrupting communications is too obvious to dwell upon and their association with critical low-level concentrations of pollution has already been considered. Neither is really capable of expression in monetary terms for the ramifications of disrupted transport are multifarious and the cost of increased electricity for lighting is difficult to estimate.

No attempt will be made here to recall the close and all-pervading effect of the broader regional climate upon the lives of its people but perhaps brief mention should be made of one interesting aspect, since this is mainly of concern to an urban community. Cottis (1959) has made a study of the part played by rain and/or low temperatures in interrupting external building work in the London area, using data for London Airport. The critical values taken for this investigation were a temperature below $1.1°C$ (34°F) and appreciable precipitation with a rate of 0.2 in. (0.5 mm) per hour or more. Lost time, on the assumption that the above values would stop external work, amounts to less than 5 per cent from April to September inclusive, but it is over 14 per cent from December to February, reaching a peak of 23 per cent in February.

Londoners live in a profoundly man-modified climate. A few of the changes wrought by the widespread substitution of houses and factories for fields and woods, and surfaced roads for cart-tracks, might be considered favourable. Such are the higher autumn, winter and spring night-time temperatures which reduce heating costs and lengthen the frost-free period, but these advantages must surely be outweighed by increased pollution and decreased sunshine. It is to be hoped that enlightened planning might do something in future years to reduce further unconscious deterioration of London's urban climate.

References

ABSALOM, H. W. L. — 1954 — Meteorological aspects of smog. *Quart. J. R. Met. Soc.*, London, 80, pp. 261–6

APPLEGATE, T. H. — 1960 — Mean dates of first and last screen frosts, 1920–55. London, Meteorological Office, *Agric. Mem.*, No. 28. (Typescript, available at the Meteorological Office)

APPLEGATE, T. H. AND SMITH, L. P. — 1960 — Humidity readings at 9 a.m. London, Meteorological Office, *Agric. Mem.*, No. 30. (Typescript, available at the Meteorological Office)

BALCHIN, W. G. V. AND PYE, N. — 1947 — A micro-climatological investigation of Bath and the surrounding district. *Quart. J. R. Met. Soc.*, London, 73, pp. 297–323

— 1949–50 — Temperature and humidity variations in an urban area of diversified relief. *J. Manch. Geogr. Soc.*, Manchester, 55, pp. 1–23

BARNES, F. A. — 1960 — The intense thunder rains of 1st July, 1952, in the northern Midlands. *East Midland Geographer*, Nottingham, No. 14, pp. 11–26

BATES, C. G. — 1945 — Shelterbelt influences II—the value of shelterbelts in home heating. *J. For.*, Washington, 43, Pt. 3

BECKER, L. — 1925 — The climatology of Glasgow. London, Meteorological Office, *Geoph. Mem.*, 3, No. 23

BEDFORD, T., WARNER, C. G. AND CHRENKO, F. A. — 1943 — Observations on the natural ventilation of buildings. *J. Roy. Inst. Brit. Architect.*, London, 51, pp. 7–11

BELASCO, J. E. — 1948 — Rainless days of London. *Quart. J. R. Met. Soc.*, London, 74, pp. 339–48

— 1951 — Freezing days in Great Britain. *Met. Mag.*, London, 80, pp. 213–24

— 1952 — Characteristics of air masses over the British Isles. London, Meteorological Office, *Geoph. Mem.*, 11, No. 87

BERG, H. — 1947 — *Einführung in die bioklimatologie.* Bonn.

BEST, A. C., KNIGHTING, E., PEDLOW, R. H. AND STORMONTH, K. — 1952 — Temperature and humidity gradients in the first 100 M over south-east England. London, Meteorological Office, *Geoph. Mem.*, 11, No. 89

BILHAM, E. G. — 1938 — *The climate of the British Isles.* London.

BILHAM, E. G. AND HAY, R. F. M. — 1934 — The frequency of heavy rains lasting from 1 to 48 hours at Kew Observatory during the period 1878 to 1927. London, Meteorological Office, *British rainfall 1934*, pp. 284–93

BISHOP, B. V. — 1947 — The frequency of thunderstorms at Kew Observatory. *Met. Mag.*, London, 76, pp. 108–11

BLACKWELL, M. J. — 1954 — Five years continuous recording of total and diffuse solar radiation at Kew Observatory. London, Meteorological Office, *Met. Res. Pap.*, No. 895. (Typescript, available at the Meteorological Office)

252   REFERENCES

BONACINA, L. C. W.   1934   Discussion of: An investigation of the statistical probability
                                  of rain in London. (Dewar, D.). *Quart. J. R. Met. Soc.*,
                                  London, 60, p. 312
                          1950   London fogs, then and now. *Weather*, London, 5, pp. 91–3
                          1960   Summer evening visibility over London in 1959; a ten-year
                                  retrospect. *Weather*, London, 15, pp. 127–30

BOOTH, R. E.   1957   The cold weather of February 1956 with special reference to
                                  temperatures at Kew during the last 75 years. *Met. Mag.*,
                                  London, 86, pp. 65–73

BOYD, J. T.   1960   Climate, air pollution and mortality. *Brit. J. Prev. Soc.
                                  Med.*, London, 14, pp. 123–35

BRAUN, R. C. AND   1961   The variation of atmospheric sulphur dioxide concentration
WILSON, M. J. G.   with altitude. *Int. J. Air Wat. Poll.*, London, 5, pp. 1–13

BRAZELL, J. H.   1963   Severe winters and the following summers in London.
                                  Weather, London, 18, pp. 322–4

BROOKS, C. E. P.   1918   The incidence of fog in London on January 31st 1918.
                                  London, Meteorological Office, *Prof. Notes*, No. 3
                          1929   The relation between the duration of bright sunshine regis-
                                  tered by the Campbell-Stokes sunshine recorder and the
                                  estimated amount of cloud. London, Meteorological Office,
                                  Prof. Notes, No. 53
                          1930   Irregularities in the annual variation of temperature in
                                  London. *Nature*, London, 126, pp. 61–3
                          1946   Annual recurrences of weather: 'singularities'. *Weather*,
                                  London, 1, pp. 107–13
                          1950   *Climate in everyday life*. London.
                          1952   Selective annotated bibliography on urban climates. *Met.
                                  Abs. Bibl.*, Lancaster Pa., 3, pp. 734–73
                          1954   *The English climate*. London

BROOKS, C. E. P. AND   1933   Variations of wind direction in the British Isles since 1341.
HUNT, T. M.   *Quart. J. R. Met. Soc.*, London, 59, pp. 376–8

BROOKS, C. E. P. AND   1930   Irregularities in the temperature of London. *Quart. J. R.
MIRRLEES, S. T. A.   Met. Soc.*, London, 56, pp. 375–88

BROWN, P. R.   1962   Low temperature and wind speed at Aberdeen, Aldergrove,
                                  Birmingham, Kew, and South Shields—Cockle Park.
                                  London, Meteorological Office, *Clim. Mem.*, No. 31.
                                  (Typescript, available at the Meteorological Office)

BRUNT, D.   1918   On the inter-relation of wind direction and cloud amount at
                                  Richmond (Kew Observatory). London, Meteorological
                                  Office, *Prof. Notes*, No. 1

BUCHAN, A.   1869   Interruptions in the regular rise and fall of temperature in
                                  the course of the year, as shown by observations made in
                                  Scotland during the past ten years, 1857–66. *J. Scot. Met.
                                  Soc.*, Edinburgh, New Series, 2, pp. 4–15
                          1892   The temperature of London for 130 years from 1763 to
                                  1892. *J. Scot. Met. Soc.*, Edinburgh, 3rd Series, 9, pp. 213–23

CALLENDAR, G. S.   1961   Temperature fluctuations and trends over the earth. *Quart.
                                  J. R. Met. Soc.*, London, 87, pp. 1–12

CARPENTER, A.   1903   *London fog inquiry, 1901–02*. Report to the Meteorological
                                  Council. London. (H.M.S.O.)

CARROLL, J. D.,   1960   Trends in the pollution of the air of Great Britain by smoke
CRAXFORD, S. R.,   and sulphur dioxide, 1952–59. *Proc. Harrogate Conf., Nat.
NEWALL, H. E. AND   Soc. Clean Air*, London
WEATHERLEY, M. L. P. M.

CHANDLER, T. J.

1960 Wind as a factor of urban temperatures—a survey in north-east London. *Weather*, London, 15, pp. 204–13

1961a The changing form of London's heat-island. *Geography*, Sheffield, 46, pp. 295–307

1961b Surface breeze effects of Leicester's heat-island. *East Midland Geographer*, Nottingham, No. 15, pp. 32–8

1962a London's urban climate. *Geogr. J.*, London, 128, Pt. III, pp. 279–302

1962b Diurnal, seasonal and annual changes in the intensity of London's heat-island. *Met. Mag.*, London, 91, pp. 146–53

1962c Temperature and humidity traverses across London. *Weather*, London, 17, pp. 235–42

CHANGNON, S. A.

1961 A climatological evaluation of precipitation patterns over an urban area. Symposium: *Air over cities*, Washington D.C., pp. 37–67. (Public Health Service)

CORBY, G. A.

1951 The visibility characteristics of Northolt Airport. London, Meteorological Office, *Met. Res. Pap.*, No. 680. (Typescript, available at the Meteorological Office)

COTTIS, J. G.

1959 Rain and/or low temperature as factors interrupting external building work in the London area. London, Meteorological Office, *Clim. Mem.*, No. 27. (Typescript, available at the Meteorological Office)

COTTIS, J. G. AND GROOM, H. J.

1958 Low temperatures related to surface wind speed and direction at London Airport, Dec. 1948 – Feb. 1958. London, Meteorological Office, *Clim. Mem.*, No. 21. (Typescript, available at the Meteorological Office)

CRADDOCK, J. M.

1957 The serial correlations of daily mean temperatures at Kew Observatory. *J. Met. Soc. Japan*. Tokyo. 75th Anniversary Volume, pp. 350–64

1963 Some facts about the 5-day mean temperature anomalies at Kew observed during the period 1901 to 1961. *Quart. J. R. Met. Soc.*, London, 89, pp. 461–8

CRAXFORD, S. R.

1961 Air pollution—past, present and future. *Inst. Petr. Rev.*, London, 15, pp. 133–9

CROWE, P. R.

1957 Some further thoughts on evapotranspiration. *Geogr. Studies*, London, 4, pp. 56–75

DALY, C.

1959 Air pollution and causes of death. *Brit. J. Prev. Soc. Med.*, London, 13, pp. 14–27

DAVIS, N. E.

1951 Fog at London Airport. *Met. Mag.*, London, 80, pp. 9–14

1954 Surface temperature and vapour pressure at London Airport. *Met. Mag.*, London, 83, pp. 297–302

1963 The 100 mb chart and dry spells at London (Heathrow). Airport. *Met. Mag.*, London, pp. 275–9

Department of Scientific and Industrial Research

1945 *Atmospheric pollution in Leicester. Technical Paper No. 1* London. (H.M.S.O.)

1955 *The investigation of atmospheric pollution, No. 27.* London. (H.M.S.O.)

1960 *The investigation of atmospheric pollution, No. 31.* London. (H.M.S.O.)

1963 *The London fog, 3rd–7th December 1962.* (Typescript, available at Warren Spring Laboratory, Stevenage)

DEWAR, D.

1934 An investigation of the statistical probability of rain in London. *Quart. J. R. Met. Soc.*, London, 60, pp. 285–312

DIGHT, F. H.　　　　　　1934　An analysis of warm spells in London from 1903–33 with special reference to the prevailing conditions of humidity. *Met. Mag.*, London, 69, pp. 109–16

DOBSON, G. M. B.　　　　1948　Meteorological aspects of atmospheric pollution. *Quart. J. R. Met. Soc.*, London, 74, pp. 133–43

DOUGLAS, C. K. M. AND STEWART, K. H.　　1953　London fog for December 5–8 1952. *Met. Mag.*, London, 82, pp. 67–71

DRUMMOND, A. J.　　　　1943　Cold winters at Kew Observatory, 1783–1942. *Quart. J. R. Met. Soc.*, London, 69, pp. 17–32, 147–55
　　　　　　　　　　　　1946　The Christmas legend. *Weather*, London, 1, pp. 245–8

DUCKWORTH, F. S. AND SANDBERG, J. S.　　1954　The effect of cities upon horizontal and vertical temperature gradients. *Bull. Amer. Met. Soc.*, Lancaster, Pa., 35, pp. 198–207

DUFTON, A. F.　　　　　1934　Degree-days. *J. Instn. Heat. Vent. Engrs.*, London, 2, pp. 83–5

DUHOT, E.　　　　　　　1948　*Les climats et l'organisme humain.* Paris.

DURST, C. S.　　　　　　1940　Winter fog and mist investigation in the British Isles. London, *Meteorological Office Memoir*, No. 372

ELLIS, W.　　　　　　　1892　Mean temperature of the air on each day of the year at the Royal Observatory, Greenwich, on the average of the fifty years 1841–90. *Quart. J. R. Met. Soc.*, London, 18, pp. 237–41
　　　　　　　　　　　　1893　Mean maximum and minimum temperature of the air on each day of the year at the Royal Observatory, Greenwich, on the average of the fifty years 1841–90. *Quart. J. R. Met. Soc.*, London, 19, pp. 211–18
　　　　　　　　　　　　1896　Mean amount of cloud on each day of the year at the Royal Observatory, Greenwich, on the average of the fifty years 1841 to 1890. *Quart. J. R. Met. Soc.*, London, 22, pp. 169–84

EVANS, B. H.　　　　　　1957　Natural air flow around buildings. *Texas Engrg. Exp. Stn. Res. Rpt., No. 79*, Texas

EVANS, D. C.　　　　　　1957　A second report of fog at London Airport. *Met. Mag.*, London, 86, pp. 333–9

EVELYN, J.　　　　　　　1661　*Fumifumigium.* London

EWART, W.　　　　　　　1902　Report on the counties of London and Middlesex. *The climates and baths of Great Britain.* London

FAIRGRIEVE, J.　　　　　1927　London fog, January 20, 1927. *Met. Mag.*, London, 62, p. 29
　　　　　　　　　　　　1928　London fog, February 21, 1928. *Met. Mag.*, London, 63, p. 38
　　　　　　　　　　　　1930　Fog of January 21 1930. *Met. Mag.*, London, 65, p. 41

FROST, B. A.　　　　　　1947　The Velocity profile in the lowest 400 ft. *Met. Mag.*, London, 76, pp. 14–17

GILCHRIST, A.　　　　　1956　*Some features of warm and cold spells at Kew, Potsdam and Uppsala.* London, Meteorological Office. (Typescript, available at the Meteorological Office)

GILDERSLEEVES, P. B.　　1962　A contribution to the problem of day-darkness over London. *Met. Mag.*, London, 91, pp. 365–9

GLASSPOOLE, J.   1934   The average annual rainfall over the County of London. London, Meteorological Office, *British rainfall 1933*, pp. 266–73

     1959   Effects of the change of site on the climatological observations at Camden Square, London. *Quart. J. R. Met. Soc.*, London, 85, pp. 65–7

GOLD, E.   1954   Discussion of: Smog. *Quart. J. R. Met. Soc.*, London, 80, pp. 273–4

     1956   Smog. The rate of influx of surrounding cleaner air. *Weather*, London, 11, pp. 230–2

Great Britain, Committee on Air Pollution   1955   *Report presented to Parliament by the Minister of Housing and Local Government, the Secretary of State for Scotland and the Minister of Fuel and Power. November 1954.* (H.M.S.O.)

Great Britain   1960   *Report of the Royal Commission on Local government in Greater London 1957–60.* (H.M.S.O.)

GREGORY, S.   1953   A note on the classification of annual rainfall-distribution types. *Quart. J. R. Met. Soc.*, London, 79, pp. 538–43

HAWKE, E. L.   1941   The frequency distribution through the year of abnormally high and low daily mean temperatures at Greenwich Observatory. *Quart. J. R. Met. Soc.*, London, 67, pp. 247–56

     1944   The incidence of extremely low relative humidity in southern England. *Quart. J. R. Met. Soc.*, London, 70, pp. 274–6

     1948   Changes in the climate of London. *Weather*, London, 3, pp. 98–102, 130–5

HAYWOOD, P.   1959   Frequencies of snow depth within given ranges at selected stations in England, Wales and Northern Ireland. London, Meteorological Office, *Clim. Mem.*, No. 24. (Typescript, available at the Meteorological Office)

HEIMANN, H.   1961   Effects of air pollution on human health. *Air pollution.* Geneva, pp. 159–220. (W.H.O.)

HELLIWELL, N. C. AND BLACKWELL, M. J.   1955   Daytime darkness over London on January 16, 1955. *Met. Mag.*, London, 84, p. 342

HELLMANN, G.   1917   Uber die Bewegung der Luft in den Untersten Schichten der Atmosphäre. *Met. 2*, Braunschweig, 32, p. 1

HILBERSHEIMER, L.   1944   *The new city, principles and planning.* Chicago

HOWARD, LUKE   1818   *The climate of London.* Vol. I. London

     1820   *The climate of London.* Vol. II. London

     1833   *The climate of London.* Vols. I-III. Second edition. London

HOWE, G. M.   1963   *National atlas of disease mortality in the United Kingdom.* Edinburgh

JACKSON, C. I.   1963   Some climatological grumbles. *Weather*, London, 18, pp. 290–3

JOHNSON, L. G.   1957   *General T. Perronet Thompson, 1783–1869; his military, literary and political campaigns.* London

JOHNSON, N. K.   1948   The vertical gradient of wind velocity in the lowest layers of the atmosphere. London, Meteorological Office, *Prof. Notes*, 6, No. 91

KELLY, T.   1963   A study of persistent and semi-persistent thick and dense
                                    fog in the London area during the decade 1947–56. *Met.
                                    Mag.*, London, 92, pp. 177–83

KNIGHT, J. C. AND   1959   Degree days and fuel consumption for office buildings. *J.
CORNELL, A. A.   Inst. Heat. Vent. Eng.*, London, 26, pp. 3–22

KRATZER, A.   1956   *Das stadtklima.* Braunschweig

KRAUS, E.   1945   Climate made by man. *Quart. J. R. Met. Soc.*, London, 71,
                                    pp. 397–412

LACY, R. E.   1951   Variations in the winter means of temperature, wind speed
                                    and sunshine, and their effect on the heating requirements
                                    of a house. *Met. Mag.*, London, 80, pp. 161–5
                             1956   Discussion of: Local temperature variations in the Reading
                                    area. (Parry, M.). *Quart. J. R. Met. Soc.*, London, 82, p. 533

LAMB, H. H.   1950   Types and spells of weather around the year in the British
                                    Isles: annual trends, seasonal structure of the year, singulari-
                                    ties. *Quart. J. R. Met. Soc.*, London, 76, pp. 393–429
                             1953   British weather around the year. *Weather*, London, 8, pp.
                                    131–6; 176–82
                             1963   What can we find out about the trend of our climate?
                                    Weather, London, 18, pp. 194–216

LANDSBERG, H. E.   1952   Climatology and its part in pollution. *Am. Met. Soc.
                                    Monogr.*, Boston, 1, pp. 7–8
                             1956   The climate of towns. *Man's role in changing the face of the
                                    earth.* (Ed. Thomas, W. L.). Chicago, pp. 584–603

LAWRENCE, E. N.   1953   London's fogs of the past. *Weather*, London, 82, pp. 367–9
                             1956   Combined distribution of hourly values of dry-bulb and
                                    wet-bulb temperatures, Croydon, 1946–55. London Meteo-
                                    rological Office, *Clim. Mem.*, No. 10. (Typescript, available
                                    at the Meteorological Office)
                             1958   Temperature and topography on radiation nights. *Met.
                                    Mag.*, London, 87, pp. 71–5

LESSING, R.   1954   Discussion of: Smog. *Quart. J. R. Met. Soc.*, London, 80,
                                    pp. 272–3

LEWIS, L. F.   1947   Variations of temperature in London, 1764–1939. *Met. Mag.*,
                                    London, 76, pp. 135–8

LOGAN, W. P. D.   1953   Mortality in the London fog incident. *Lancet*, London,
                                    264, 1, pp. 336–8

London, Meteorological Office 1900– *Monthly weather reports.* (H.M.S.O.)
                             63
                             1927– *Observatories' year books.* (H.M.S.O.)
                             56
                             1934– *British rainfall* 1933–58. (H.M.S.O.)
                             63
                             1925   *Report of the Advisory Committee on Atmospheric Pollution.*
                                    London
                             1933   *Averages of temperature for the British Isles for periods end-
                                    ing 1930.* M.O. 364. (H.M.S.O.)
                             1943   Tables of wind direction and force over the British Isles.
                                    2nd Edition *Meteorological Office Mem.*, No. 370
                             1951   *Climate of Kew Observatory, 1871–1950.* (Typescript, avail-
                                    able at the Meteorological Office)

1952 *Climatological atlas of the British Isles.* (H.M.S.O.)

1953 *Averages of bright sunshine for Great Britain and Northern Ireland 1921–50.* M.O. 572. (H.M.S.O.)

1958 *Averages of rainfall for Great Britain and Northern Ireland 1916–50.* M.O. 635. (H.M.S.O.)

1959 *Averages of humidity for the British Isles.* M.O. 421. (H.M.S.O.)

1960 *Averages of earth temperature for the British Isles.* M.O. 665. (H.M.S.O.)

1963a *Averages of temperature for Great Britain and Northern Ireland 1931–60.* M.O. 735. (H.M.S.O.)

1963b Rainfall over the areas of East Suffolk and Norfolk and the Essex river boards, 1916–50. *Hydro. Mem.* No. 20. (Typescript, available at the Meteorological Office).

1963c Rainfall over the areas of the Kent and West Sussex river boards, 1916–50. *Hydro. Mem.* No. 21. (Typescript, available at the Meteorological Office)

1963d Rainfall over the areas of the Thames and Lea Conservancies, London, and the Brent, the Wandle and the Ravensbourne valleys, 1916–50. *Hydro. Mem.* No. 22. (Typescript, available at the Meteorological Office)

1911–63 *Monthly return of daily observations, Forms F 3203 and F 3208.* (MS, available at the Meteorological Office)

1950–60 *Daily return of hourly observations, Form 3257(B).* (MS, available at the Meteorological Office)

1947–63 *Hourly values of radiation, Form 3265 (A) and 3265(B).* (MS, available at the Meteorological Office).

Tables for the evaluation of daily values of accumulated temperature above and below 42°F from daily values of maximum and minimum temperature, Form 3300

1961–2 *Hourly values of wind speed, Form 3431.* (MS, available at the Meteorological Office)

Tabulations of wind direction and velocity compiled from hourly observations, Form 3433. (MS, available at the Meteorological Office)

1957–62 *Hourly values of sunshine, Form 3445.* (MS, available at Kew Observatory)

1952–62 *Hourly values of pollution, Form 3745.* (MS, available at Kew Observatory)

1958–60 *Daily values of maximum and minimum temperature recorded in the Stevenson (Garden) Screen, Kew Observatory.* (MS, available at Kew Observatory)

London Transport Executive

1959 *Night minimum rail temperatures in the London area during the winter 1958–59.* (Typescript)

LOWNDES, C. A. S.

1960 Dry spells of three days or more at London from May to October. *Met. Mag.*, London, 89, pp. 105–11

1962 Wet spells at London. *Met. Mag.*, London, 91, pp. 98–104

1963 Cold spells at London, *Met Mag.*, London, 92, pp. 165–76

LUCAS, D. H.

1958 The atmospheric pollution of cities. *Int. J. Air Poll.*, London, 1, pp. 71–86

MANLEY, G.

1944 Topographical features and the climate of Britain. *Geogr. J.* London, 103, pp. 241–63

1945 The effective rate of altitudinal change in temperate Atlantic climates. *Geogr. Rev.*, New York, 35, pp. 408–17

R

1946   Variations in the length of the frost-free season. *Quart. J. R. Met. Soc.*, London, 72, pp. 180–4

1952   *Climate and the British scene.* London

1956   Discussion of: Local temperature variations in the Reading area. (Parry, M.). *Quart. J. R. Met. Soc.*, London, 82, p. 532

1957a   Studies of the frequency of snowfall in England, 1668–1956. and the relationship with glacier behaviour. *Proc. Comm. Snow and Ice, I.U.G.G.*, Toronto Assembly, Toronto, pp. 40–5

1957b   Climatic fluctuations and fuel requirements. *Scot. Geogr. Mag.*, Edinburgh, 73, pp. 19–28

1958   On the frequency of snowfall in metropolitan England. *Quart. J. R. Met. Soc.*, London, 84, pp. 70–2

1961   A preliminary note on early meteorological observations in the London region, 1680–1717, with estimates of the monthly mean temperatures, 1680–1706. *Met. Mag.*, London, 90, pp. 303–10

1963a   Seventeenth-century London temperatures: some further experiments. *Weather*, London, 18, pp. 98–105

1963b   Severe winters in Britain. *The Guardian*, 14 January 1963

MARSHALL, W. A. L.

1948   London temperatures. *Met. Mag.*, London, 77, pp. 54–9

1950   Sea breeze across London. *Met. Mag.*, London, 79, pp. 165–8

1952   *A century of London weather.* London. (H.M.S.O.)

1954   Mean maximum and mean minimum temperatures as criteria of the temperature characteristics of a month. *Met. Mag.*, London, 83, pp. 100–7

MCINTOSH, D. H.

1955   The occurrence of spells in London rainfall and temperature. *Met. Mag.*, London, 84, pp. 366–72

Medical Officer of Health, London County Council

1956   *Annual report*

1958   *Annual report*

MEETHAM, A. R.

1950   Natural removal of pollution from the atmosphere. *Quart. J. R. Met. Soc.*, London, 76, pp. 359–71

1956   *Atmospheric pollution.* London

Ministry of Health

1954   *Mortality and morbidity during the London fog of December 1952.* (Reports on public health and medical subjects, No. 95). (H.M.S.O.)

MITCHELL, J. M.

1953   On the causes of instrumentally observed secular temperature trends. *J. Met.*, Lancaster, Pa., 10, pp. 244–61

1961   The temperature of cities. *Weatherwise*, Lancaster, Pa., 14, p. 229

OLGYAY, V.

1963   *Design with climate, bioclimatic approach to architectural regionalism.* Oxford

PARRY, M.

1954   Local degree-day variations in the Reading area. *Met. Mag.*, London, 83, pp. 307–09

1956a   Local temperature variations in the Reading area. *Quart. J. R. Met. Sec.*, London, 82, pp. 45–57

1956b   An 'urban rainstorm' in the Reading area. *Weather*, London, 11, pp. 41–8

1957   Local climates and house heating. *Adv. Sci.*, London, 13, pp. 326–31

PENMAN, H. L.   1950 Evaporation over the British Isles. *Quart. J. R. Met. Soc.* London, 76, pp. 372–83

PICK, W. H.   1929 Fogs during winter with unsaturated air at various towns, rural and seaside stations in the British Isles. *Quart. J. R. Met. Soc.*, London, 55, pp. 305–6

    1931 A note on the relationship between fog and relative humidity. *Quart. J. R. Met. Soc.*, London, 57, pp. 288–95

PINARD, T. S. AND WILKINS, E. T.   1958 Air pollution in London and its smokeless zones. *Proc. Llandudno Conf., Nat. Soc. Clean Air*, London

POOLER, F.   1963 Airflow over a city in terrain of moderate relief. *J. App. Met.*, Lancaster Pa., 35, pp. 446–56

POULTER, R. M.   1962 The next few summers in London. *Weather*, London, 17, pp. 253–5

REYNOLDS, G.   1957 Variations in visibility over urban and rural areas. *Weather*, London, 12, pp. 314–20

ROGERS, P.   1960 London summers of the 1950s. *Weather*, London, 15, pp. 234–41

SCHLESINGER, M.   1853 *Saunterings in and about London.* London

SCORER, R. S.   1957 The cost in Britain of air pollution from different types of source. *J. Inst. Fuel*, 30, pp. 110–23

SCOTT, J. A.   1959 Fog and atmospheric pollution in London, winter 1958–9. *The Medical Officer*, London, 102, pp. 191–3

SELF, P.   1957 *Cities in flood.* London

SHELLARD, H. C.   1959a Averages of accumulated temperature and standard deviation of monthly mean temperature over Britain, 1921–50. London, Meteorological Office, *Prof. Notes*, No. 125

    1959b The frequency of fog in the London area compared with that in rural areas of East Anglia and south-east England. *Met. Mag.*, London, 88, pp. 321–3

    1962 Extreme wind speeds over the United Kingdom for periods ending 1959. *Met. Mag.*, London, 91, pp. 39–47

SHELLARD, H. C. AND BROWN, P. R.   1961 Frequency distribution of the daily range of temperature at Kew Observatory and London Airport. London, Meteorological Office, *Clim. Mem.* No. 28. (Typescript, available at the Meteorological Office)

SMITH, L. P.   1954 Length of the frost-free period. *Met. Mag.*, London, 83, pp. 81–3

    1956 Winter's worst moves into February. *Grower*, London, 45, No. 1, p. 27

    1957 Monthly temperature persistence. London, Meteorological Office, *Agric. Mem.* No. 14. (Typescript, available at the Meteorological Office)

    1961 Frequencies of poor afternoon visibilities in England and Wales. *Met. Mag.*, London, 90, pp. 355–9

SPENCE, M. T.   1936 Temperature changes over short distances as shown by records in the Edinburgh district. *Quart. J. R. Met. Soc.*, London, 62, pp. 25–31

STAGG, J. M.   1950 Solar radiation at Kew Observatory. London, Meteorological Office, *Geoph. Mem.* 11, No. 86

R*

260 REFERENCES

STANHILL, G.   1960   The variance of evaporation, rainfall, soil moisture deficit and run-off. *British rainfall 1957*, III, pp. 240–5. (H.M.S.O.)

STEINHAUSER, F., ECKEL, O. AND SAUBERER, F.   1957   *Klima und bioklima von Wien.* Teil II. Vienna

STEWART, K. H.   1953   *Data on fog in the London area, December 5–9th, 1952.* (Typescript, available at the Meteorological Office).

STOCKS, P.   1959   Cancer and bronchitis mortality in relation to atmospheric deposit and smoke. *Brit. Med. J.*, London, 1, pp. 74–9

SUGDEN, L.   1952   Diurnal and seasonal variation of visibility. Meteorological Office discussion. *Met. Mag.*, London, 81, pp. 174–85

SUNBORG, A.   1951   Climatological studies in Uppsala with special regard to the temperature conditions in the urban area. *Geographica*, (Geographical Institute, University of Uppsala), Uppsala, 22

SUTTON, O. G.   1937   The logarithmic law of wind structure near the ground. *Quart. J. R. Met. Soc.*, London, 63, pp. 105–7

TINN, A.B.   1938   Local temperature variations in the Nottingham district. *Quart. J. R. Met. Soc.*, London, 64, pp. 391–401
   1939   Depths of snow lying at Nottingham. *Met. Mag.*, London, 74, pp. 214–15
   1940   Local distribution of thunder rains round Nottingham. *Quart. J. R. Met. Soc.*, London, 66, pp. 47–65

TOWNSHEND, G. K.   1948   Some microclimatological aspects of the Aberdeen area. *Scot. Geogr. Mag.*, Edinburgh, 64, pp. 66–70

VERYARD, R. G.   1958   Some climatological aspects of air pollution. *Smokeless Air*, London, 28, pp. 277–84

WAINWRIGHT, C. W. K. AND WILSON, M. J. G.   1962   Atmospheric pollution in a London park. *Int. J. Air Wat. Poll.*, London, 6, pp. 337–47

WHITEN, A. J.   1956   The ventilation of Oxford Circus. *Weather*, London, 11, pp. 227–9

WILKINS, E. T.   1954   Air pollution aspects of the London fog of December 1952. *Quart. J. R. Met. Soc.*, London, 80, pp. 267–71

WILLIAMS, F. P.   1960   Pollution levels in cities. *Proc. Harrogate Conf. Nat. Soc. Clean Air.* London

WRIGHT, H. L.   1932   Observations of smoke particles and condensation nuclei at Kew Observatory. London, Meteorological Office, *Geoph. Mem.* 6, No. 57
   1935   Visibility and atmospheric suspensoids at Kew Observatory. *Quart. J. R. Met. Soc.*, London, 61, pp. 71–80
   1939   Atmospheric opacity: a study of visibility observations in the British Isles. *Quart. J. R. Met. Soc.*, London, 65, pp. 411–42

Appendix 1

AVERAGE AND EXTREME MEAN DAILY WIND SPEEDS, KEW, 1927–56

Date		Average	Highest	Lowest	Date		Average	Highest	Lowest
			m/sec					m/sec	
January	1	4·2	9·8	0·2	February	1	5·4	10·3	1·3
	2	4·6	8·4	0·9		2	4·7	8·9	1·4
	3	4·6	11·2	1·5		3	4·3	8·1	0·6
	4	4·6	6·9	0·6		4	4·1	8·8	0·6
	5	4·1	8·0	0·2		5	4·1	8·2	0·9
	6	4·1	9·5	1·0		6	3·6	9·2	1·3
	7	4·0	6·7	1·0		7	4·2	7·7	0·9
	8	3·5	6·2	0·5		8	5·0	9·6	1·8
	9	4·0	8·7	0·3		9	5·3	8·5	1·4
	10	4·3	8·8	1·3		10	5·1	11·3	1·3
	11	4·5	8·5	1·3		11	4·6	9·7	0·5
	12	4·2	8·0	0·9		12	4·5	8·8	0·6
	13	4·3	8·9	0·9		13	3·8	7·8	0·5
	14	4·0	8·7	1·0		14	3·3	7·3	0·4
	15	4·2	11·1	0·9		15	3·7	9·0	1·0
	16	4·1	9·2	0·6		16	4·2	10·6	1·1
	17	4·3	7·6	0·8		17	4·0	7·3	1·0
	18	4·3	9·1	1·5		18	4·2	7·8	1·2
	19	3·5	8·2	0·6		19	4·1	7·5	1·1
	20	3·5	7·9	0·7		20	4·1	9·4	0·4
	21	3·4	6·9	0·4		21	4·1	8·2	0·8
	22	3·3	10·3	0·8		22	4·0	7·4	0·8
	23	3·7	8·7	1·0		23	3·9	8·7	0·7
	24	3·9	7·9	0·5		24	3·7	7·3	1·1
	25	4·3	8·1	1·2		25	4·3	9·0	1·4
	26	4·4	8·8	0·6		26	4·6	8·5	0·3
	27	4·3	7·2	0·8		27	4·3	9·1	0·9
	28	4·5	10·6	0·7		28	4·2	10·4	0·9
	29	4·8	10·2	0·5					
	30	4·3	9·5	1·0					
	31	5·1	9·6	1·6					

Date		Average	Highest m/sec	Lowest	Date		Average	Highest m/sec	Lowest
March	1	4·3	10·0	1·2	April	1	5·1	10·3	1·4
	2	3·9	7·1	0·8		2	4·3	7·4	1·7
	3	3·5	7·6	0·5		3	4·2	9·3	0·8
	4	3·9	8·2	0·7		4	4·2	10·6	0·9
	5	3·7	8·2	1·3		5	4·3	7·4	1·0
	6	3·8	10·9	1·2		6	4·2	7·9	0·9
	7	3·8	10·3	0·8		7	4·5	8·7	1·4
	8	3·9	7·9	1·4		8	4·1	8·1	0·8
	9	3·5	9·8	1·6		9	4·3	8·6	1·6
	10	3·1	8·6	0·4		10	4·3	11·0	1·7
	11	3·5	8·0	0·8		11	3·8	8·0	0·7
	12	4·0	7·9	1·1		12	3·6	8·4	1·3
	13	4·0	8·1	0·8		13	3·2	6·2	1·2
	14	4·0	8·7	1·5		14	4·0	9·7	0·6
	15	3·7	7·6	1·2		15	4·0	7·7	1·3
	16	4·3	9·0	0·9		16	3·9	7·4	0·7
	17	3·9	7·6	0·9		17	3·9	6·9	0·7
	18	4·3	8·7	1·7		18	3·8	6·7	1·3
	19	4·3	8·7	1·8		19	4·0	7·8	1·0
	20	3·7	6·9	1·4		20	3·5	7·3	1·5
	21	3·9	6·7	1·3		21	4·1	9·5	1·6
	22	3·9	6·9	1·7		22	3·9	7·7	1·4
	23	4·2	9·1	0·8		23	3·8	10·3	1·1
	24	3·7	7·6	0·5		24	4·0	8·1	1·5
	25	3·5	6·1	0·8		25	4·4	9·8	1·3
	26	4·1	9·1	0·9		26	4·0	8·9	1·0
	27	3·8	7·8	0·7		27	4·0	8·0	1·5
	28	4·0	8·7	1·4		28	4·1	11·0	1·0
	29	4·6	10·8	0·9		29	3·8	10·7	1·6
	30	4·9	8·6	1·0		30	4·0	7·5	1·6
	31	4·7	8·5	2·2					

Date		Average	Highest m/sec	Lowest	Date		Average	Highest m/sec	Lowest
May	1	3·7	7·9	1·5	June	1	4·1	7·1	1·8
	2	4·8	9·2	1·5		2	4·6	9·3	1·5
	3	4·3	8·7	1·1		3	4·0	7·2	0·9
	4	4·1	8·2	1·3		4	4·1	7·2	1·2
	5	4·1	7·7	0·9		5	4·3	9·3	1·5
	6	4·0	8·0	1·7		6	4·1	7·6	1·8
	7	3·8	8·2	1·5		7	3·9	9·4	1·0
	8	3·8	9·6	1·3		8	3·4	6·0	1·4
	9	4·0	8·0	1·0		9	3·4	7·0	0·8
	10	3·8	9·1	1·2		10	3·7	6·9	0·5
	11	3·5	6·6	1·1		11	3·4	6·3	1·7
	12	3·5	7·3	0·8		12	3·5	7·0	1·4
	13	3·6	7·5	1·1		13	3·3	6·3	0·8
	14	3·9	7·6	1·3		14	3·6	6·8	1·6
	15	3·9	5·9	1·7		15	3·8	6·4	1·7
	16	3·8	7·0	1·3		16	3·4	5·4	1·6
	17	3·4	6·2	1·2		17	3·5	6·8	0·9
	18	3·8	6·4	1·1		18	3·7	6·2	1·0
	19	3·5	6·0	1·0		19	3·8	6·9	1·4
	20	3·2	7·3	1·0		20	3·5	7·8	1·4
	21	3·5	6·2	1·4		21	3·6	7·4	1·2
	22	3·4	7·6	1·1		22	3·5	7·0	1·5
	23	3·2	8·4	1·4		23	3·4	6·2	0·9
	24	3·7	8·5	1·0		24	3·1	6·0	1·4
	25	3·8	7·2	1·5		25	3·1	6·3	1·4
	26	3·5	5·8	1·4		26	3·0	7·1	1·1
	27	3·7	7·5	1·2		27	3·2	8·0	0·7
	28	3·7	9·7	1·0		28	3·7	9·3	1·7
	29	3·2	6·8	1·3		29	4·0	7·5	1·5
	30	3·6	7·1	0·9		30	3·5	5·6	1·2
	31	3·9	7·6	1·0					

APPENDICES

Date		Average	Highest m/sec	Lowest	Date		Average	Highest m/sec	Lowest
July	1	3·3	7·4	1·2	August	1	3·4	6·7	1·1
	2	3·3	5·3	1·7		2	3·9	6·8	0·9
	3	3·3	5·1	1·2		3	3·1	8·0	1·0
	4	4·0	6·4	1·1		4	3·0	5·6	0·8
	5	4·0	8·4	0·9		5	2·7	6·0	0·7
	6	3·6	7·2	1·9		6	2·6	4·7	1·1
	7	3·5	8·0	1·5		7	2·9	6·0	0·5
	8	3·7	7·8	1·0		8	2·9	6·8	1·0
	9	3·7	6·0	0·9		9	3·2	7·0	0·8
	10	3·5	6·7	1·6		10	3·7	6·4	0·6
	11	3·4	6·4	1·2		11	3·6	5·7	1·0
	12	3·2	6·7	1·1		12	3·6	7·6	1·3
	13	3·5	6·3	0·9		13	3·6	6·5	1·1
	14	3·2	5·7	1·2		14	2·9	5·7	0·8
	15	3·4	5·2	1·1		15	3·1	5·5	0·9
	16	3·2	5·9	0·9		16	3·0	7·4	1·0
	17	3·4	6·5	1·5		17	3·5	7·5	1·3
	18	3·9	8·8	0·9		18	3·6	8·8	1·0
	19	3·5	6·0	1·4		19	3·6	7·0	0·9
	20	3·3	6·5	1·1		20	3·5	7·6	1·3
	21	3·3	6·6	1·1		21	3·6	7·1	1·1
	22	3·1	5·9	0·7		22	3·5	8·6	0·7
	23	3·0	6·0	1·1		23	2·9	5·7	0·9
	24	3·1	7·4	1·0		24	3·1	6·7	0·9
	25	2·8	5·6	1·1		25	3·1	7·8	0·5
	26	3·1	5·6	1·3		26	2·7	5·7	0·8
	27	3·7	6·9	1·4		27	3·1	5·9	1·5
	28	3·7	6·8	1·7		28	3·3	8·6	0·7
	29	3·7	9·3	1·2		29	3·2	8·5	0·6
	30	3·5	7·4	1·3		30	3·1	6·4	1·1
	31	3·5	6·5	1·0		31	3·1	5·9	1·3

Date		Average	Highest m/sec	Lowest	Date		Average	Highest m/sec	Lowest
September	1	3·1	7·8	1·2	October	1	3·2	5·9	0·5
	2	3·5	7·3	0·3		2	3·1	5·7	1·6
	3	3·6	5·7	0·7		3	2·8	7·5	0·5
	4	3·2	8·3	0·7		4	3·2	10·0	0·1
	5	3·1	6·7	0·6		5	3·4	6·0	0·1
	6	3·1	5·5	1·3		6	3·7	8·9	0·5
	7	3·3	8·2	1·1		7	2·9	5·8	0·3
	8	3·2	7·0	0·7		8	3·0	7·6	0·7
	9	3·1	7·8	0·1		9	3·2	7·6	1·0
	10	3·1	7·1	1·0		10	3·0	9·3	0·9
	11	3·3	5·8	0·6		11	2·9	6·8	0·2
	12	3·3	5·8	1·0		12	2·5	5·2	0·8
	13	3·4	7·8	1·1		13	2·7	7·3	0·7
	14	3·5	6·3	0·8		14	3·1	5·9	1·1
	15	3·4	6·2	1·0		15	3·0	6·0	0·6
	16	3·5	7·6	1·2		16	3·0	6·4	0·5
	17	3·5	9·7	0·7		17	3·8	7·0	0·8
	18	2·9	6·0	0·6		18	4·0	7·7	0·7
	19	3·1	8·5	1·0		19	3·9	8·5	0·5
	20	4·0	9·2	1·0		20	3·5	7·2	0·9
	21	3·4	8·4	0·9		21	3·2	7·0	0·7
	22	3·5	6·5	0·5		22	3·3	6·7	0·8
	23	3·1	5·4	0·9		23	3·5	6·3	1·1
	24	3·6	6·7	0·5		24	4·1	8·6	0·8
	25	3·1	5·7	1·1		25	4·3	8·0	0·7
	26	3·0	6·2	0·9		26	4·1	9·5	0·6
	27	3·1	6·5	0·8		27	3·8	8·0	0·6
	28	3·6	6·6	1·1		28	3·9	8·3	0·8
	29	3·2	6·5	0·9		29	3·6	7·3	0·8
	30	3·2	5·2	0·9		30	3·8	7·8	0·3
						31	3·5	7·9	0·9

Date	Average	Highest m/sec	Lowest	Date	Average	Highest m/sec	Lowest
November 1	3·1	7·2	0·2	December 1	3·6	7·9	0·7
2	3·5	7·7	0·5	2	4·0	9·3	1·5
3	3·7	10·5	0·9	3	4·2	9·0	1·0
4	3·9	9·5	1·4	4	4·1	9·4	0·8
5	3·5	7·4	0·8	5	4·4	9·3	0·2
6	3·5	6·1	0·3	6	3·7	9·7	0·2
7	3·9	7·6	1·5	7	3·8	10·2	0·2
8	3·8	8·0	1·2	8	4·1	10·7	0·5
9	3·9	7·5	0·4	9	4·4	8·5	0·9
10	3·8	6·2	1·0	10	4·3	9·1	0·4
11	3·7	8·6	0·3	11	4·3	9·0	1·0
12	3·9	9·6	0·7	12	3·9	8·0	1·1
13	3·6	8·0	0·6	13	4·0	10·7	0·5
14	3·2	6·2	0·9	14	3·9	12·0	0·6
15	3·2	6·7	0·3	15	3·6	9·6	1·1
16	3·3	8·1	1·3	16	4·2	9·7	1·3
17	3·7	7·5	0·4	17	4·1	8·5	0·3
18	3·8	9·1	0·9	18	3·7	10·2	0·4
19	3·9	8·2	0·0	19	3·5	9·6	0·2
20	3·7	8·0	0·6	20	3·4	6·8	0·9
21	3·5	7·5	0·2	21	3·2	7·4	0·9
22	3·7	8·0	1·3	22	3·4	8·5	0·6
23	3·7	9·0	1·1	23	3·1	9·0	0·6
24	3·9	8·3	0·9	24	3·7	9·4	1·0
25	3·9	8·8	0·7	25	3·4	9·4	0·8
26	3·9	7·9	0·6	26	3·3	9·8	0·3
27	3·8	10·7	0·9	27	3·7	8·6	0·5
28	3·7	8·0	0·3	28	4·2	9·2	1·2
29	3·6	7·3	0·5	29	4·0	9·5	0·6
30	3·7	8·5	0·6	30	3·8	8·4	0·7
				31	3·5	7·6	1·0

Source of data: London, Meteorological Office *Observatories' year book*, 1927–56.

Appendix 2

AVERAGE AND EXTREME MAXIMUM TEMPERATURES, KEW, 1871–1950

Date		Average	Highest °F	Lowest	Date		Average	Highest °F	Lowest
January	1	43·8	56·1	22·9	February	1	44·2	56·3	31·0
	2	44·9	57·2	28·0		2	44·4	58·1	29·3
	3	44·6	55·6	30·2		3	44·7	54·0	33·5
	4	44·2	55·8	23·9		4	44·7	55·2	28·6
	5	43·7	53·6	22·2		5	44·3	55·9	29·6
	6	43·7	55·2	26·5		6	44·5	55·6	25·1
	7	43·6	53·8	25·1		7	45·0	57·6	25·1
	8	43·8	53·6	28·4		8	45·0	54·9	27·8
	9	43·7	56·1	31·6		9	44·8	57·0	23·1
	10	44·3	55·2	27·4		10	45·5	62·3	30·2
	11	43·8	55·2	25·7		11	44·2	55·5	31·1
	12	43·3	55·8	32·0		12	44·5	56·3	27·0
	13	44·0	56·7	31·0		13	44·8	55·6	25·9
	14	44·0	54·7	25·6		14	45·2	57·0	27·1
	15	43·6	54·1	25·0		15	45·9	55·2	27·0
	16	43·3	55·2	27·9		16	45·6	54·9	29·7
	17	43·2	55·8	28·8		17	45·7	58·1	27·7
	18	45·4	55·0	30·0		18	45·5	61·2	29·7
	19	44·1	56·1	30·2		19	45·4	57·6	30·2
	20	43·4	53·8	27·7		20	44·8	57·4	28·9
	21	43·1	55·4	27·9		21	45·2	56·5	30·2
	22	43·2	54·7	26·6		22	45·2	56·8	29·5
	23	43·1	54·2	29·8		23	44·8	57·2	30·9
	24	43·0	54·7	28·9		24	45·1	58·8	30·0
	25	43·2	54·1	28·0		25	45·9	58·3	33·8
	26	43·5	52·7	31·0		26	46·3	57·0	31·3
	27	43·5	54·5	25·0		27	46·3	57·7	30·4
	28	43·8	54·0	25·1		28	46·0	57·1	32·4
	29	43·7	54·0	29·8					
	30	44·5	54·6	31·6					
	31	45·8	55·0	30·4					

Date		Average	Highest °F	Lowest	Date		Average	Highest °F	Lowest
March	1	46·4	56·2	33·7	April	1	53·0	67·2	40·3
	2	46·7	57·1	33·1		2	53·2	70·5	41·0
	3	46·8	62·2	31·8		3	52·9	74·5	37·9
	4	47·3	63·7	32·9		4	53·2	73·4	42·3
	5	47·9	60·3	33·4		5	53·1	68·7	34·5
	6	48·3	60·6	32·0		6	52·8	65·0	37·2
	7	47·7	61·0	34·9		7	53·5	66·6	41·2
	8	47·9	61·0	33·8		8	54·0	70·4	40·6
	9	48·0	70·5	31·3		9	53·0	68·0	41·9
	10	47·9	60·6	34·3		10	53·6	68·6	40·5
	11	48·5	63·0	35·7		11	54·5	72·1	39·0
	12	48·1	60·6	35·5		12	54·6	71·1	38·7
	13	47·3	63·5	34·7		13	54·7	68·7	39·0
	14	48·4	64·0	34·4		14	54·8	67·5	43·6
	15	48·2	65·3	33·2		15	55·4	74·5	41·4
	16	49·3	65·0	35·8		16	55·1	77·9	41·2
	17	49·9	63·4	35·7		17	54·5	75·4	41·0
	18	50·5	61·7	34·3		18	55·4	75·4	41·5
	19	50·0	63·9	34·4		19	56·3	73·7	41·0
	20	50·4	65·8	34·5		20	56·8	80·3	41·5
	21	50·2	64·8	36·8		21	57·0	75·0	42·3
	22	50·3	64·0	35·3		22	56·2	71·9	42·3
	23	50·7	68·9	36·2		23	56·1	76·3	44·1
	24	51·5	68·0	34·0		24	56·1	75·4	42·3
	25	51·7	65·3	33·7		25	55·9	73·9	44·8
	26	50·9	68·0	35·8		26	56·2	73·6	45·6
	27	51·2	67·8	38·5		27	57·3	74·0	43·7
	28	51·7	66·9	38·7		28	56·7	70·1	44·7
	29	51·2	67·6	37·2		29	57·2	68·0	45·9
	30	51·6	67·5	41·0		30	57·5	71·2	44·2
	31	52·7	63·4	38·5					

Date		Average	Highest	Lowest	Date		Average	Highest	Lowest
			°F					°F	
May	1	57·4	73·9	46·0	June	1	66·0	84·9	52·7
	2	57·4	74·5	46·6		2	66·5	88·9	52·5
	3	58·3	74·1	45·7		3	66·9	90·9	53·6
	4	58·9	77·0	47·1		4	67·4	82·9	51·1
	5	59·9	77·9	46·7		5	66·6	85·5	55·5
	6	60·1	74·7	49·1		6	66·7	85·8	50·7
	7	60·2	72·9	46·4		7	66·8	85·3	53·8
	8	59·4	77·9	48·0		8	66·7	85·6	55·0
	9	59·8	76·1	46·4		9	67·0	82·8	54·0
	10	60·0	72·1	48·0		10	66·1	80·7	53·7
	11	61·7	79·9	47·0		11	66·8	86·5	55·0
	12	62·3	82·9	48·2		12	66·9	81·7	50·4
	13	62·1	80·4	47·7		13	67·0	81·1	54·0
	14	61·8	79·9	48·4		14	66·3	79·7	51·6
	15	61·2	78·1	48·7		15	66·5	82·5	51·1
	16	60·9	77·0	48·6		16	67·6	84·4	54·3
	17	61·5	77·2	47·1		17	68·2	87·8	52·9
	18	61·5	76·6	43·0		18	68·3	84·2	51·7
	19	61·8	75·4	50·2		19	68·7	86·1	50·2
	20	61·9	76·1	48·7		20	67·7	85·5	52·9
	21	63·6	82·0	48·3		21	68·8	85·6	56·7
	22	64·9	86·0	51·0		22	69·5	87·1	57·4
	23	65·0	86·4	51·3		23	68·9	81·8	59·0
	24	64·7	86·5	51·4		24	69·3	84·0	53·6
	25	64·6	79·2	46·8		25	68·8	84·9	59·0
	26	63·9	81·0	50·1		26	68·9	85·6	56·8
	27	64·7	79·5	51·4		27	69·5	84·4	58·1
	28	65·2	82·2	52·3		28	70·9	81·7	56·8
	29	66·1	86·4	50·4		29	70·0	83·4	58·3
	30	66·2	86·2	54·5		30	69·9	84·4	58·3
	31	65·7	85·6	52·3					

Date		Average	Highest °F	Lowest	Date		Average	Highest °F	Lowest
July	1	70·3	89·1	58·6	August	1	70·8	83·8	57·2
	2	70·5	83·3	58·1		2	70·3	83·1	61·7
	3	70·7	85·3	58·0		3	70·2	85·1	60·8
	4	70·3	84·7	56·7		4	70·7	87·7	60·8
	5	70·5	90·0	53·6		5	70·9	86·6	61·5
	6	70·7	86·4	60·0		6	71·4	89·4	58·8
	7	70·7	88·3	57·1		7	70·9	84·2	55·3
	8	70·7	88·0	55·4		8	71·5	88·0	59·3
	9	70·9	86·9	57·6		9	71·1	93·9	60·2
	10	70·9	89·2	59·2		10	70·9	82·6	60·4
	11	71·8	89·1	55·0		11	70·7	89·2	60·6
	12	71·7	90·1	54·0		12	71·1	88·2	60·6
	13	71·9	89·6	60·3		13	70·8	92·3	58·9
	14	72·1	85·6	58·0		14	71·5	87·1	62·2
	15	71·3	89·8	58·1		15	70·9	87·3	61·3
	16	71·3	89·4	58·5		16	71·2	87·3	59·9
	17	71·1	85·0	57·9		17	71·0	88·6	55·6
	18	71·3	85·6	57·9		18	70·7	88·3	62·6
	19	71·5	89·4	58·3		19	69·7	91·6	58·7
	20	71·6	89·4	57·7		20	69·7	83·8	60·6
	21	71·9	87·4	56·8		21	69·4	82·8	59·2
	22	71·5	88·3	58·5		22	69·8	86·0	61·0
	23	70·4	82·7	58·8		23	68·7	81·1	58·8
	24	71·3	86·0	59·9		24	69·2	85·4	56·7
	25	71·6	89·3	62·1		25	69·1	86·1	60·3
	26	71·3	88·3	58·5		26	68·9	84·0	59·2
	27	70·4	87·3	59·9		27	68·5	88·0	58·1
	28	70·5	92·8	59·1		28	69·5	88·0	59·5
	29	70·8	91·4	58·4		29	68·6	89·1	58·5
	30	71·5	88·5	60·3		30	68·4	84·4	57·2
	31	71·1	90·5	56·7		31	67·9	90·9	55·6

Date		Average	Highest °F	Lowest	Date		Average	Highest °F	Lowest
September	1	67·4	91·8	55·3	October	1	61·7	74·9	52·1
	2	67·6	91·8	57·4		2	60·3	76·3	43·2
	3	67·7	84·9	56·4		3	60·2	75·9	46·9
	4	67·4	85·8	54·3		4	59·9	76·7	46·6
	5	67·8	84·2	57·2		5	59·8	81·9	47·4
	6	67·5	82·9	56·7		6	60·0	80·8	48·9
	7	67·7	87·3	56·7		7	59·8	73·6	48·9
	8	67·5	88·3	54·0		8	59·0	75·0	48·2
	9	66·7	82·4	58·1		9	58·7	79·7	51·1
	10	65·8	78·0	54·3		10	58·6	76·1	46·2
	11	66·5	82·9	52·3		11	58·3	71·6	46·6
	12	66·1	84·0	56·3		12	58·0	68·4	46·0
	13	65·7	79·0	54·0		13	57·4	68·0	47·4
	14	65·1	79·2	55·2		14	57·2	69·3	47·7
	15	65·1	80·6	55·6		15	56·6	69·6	45·5
	16	65·2	83·2	57·5		16	56·6	65·3	47·3
	17	65·9	86·4	58·0		17	57·3	69·1	47·5
	18	65·1	80·6	53·4		18	56·5	73·9	46·8
	19	63·9	83·7	54·7		19	56·2	67·8	46·2
	20	63·5	75·6	53·0		20	55·2	64·9	40·0
	21	62·3	71·3	52·9		21	55·1	66·6	44·1
	22	62·6	75·2	54·2		22	54·7	65·8	43·5
	23	62·3	75·4	52·0		23	54·1	63·0	43·7
	24	62·5	80·2	49·7		24	53·4	62·8	43·6
	25	62·6	77·2	52·4		25	53·6	65·5	42·5
	26	63·0	79·4	51·6		26	52·7	61·6	39·0
	27	63·1	78·6	49·9		27	52·5	66·9	41·2
	28	62·5	77·2	53·5		28	53·5	63·7	42·7
	29	61·9	73·3	51·4		29	52·9	64·9	37·5
	30	61·6	75·9	51·3		30	52·9	64·0	42·6
						31	52·3	62·1	39·8

Date		Average	Highest °F	Lowest	Date		Average	Highest °F	Lowest
November	1	52·2	61·9	39·4	December	1	46·2	55·0	32·9
	2	52·2	60·8	41·9		2	46·1	55·8	31·8
	3	52·3	62·4	37·2		3	46·4	55·8	30·2
	4	52·2	62·4	35·2		4	45·9	59·2	32·0
	5	52·1	66·2	38·8		5	45·7	57·3	31·2
	6	52·3	60·1	36·7		6	46·1	55·9	33·1
	7	50·5	59·1	38·7		7	45·3	56·8	30·6
	8	50·3	59·4	39·7		8	45·6	56·7	31·2
	9	50·3	60·1	40·0		9	44·9	55·0	33·4
	10	50·2	59·2	36·8		10	44·1	55·8	27·4
	11	49·8	61·3	37·8		11	44·0	55·4	27·6
	12	49·9	61·3	37·9		12	44·2	57·0	30·0
	13	49·4	61·3	37·6		13	45·1	57·9	28·2
	14	48·7	62·9	35·8		14	44·8	56·8	21·5
	15	48·6	62·4	35·0		15	44·7	55·6	28·5
	16	47·6	61·6	30·6		16	45·2	56·1	31·2
	17	47·7	57·2	36·7		17	44·7	54·7	29·0
	18	47·6	58·1	33·7		18	44·6	55·2	28·6
	19	47·9	57·4	34·9		19	43·7	54·9	29·1
	20	47·8	57·6	35·6		20	43·2	54·1	26·8
	21	47·0	59·0	34·6		21	43·0	53·4	25·9
	22	47·6	59·0	33·3		22	43·9	53·9	25·0
	23	47·5	59·0	33·9		23	42·8	54·1	28·5
	24	47·2	57·0	33·6		24	43·5	53·8	27·9
	25	47·3	56·7	32·0		25	43·5	53·6	29·2
	26	46·7	57·4	30·4		26	43·8	54·1	32·5
	27	46·0	56·1	30·2		27	44·3	57·1	28·8
	28	46·7	57·6	25·5		28	44·8	57·0	28·3
	29	46·7	57·7	33·1		29	44·4	55·6	29·8
	30	46·1	58·4	33·3		30	44·2	54·9	28·2
						31	43·5	55·9	24·5

Source: London, Meteorological Office 1951 *Climate of Kew Observatory, 1871–1950.*

Appendix 3

AVERAGE AND EXTREME MINIMUM TEMPERATURES, KEW, 1871–1950

Date		Average	Highest	Lowest	Date		Average	Highest	Lowest
			°F					°F	
January	1	34·4	52·0	17·1	February	1	36·0	50·7	24·6
	2	36·3	50·4	14·9		2	34·6	51·4	21·6
	3	36·9	52·9	20·7		3	35·5	50·2	20·3
	4	36·5	51·4	16·2		4	35·4	50·4	21·9
	5	34·8	46·9	13·1		5	34·9	49·3	19·7
	6	34·7	50·5	19·7		6	35·5	49·6	14·5
	7	35·2	47·7	15·8		7	35·4	50·4	10·8
	8	35·3	48·7	16·3		8	35·6	50·4	11·6
	9	35·5	50·2	19·0		9	35·7	49·1	11·7
	10	35·2	48·6	15·2		10	35·7	51·6	18·7
	11	35·4	50·4	13·3		11	34·8	49·8	20·7
	12	34·5	45·5	19·1		12	34·1	46·1	17·2
	13	35·0	47·8	19·7		13	34·7	46·1	14·9
	14	35·6	50·4	12·0		14	36·3	49·6	20·1
	15	35·2	49·6	10·9		15	36·5	51·6	22·6
	16	35·0	48·7	15·1		16	35·9	48·7	17·8
	17	34·5	48·4	9·4		17	35·6	48·6	19·2
	18	35·3	50·2	18·3		18	35·1	49·1	17·8
	19	35·3	47·9	20·8		19	35·8	49·4	23·5
	20	34·5	48·3	15·0		20	35·5	48·4	22·6
	21	34·7	50·6	16·0		21	35·0	47·5	23·0
	22	34·8	47·8	10·1		22	34·7	46·9	22·6
	23	34·4	46·9	19·4		23	35·3	48·9	20·5
	24	34·5	48·6	19·4		24	34·7	49·2	14·5
	25	34·7	46·9	19·0		25	35·5	49·0	17·4
	26	34·5	46·9	18·0		26	36·2	49·1	22·8
	27	34·6	49·3	18·9		27	36·1	49·8	23·1
	28	35·0	48·6	17·6		28	35·1	50·4	21·9
	29	35·1	49·6	14·9					
	30	35·1	47·5	20·1					
	31	36·3	47·7	24·3					

Date		Average	Highest °F	Lowest	Date		Average	Highest °F	Lowest
March	1	35·3	50·8	23·5	April	1	38·3	51·4	27·0
	2	35·1	48·2	23·5		2	38·7	48·9	26·2
	3	34·9	49·1	22·4		3	39·0	50·7	28·9
	4	35·3	46·0	18·3		4	39·1	53·1	30·4
	5	36·0	50·0	17·1		5	39·2	49·9	30·3
	6	37·2	47·9	25·9		6	39·5	51·0	28·2
	7	35·6	49·5	22·3		7	39·3	50·7	28·6
	8	35·9	51·0	23·5		8	39·1	49·8	30·2
	9	35·2	49·5	18·7		9	39·6	49·6	28·0
	10	35·4	50·6	18·1		10	39·3	50·4	29·3
	11	35·7	50·0	23·2		11	39·2	50·9	28·3
	12	34·9	47·6	23·9		12	39·7	52·3	28·9
	13	35·6	47·1	24·3		13	39·7	50·9	29·8
	14	36·5	49·6	25·0		14	40·4	52·7	30·0
	15	35·9	46·7	27·0		15	40·3	51·1	27·9
	16	36·8	48·9	24·1		16	40·3	52·7	30·0
	17	37·2	48·7	22·2		17	40·1	53·1	27·4
	18	37·0	50·9	24·8		18	40·4	51·3	30·0
	19	37·2	47·3	23·8		19	40·4	52·3	30·0
	20	37·7	48·9	26·4		20	40·3	49·5	29·6
	21	36·7	48·0	22·5		21	40·9	52·0	29·9
	22	36·9	51·1	23·9		22	41·3	51·8	31·8
	23	37·0	51·3	23·0		23	40·9	52·9	28·1
	24	36·7	47·1	22·6		24	41·3	52·0	29·6
	25	37·2	51·6	24·4		25	41·3	53·0	30·2
	26	37·4	50·0	27·0		26	40·8	52·2	30·0
	27	37·3	49·6	27·0		27	41·9	50·2	31·3
	28	37·5	50·5	25·7		28	42·2	51·8	32·4
	29	38·3	51·3	26·1		29	41·9	50·7	30·5
	30	38·4	50·0	26·3		30	42·0	50·0	31·9
	31	39·1	49·3	28·4					

Date		Average	Highest	Lowest	Date		Average	Highest	Lowest
			°F					°F	
May	1	41·7	53·8	30·7	June	1	49·1	62·1	38·0
	2	41·9	50·9	32·2		2	49·7	64·4	40·9
	3	42·5	52·2	32·0		3	49·4	64·2	37·4
	4	42·4	53·8	30·9		4	49·8	58·8	39·2
	5	42·5	52·2	30·0		5	50·2	59·9	37·4
	6	43·7	54·9	32·3		6	49·8	61·5	41·4
	7	43·7	55·3	31·2		7	50·4	61·0	41·2
	8	43·9	56·8	31·8		8	50·5	61·5	41·7
	9	43·4	55·6	33·4		9	50·6	59·0	38·5
	10	43·4	54·7	31·2		10	50·4	59·5	40·1
	11	43·6	54·1	32·5		11	49·8	59·7	40·2
	12	45·1	58·3	34·0		12	50·4	61·9	42·1
	13	45·7	57·2	33·7		13	50·4	58·8	39·4
	14	45·3	55·7	32·4		14	50·4	59·2	41·9
	15	45·1	55·4	34·2		15	50·2	59·4	38·2
	16	44·9	55·4	35·2		16	50·9	59·4	41·4
	17	45·1	57·0	30·2		17	50·4	61·7	40·6
	18	45·5	56·5	33·1		18	51·0	61·9	41·9
	19	45·2	55·6	34·0		19	51·6	61·2	40·3
	20	45·2	57·4	32·5		20	52·5	63·9	40·5
	21	45·8	56·3	33·8		21	52·0	61·9	44·0
	22	46·5	57·4	34·2		22	52·1	63·5	41·0
	23	47·6	62·4	34·7		23	52·8	63·5	44·2
	24	48·0	58·8	38·1		24	52·9	64·8	44·4
	25	47·8	61·9	38·9		25	52·6	65·1	42·3
	26	47·8	57·2	36·7		26	52·2	60·3	43·2
	27	48·3	59·0	36·3		27	52·6	63·9	41·3
	28	48·0	56·3	37·0		28	53·9	63·3	45·1
	29	48·5	57·9	36·3		29	53·4	60·8	44·2
	30	49·1	62·6	38·0		30	52·9	62·2	44·0
	31	48·6	58·5	37·8					

Date		Average	Highest °F	Lowest	Date		Average	Highest °F	Lowest
July	1	53·2	61·3	42·8	August	1	54·8	64·0	45·3
	2	53·9	62·4	46·8		2	54·1	63·5	45·1
	3	54·4	63·3	45·9		3	53·8	66·2	44·1
	4	54·0	63·3	46·4		4	54·5	63·3	48·3
	5	54·3	61·1	46·2		5	54·1	62·6	45·1
	6	54·3	60·6	47·9		6	55·5	62·8	46·3
	7	54·1	63·1	45·2		7	55·1	64·4	46·9
	8	53·5	61·5	43·6		8	54·8	63·1	46·6
	9	53·9	63·0	43·5		9	55·1	62·2	47·3
	10	54·3	63·7	47·5		10	55·2	64·2	46·2
	11	54·5	63·0	43·5		11	54·4	63·9	43·8
	12	55·1	66·4	44·0		12	54·2	63·8	46·0
	13	55·1	68·0	43·9		13	54·9	66·9	46·0
	14	55·2	65·3	46·6		14	55·4	63·3	42·1
	15	55·4	63·7	46·6		15	54·9	63·4	41·5
	16	55·2	63·1	44·1		16	53·9	62·9	44·4
	17	55·2	61·5	44·8		17	54·6	64·6	46·7
	18	55·3	62·2	45·3		18	55·2	65·9	44·4
	19	55·2	63·1	45·4		19	54·7	65·8	43·4
	20	55·1	66·2	47·1		20	54·3	66·0	46·4
	21	56·0	63·5	46·4		21	54·3	64·4	45·3
	22	56·1	63·9	48·6		22	53·7	63·3	45·0
	23	56·1	67·4	46·6		23	53·4	62·2	45·0
	24	55·1	63·3	47·0		24	53·6	62·4	42·0
	25	55·0	66·1	45·5		25	53·1	62·4	43·5
	26	55·5	64·4	43·2		26	53·3	61·6	43·5
	27	54·9	66·0	45·9		27	53·6	63·9	45·0
	28	54·9	68·0	44·1		28	53·3	63·9	43·1
	29	54·8	68·2	45·3		29	53·2	62·2	43·6
	30	55·1	64·8	46·3		30	53·1	64·2	41·7
	31	55·2	64·0	47·1		31	52·4	61·0	40·5

Date		Average	Highest °F	Lowest	Date		Average	Highest °F	Lowest
September	1	52·5	61·2	36·9	October	1	47·0	59·2	34·7
	2	53·0	63·9	40·8		2	46·3	58·5	35·0
	3	52·2	61·3	42·1		3	45·6	58·1	28·1
	4	52·5	62·4	41·9		4	46·2	58·6	32·4
	5	52·5	64·8	39·7		5	46·1	58·1	31·1
	6	52·1	61·9	40·5		6	46·6	61·0	30·9
	7	51·6	61·7	41·0		7	46·2	59·5	30·0
	8	51·3	59·9	37·9		8	46·2	58·8	29·0
	9	51·2	61·2	40·0		9	45·3	59·4	32·0
	10	51·3	61·5	40·1		10	45·5	61·0	31·4
	11	50·2	61·5	38·8		11	45·6	58·1	32·9
	12	51·1	62·4	40·3		12	44·0	59·0	30·1
	13	50·3	61·2	39·6		13	43·1	60·3	28·2
	14	51·3	61·9	39·9		14	43·6	59·0	30·2
	15	50·3	60·1	35·5		15	43·6	59·0	30·8
	16	49·5	63·1	37·0		16	44·6	58·5	30·0
	17	50·9	60·0	34·7		17	44·8	55·0	25·4
	18	50·4	60·8	33·9		18	43·7	56·7	29·0
	19	49·7	63·0	37·0		19	44·2	54·0	28·2
	20	49·9	58·6	36·0		20	43·6	55·2	32·7
	21	47·4	59·9	37·9		21	42·9	58·8	28·4
	22	47·7	61·0	36·4		22	42·6	58·6	27·4
	23	48·3	59·9	35·0		23	41·8	54·5	28·4
	24	48·3	60·8	37·0		24	41·7	52·1	28·6
	25	48·0	59·9	34·5		25	40·8	55·3	29·7
	26	47·9	58·1	35·6		26	40·7	56·8	25·3
	27	47·6	60·1	33·8		27	39·3	56·9	27·5
	28	47·9	59·4	35·3		28	41·4	55·9	25·1
	29	47·9	59·1	30·9		29	41·3	53·4	27·1
	30	47·1	57·4	30·7		30	41·6	53·6	26·4
						31	41·1	51·9	26·6

S

Date		Average	Highest	Lowest	Date		Average	Highest	Lowest
			°F					°F	
November	1	41·1	54·6	28·9	December	1	37·3	52·0	23·0
	2	41·8	55·1	26·4		2	36·9	51·1	18·0
	3	41·7	55·0	29·1		3	37·4	51·3	18·3
	4	40·9	53·8	28·2		4	37·1	53·4	21·0
	5	41·2	57·9	28·2		5	37·0	53·1	23·0
	6	40·3	53·8	29·0		6	36·6	49·9	18·0
	7	39·5	51·8	25·6		7	36·5	54·1	13·5
	8	39·0	53·2	22·6		8	36·4	49·6	21·8
	9	39·8	52·2	28·3		9	35·4	48·2	23·2
	10	39·2	50·4	23·7		10	35·8	49·8	20·5
	11	39·5	50·0	27·3		11	35·5	50·6	19·7
	12	39·4	54·3	26·6		12	36·1	51·0	22·6
	13	38·9	52·6	23·5		13	36·6	51·6	16·4
	14	38·2	53·2	23·0		14	36·8	52·5	16·7
	15	38·1	50·5	24·2		15	36·5	48·9	21·2
	16	38·7	51·6	21·9		16	36·1	49·3	23·6
	17	38·5	51·1	21·0		17	36·7	50·2	21·9
	18	37·6	53·0	24·6		18	36·6	51·5	24·0
	19	38·6	51·5	20·2		19	35·9	51·3	21·4
	20	38·5	50·1	25·0		20	34·7	49·8	15·5
	21	38·2	56·7	23·9		21	35·0	48·4	18·6
	22	37·9	57·4	22·5		22	34·9	46·2	10·8
	23	37·9	52·3	24·1		23	34·5	49·8	16·9
	24	38·1	49·8	24·3		24	34·8	48·4	14·7
	25	37·3	52·2	25·6		25	34·6	48·0	16·0
	26	36·8	50·0	24·1		26	35·7	49·3	21·7
	27	36·7	48·5	22·5		27	36·1	48·6	17·9
	28	37·3	50·4	21·5		28	36·1	51·4	24·4
	29	37·3	50·9	21·6		29	36·7	50·3	20·0
	30	37·3	54·3	21·5		30	35·4	47·7	14·7
						31	35·0	51·3	17·0

Source: London, Meteorological Office, 1951, *Climate of Kew Observatory, 1871–1950.*

Appendix 4

AVERAGE AND EXTREME MEAN* DAILY RELATIVE
HUMIDITY, KEW, 1927–56

Date		Average	Highest	Lowest	Date		Average	Highest	Lowest
			per cent					per cent	
January	1	87·0	98·7	63·5	February	1	82·0	97·9	52·5
	2	83·7	96·6	65·7		2	81·9	94·3	58·2
	3	83·9	93·0	62·9		3	82·3	97·2	62·3
	4	82·8	96·9	59·5		4	82·5	98·7	61·5
	5	83·3	97·9	72·5		5	79·5	97·5	65·5
	6	86·9	97·1	73·1		6	81·3	94·3	65·4
	7	87·5	98·2	68·5		7	84·0	95·0	64·2
	8	86·6	94·6	74·6		8	81·4	93·1	61·5
	9	86·2	96·3	75·5		9	79·9	96·5	59·6
	10	85·8	96·7	62·9		10	80·0	93·2	66·2
	11	84·8	95·2	67·6		11	78·7	96·5	53·6
	12	85·6	96·4	68·5		12	79·9	98·3	62·2
	13	86·3	97·5	75·5		13	81·8	94·8	59·0
	14	86·5	98·0	61·3		14	82·0	98·0	62·9
	15	85·0	99·0	64·1		15	81·6	96·5	61·9
	16	84·2	98·9	60·2		16	80·3	96·0	59·9
	17	82·3	97·4	64·0		17	81·3	94·5	61·5
	18	83·6	97·4	62·8		18	81·2	97·0	59·6
	19	84·6	97·8	64·1		19	82·2	95·5	64·9
	20	84·7	97·2	68·8		20	79·5	96·3	56·3
	21	85·9	98·0	68·1		21	78·7	94·5	55·3
	22	86·6	98·3	70·8		22	79·8	92·9	66·0
	23	86·9	97·3	71·2		23	80·0	94·3	62·0
	24	84·5	98·6	66·2		24	80·1	94·4	58·8
	25	82·6	95·6	64·9		25	80·3	93·9	65·7
	26	83·5	94·3	60·7		26	79·0	92·0	55·0
	27	82·9	94·9	64·0		27	77·8	94·0	61·8
	28	84·8	97·1	63·0		28	80·0	92·5	58·0
	29	83·9	97·8	63·0					
	30	86·6	96·3	64·8					
	31	84·5	97·7	64·3					

* of 24 hourly readings

Date		Average	Highest per cent	Lowest	Date		Average	Highest per cent	Lowest
March	1	75·9	90·0	46·7	April	1	75·6	93·4	43·7
	2	77·7	93·3	56·5		2	77·4	91·7	55·9
	3	78·0	94·9	63·2		3	76·8	94·6	56·9
	4	79·2	93·1	59·2		4	77·3	93·5	60·0
	5	78·9	92·5	55·7		5	75·9	87·5	60·9
	6	79·8	94·1	57·2		6	75·7	94·3	49·0
	7	79·2	94·1	55·3		7	73·5	90·0	58·3
	8	76·8	92·6	58·7		8	72·3	91·8	52·9
	9	76·3	94·5	54·0		9	70·9	87·9	56·3
	10	77·1	95·0	58·5		10	71·5	84·9	58·2
	11	78·6	93·2	61·7		11	71·4	81·8	57·0
	12	76·6	89·9	61·3		12	74·3	90·6	60·8
	13	76·7	97·0	58·9		13	73·1	93·6	57·0
	14	76·0	89·4	60·5		14	74·3	88·3	60·8
	15	77·0	91·5	61·1		15	71·4	87·8	43·5
	16	78·3	93·2	61·7		16	69·4	89·6	41·5
	17	77·7	95·2	52·8		17	70·7	87·0	53·7
	18	76·8	92·4	59·0		18	70·7	87·0	55·2
	19	79·1	89·8	62·3		19	70·2	84·7	58·0
	20	75·7	91·6	60·5		20	68·8	87·5	55·3
	21	78·3	91·3	60·1		21	71·2	83·7	56·2
	22	78·6	96·3	59·0		22	69·8	86·5	54·8
	23	77·5	93·5	54·2		23	70·8	87·7	54·4
	24	75·9	89·8	55·4		24	69·7	94·3	55·8
	25	77·4	89·8	51·0		25	69·3	91·7	52·0
	26	74·7	92·0	52·7		26	70·1	85·4	48·3
	27	75·1	91·7	58·0		27	70·6	85·6	54·8
	28	73·2	92·6	53·5		28	73·6	89·8	44·3
	29	78·9	93·0	48·7		29	73·3	94·3	45·3
	30	68·6	91·2	47·8		30	72·0	91·1	43·3
	31	75·0	93·5	53·7					

Date		Average	Highest per cent	Lowest	Date		Average	Highest per cent	Lowest
May	1	75·4	92·8	54·9	June	1	72·6	89·6	54·9
	2	74·2	91·5	56·2		2	70·4	85·0	50·3
	3	73·8	89·7	49·5		3	69·3	86·1	41·8
	4	73·0	94·1	55·7		4	70·4	83·1	40·7
	5	73·1	92·4	55·7		5	69·4	88·4	41·5
	6	71·9	90·4	45·2		6	70·7	90·2	54·9
	7	69·6	89·1	51·9		7	70·5	83·0	47·2
	8	71·5	93·9	57·4		8	72·6	93·3	50·5
	9	70·0	90·9	54·3		9	71·8	91·5	56·4
	10	69·6	88·3	55·8		10	73·1	92·3	56·6
	11	70·6	86·9	52·5		11	72·7	88·8	49·3
	12	72·0	89·3	51·0		12	72·1	90·5	54·5
	13	71·1	88·4	57·0		13	72·8	90·1	59·0
	14	71·7	87·0	56·5		14	73·5	88·6	50·2
	15	71·4	94·5	51·4		15	71·3	85·2	61·5
	16	71·9	90·1	53·0		16	72·3	87·6	59·2
	17	71·1	89·8	56·5		17	71·4	87·7	58·0
	18	70·5	87·9	52·2		18	72·7	90·1	50·7
	19	69·8	87·1	50·7		19	72·5	95·9	52·9
	20	72·1	89·6	49·4		20	72·1	90·5	57·1
	21	70·9	88·7	51·2		21	73·0	88·0	58·0
	22	71·3	87·0	52·3		22	72·2	88·5	54·6
	23	72·0	86·8	47·1		23	70·4	89·6	58·4
	24	73·1	87·0	59·2		24	70·5	85·7	58·0
	25	71·6	90·0	58·9		25	69·7	88·5	59·3
	26	74·6	89·4	56·0		26	70 8	96·5	53·7
	27	73·6	89·6	52·2		27	69·9	89·6	57·4
	28	72·0	91·3	55·4		28	73·7	89·1	57·1
	29	71·7	86·4	60·5		29	70·6	88·1	55·9
	30	70·4	89·2	57·2		30	71·5	84·1	59·0
	31	71·2	88·8	55·7					

Date		Average	Highest	Lowest	Date		Average	Highest	Lowest
			per cent					per cent	
July	1	73·4	87·5	52·9	August	1	75·6	88·1	58·6
	2	71·5	89·5	52·5		2	75·3	85·4	61·0
	3	73·0	92·1	50·5		3	74·8	87·1	58·4
	4	72·3	90·1	55·0		4	74·5	84·9	62·1
	5	70·5	91·7	56·4		5	75·4	91·2	64·0
	6	72·2	88·6	56·5		6	77·5	93·3	61·5
	7	69·9	80·4	53·4		7	76·5	90·0	59·6
	8	68·6	84·8	52·8		8	76·4	89·5	58·5
	9	72·9	88·2	52·8		9	75·4	88·3	60·2
	10	73·1	92·3	45·3		10	76·4	91·7	52·3
	11	69·0	88·3	50·1		11	76·4	93·6	56·0
	12	72·2	93·2	50·5		12	73·1	88·4	58·4
	13	74·4	90·3	59·2		13	74·6	91·0	58·9
	14	72·8	93·0	53·5		14	74·5	93·2	58·3
	15	74·4	88·2	53·0		15	73·8	92·0	50·1
	16	75·3	91·1	57·3		16	73·7	94·8	58·3
	17	75·0	90·3	61·2		17	74·7	94·5	56·9
	18	76·2	87·0	58·3		18	75·1	90·5	58·3
	19	73·0	88·9	58·1		19	75·6	94·1	55·1
	20	74·5	91·3	60·5		20	77·1	92·0	59·9
	21	74·0	93·4	56·5		21	76·6	90·4	57·7
	22	73·6	91·1	52·2		22	77·7	92·6	58·5
	23	73·5	93·1	56·7		23	78·4	95·4	66·5
	24	72·9	86·3	60·2		24	77·0	88·7	61·1
	25	73·2	94·2	60·3		25	76·2	91·5	60·1
	26	73·4	91·1	59·2		26	76·7	88·7	64·0
	27	72·5	93·5	56·9		27	75·5	88·5	60·0
	28	72·9	93·6	57·8		28	76·4	90·9	60·8
	29	72·8	88·3	55·1		29	75·1	92·0	63·9
	30	73·1	86·8	56·9		30	77·7	89·4	59·4
	31	75·0	90·7	62·7		31	77·7	92·0	61·3

Date		Average	Highest per cent	Lowest	Date		Average	Highest per cent	Lowest
September	1	78·1	89·9	59·1	October	1	80·5	97·5	66·2
	2	78·3	89·0	68·1		2	80·4	93·0	61·5
	3	79·3	90·3	68·6		3	81·0	92·6	65·7
	4	79·1	92·0	66·4		4	81·2	94·8	62·3
	5	74·7	91·5	63·7		5	82·3	99·3	71·3
	6	76·5	90·8	58·3		6	79·5	92·3	60·5
	7	73·2	91·1	64·4		7	82·0	96·0	69·5
	8	77·8	94·4	62·4		8	83·5	93·9	70·8
	9	78·8	93·9	62·6		9	83·3	92·7	72·0
	10	78·1	93·1	61·2		10	82·9	93·5	65·9
	11	77·8	92·9	54·8		11	82·7	97·1	63·9
	12	80·0	91·1	68·4		12	85·8	96·7	73·3
	13	80·6	89·6	68·5		13	86·3	94·0	77·6
	14	78·7	91·3	63·7		14	85·2	95·4	72·4
	15	78·1	90·6	64·2		15	83·5	95·1	72·0
	16	79·2	91·4	67·0		16	84·7	96·0	63·7
	17	80·1	92·7	68·6		17	83·6	95·0	71·5
	18	80·9	92·5	65·1		18	82·3	95·6	65·3
	19	81·6	90·5	71·3		19	82·0	91·1	68·7
	20	79·6	89·5	59·1		20	84·5	95·1	69·5
	21	79·4	92·3	63·3		21	84·1	97·8	73·3
	22	80·9	93·6	65·2		22	86·8	95·5	74·0
	23	81·3	96·2	67·2		23	85·0	94·8	64·2
	24	79·1	92·4	70·4		24	82·3	95·5	64·8
	25	81·5	94·3	69·5		25	82·0	96·6	66·5
	26	79·9	92·7	63·1		26	81·6	96·6	62·5
	27	81·9	96·0	69·8		27	82·7	95·5	61·0
	28	80·9	95·6	65·8		28	82·9	96·1	63·6
	29	82·4	89·5	65·9		29	82·1	94·1	63·8
	30	82·6	95·5	68·2		30	82·8	97·3	71·6
						31	84·2	94·3	70·8

Date		Average	Highest per cent	Lowest	Date		Average	Highest per cent	Lowest
November	1	86·4	95·8	72·6	December	1	86·2	98·3	69·9
	2	87·3	97·6	69·6		2	85·4	97·4	67·5
	3	84·3	97·7	68·5		3	85·3	95·1	66·1
	4	85·1	97·0	72·8		4	83·3	94·7	68·6
	5	84·2	96·7	72·9		5	83·4	97·0	70·5
	6	85·0	98·1	65·6		6	85·0	100·0	59·9
	7	84·3	92·6	60·6		7	85·5	99·2	66·5
	8	84·3	95·1	67·1		8	84·3	97·7	60·8
	9	84·5	94·7	68·8		9	85·6	96·9	59·7
	10	83·5	97·1	68·7		10	85·2	96·7	62·3
	11	85·1	98·6	68·3		11	85·4	93·9	69·8
	12	84·5	94·6	71·6		12	84·1	95·2	69·6
	13	84·0	94·0	69·5		13	86·8	98·5	55·7
	14	86·2	94·9	72·0		14	88·1	99·1	51·3
	15	86·8	97·0	72·5		15	85·5	96·3	69·0
	16	86·1	95·0	72·5		16	85·7	98·0	69·7
	17	85·1	98·4	70·6		17	85·0	93·5	69·9
	18	86·5	95·7	70·3		18	85·6	98·6	63·0
	19	87·9	97·5	71·2		19	86·9	98·6	68·3
	20	87·6	97·9	69·7		20	85·4	99·7	64·3
	21	88·6	98·6	77·7		21	87·2	95·8	75·0
	22	87·3	96·6	72·9		22	87·6	96·6	72·3
	23	86·6	97·1	70·2		23	86·9	97·3	64·6
	24	84·8	94·2	65·9		24	87·1	99·6	75·1
	25	86·1	97·7	64·3		25	87·5	100·0	74·6
	26	84·9	98·5	68·5		26	90·2	98·1	73·0
	27	85·6	97·9	66·4		27	86·3	97·7	68·0
	28	85·3	99·0	71·2		28	85·9	95·2	63·2
	29	85·7	98·1	63·2		29	82·8	97·2	63·8
	30	85·4	98·7	66·6		30	85·6	97·2	67·7
						31	86·7	97·6	74·5

Source: London, Meteorological Office *Observatories' year book, 1927–56*

Appendix 5

AVERAGE DAILY PRECIPITATION, KEW, 1871–1950

Date		Average in.	Date		Average in.	Date		Average in.	Date		Average in.
January	1	·09	February	1	·07	March	1	·06	April	1	·04
	2	·07		2	·08		2	·04		2	·07
	3	·07		3	·06		3	·05		3	·07
	4	·06		4	·04		4	·06		4	·06
	5	·06		5	·05		5	·05		5	·04
	6	·07		6	·05		6	·06		6	·05
	7	·09		7	·05		7	·07		7	·07
	8	·06		8	·06		8	·04		8	·05
	9	·07		9	·06		9	·06		9	·05
	10	·08		10	·07		10	·04		10	·07
	11	·07		11	·04		11	·05		11	·06
	12	·05		12	·04		12	·05		12	·05
	13	·05		13	·07		13	·05		13	·05
	14	·04		14	·05		14	·07		14	·05
	15	·06		15	·07		15	·05		15	·05
	16	·06		16	·05		16	·04		16	·08
	17	·07		17	·06		17	·04		17	·05
	18	·08		18	·05		18	·04		18	·04
	19	·06		19	·04		19	·04		19	·04
	20	·05		20	·05		20	·05		20	·06
	21	·06		21	·06		21	·04		21	·05
	22	·06		22	·05		22	·05		22	·04
	23	·07		23	·04		23	·05		23	·05
	24	·06		24	·05		24	·03		24	·05
	25	·07		25	·07		25	·05		25	·08
	26	·04		26	·07		26	·07		26	·08
	27	·05		27	·07		27	·05		27	·07
	28	·08		28	·05		28	·05		28	·08
	29	·06					29	·06		29	·07
	30	·06					30	·04		30	·06
	31	·08					31	·05			

Date		Average	Date		Average	Date		Average	Date		Average
		in.			in.			in.			in.
May	1	·04	June	1	·08	July	1	·09	August	1	·07
	2	·05		2	·07		2	·07		2	·08
	3	·09		3	·05		3	·08		3	·08
	4	·04		4	·08		4	·06		4	·10
	5	·05		5	·06		5	·07		5	·08
	6	·04		6	·08		6	·09		6	·06
	7	·07		7	·06		7	·05		7	·06
	8	·06		8	·05		8	·05		8	·09
	9	·05		9	·08		9	·07		9	·05
	10	·05		10	·10		10	·08		10	·08
	11	·04		11	·06		11	·07		11	·05
	12	·04		12	·06		12	·07		12	·05
	13	·07		13	·07		13	·06		13	·07
	14	·04		14	·08		14	·09		14	·06
	15	·04		15	·08		15	·10		15	·04
	16	·05		16	·08		16	·07		16	·05
	17	·07		17	·07		17	·08		17	·08
	18	·06		18	·09		18	·09		18	·09
	19	·05		19	·05		19	·09		19	·07
	20	·06		20	·06		20	·07		20	·08
	21	·05		21	·05		21	·09		21	·06
	22	·06		22	·03		22	·09		22	·06
	23	·07		23	·04		23	·06		23	·11
	24	·06		24	·08		24	·08		24	·10
	25	·06		25	·07		25	·08		25	·06
	26	·08		26	·05		26	·13		26	·08
	27	·08		27	·06		27	·10		27	·07
	28	·06		28	·05		28	·07		28	·10
	29	·05		29	·10		29	·08		29	·09
	30	·06		30	·07		30	·06		30	·06
	31	·06					31	·05		31	·10

Date		Average in.	Date		Average in.	Date		Average in.	Date		Average in.
September	1	·06	October	1	·07	November	1	·10	December	1	·09
	2	·07		2	·07		2	·07		2	·07
	3	·07		3	·05		3	·10		3	·05
	4	·10		4	·07		4	·07		4	·06
	5	·08		5	·04		5	·10		5	·07
	6	·05		6	·09		6	·09		6	·08
	7	·05		7	·08		7	·10		7	·08
	8	·07		8	·07		8	·08		8	·08
	9	·05		9	·08		9	·07		9	·08
	10	·08		10	·06		10	·08		10	·08
	11	·08		11	·09		11	·12		11	·05
	12	·05		12	·07		12	·09		12	·08
	13	·07		13	·04		13	·07		13	·07
	14	·06		14	·08		14	·07		14	·10
	15	·05		15	·06		15	·08		15	·06
	16	·05		16	·09		16	·10		16	·06
	17	·05		17	·06		17	·07		17	·05
	18	·08		18	·05		18	·07		18	·05
	19	·06		19	·09		19	·05		19	·05
	20	·06		20	·11		20	·06		20	·05
	21	·06		21	·07		21	·07		21	·05
	22	·06		22	·12		22	·04		22	·07
	23	·07		23	·10		23	·05		23	·06
	24	·09		24	·10		24	·06		24	·07
	25	·07		25	·06		25	·07		25	·07
	26	·03		26	·13		26	·08		26	·09
	27	·05		27	·10		27	·07		27	·08
	28	·06		28	·08		28	·09		28	·09
	29	·13		29	·08		29	·08		29	·05
	30	·09		30	·12		30	·08		30	·10
				31	·09					31	·07

Source: London, Meteorological Office 1951 *Climate of Kew Observatory, 1871–1960* (Typescript)

Index